THE SOLOMON R. GUGGENHEIM MUSEUM COLLECTION

Selections

from the Guggenheim Museum

Collection

1900-1970

THE SOLOMON R. GUGGENHEIM MUSEUM, NEW YORK

PUBLISHED BY

THE SOLOMON R. GUGGENHEIM FOUNDATION

NEW YORK, 1970

LIBRARY OF CONGRESS

CARD CATALOGUE NUMBER: 74-122468

PRINTED IN THE NETHERLANDS

PREFACE

In a museum, collecting aims and their rationalizations necessarily evolve with changing times and the changing texture of the institution itself. The Solomon R. Guggenheim Museum has developed from private beginnings toward public ends and the brief historical review that follows this preface will draw attention to the main currents of such a progression. It may be stated in advance, however, that collecting policies in the original *Museum of Non-Objective Painting* purported to be dogmatic. An exclusive stylistic commitment to non-objective painting was implicit in the Museum's name but, despite it, the Cubists, Klee, Chagall, Marc, Modigliani, and the early Kandinsky – who were certainly not non-objective – were collected from the very beginning in wholesome disregard of the stated collecting plan. During the years of transition from the Foundation's relatively private to its public role, when the *Museum of Non-Objective Painting* gave way to *The Solomon R. Guggenheim Museum*, stylistic limitations were relaxed, collecting became pointedly ahistorical, and *quality* became the guiding criterion. The present fully public stage (which goes back to the transfer of museum activities to the Frank Lloyd Wright building on Fifth Avenue) also embraces quality but seeks, in addition, a measure of historical and didactic continuity.

Such a development leads inevitably toward a more comprehensive Collection ideal and brings with it an awareness of what is missing. Gaps, as these are felt today, had no conscious part in the tightly drawn collection policies of the Museum's original phase. In the transitional stage of the 1950's, a sense of uneasiness at interruptions in the chronological sequence began to be felt as emerging relationships among individual objects began to assert their relevance to art history. It would have been premature however to think of gaps, if only because the existing chronologically compact areas floated like small islands on the sea of modern art. After more than thirty years of institutional collecting, modern art as mirrored in the Museum's Collection has ceased to be a sea inhabited by islands and has instead become a landmass, dotted by lakes. The Collection gaps can no longer be ignored since too much now exists not to point up what is missing. The reduction of gaps therefore has become an implicit objective. It is understood, of course, that this can be attempted only if the search for *works of exceptional importance* rather than for merely *representative examples* remains paramount.

The Guggenheim Museum Collection, as presently constituted, suffers from conspicuous omissions: Matisse and the Fauves; the *Brücke* painters and late German Expressionism; Dada and Surrealism (splendidly illuminated, to be sure, in Peggy Guggenheim's Collection in Venice). On the other hand, exceedingly well represented are: Cubism and its satellite movements; the pioneers of abstraction, particularly through the work of Kandinsky; the Bauhaus painters and those of *de Stijl*. As in most collections that move toward the boundless expanse of current art, the measure of continuity that is in evidence from the turn of our century to World War II loses its coherence and breaks down thereafter. Gaps disappear because the void becomes too pervasive.

The Collection of The Solomon R. Guggenheim Museum contains approximately 3,000 works of which less than 250 paintings, sculptures, and works on paper have been selected to observe the first decade of Frank Lloyd Wright's famous building on Fifth Avenue. Since, however, every effort has been made to include most of the finest works in each of the chronologically defined periods, the remarks relating to the Collection as a whole are largely applicable to the sampling covered by this catalogue. This publication, therefore, serves a double purpose: first, as an exhibition catalogue, accompanying a survey of the Collection; and second, as the first selective *Handbook* published about the Guggenheim Museum Collection in a decade's time.

Such publications and exhibitions are the result of a concerted staff effort involving virtually every museum department. Works included were checked and many were treated in the department of conservation, photographed by the staff photographers, and minutely described by registrars for reliable identification. All research and library personnel were involved in the catalogue's documentation, to which former as well as present members of the curatorial staff have contributed their specialized knowledge. The publication of this *Handbook*, however, ultimately depended upon extensive writing by Margit Rowell and the production skill of Linda Konheim, both research fellows at the Guggenheim Museum. They, in turn, depended heavily upon the editorial work of Dr. Louise Averill Svendsen, who, as the Museum's curator, brought to this task a familiarity with the Collection that was acquired over a long period of time. These acknowledgments would, however, be incomplete were one not to record the aid received in various areas of special competence from scholars throughout the world who have always and without exception responded to requests for information, who generously shared their knowledge, and thereby substantially aided our task.

Thomas M. Messer
Director

INTRODUCTION

When Solomon R. Guggenheim conceived the idea of establishing a museum, he was following in a tradition peculiarly American. Lacking the European system of separate, government-supported community collections and exhibition halls, many American organizations were then supported by wealthy individuals. As great fortunes were amassed, great art collections and philanthropic institutions followed, and, as income and inheritance taxes rose, it was a natural sequence that museums and foundations were established. Outstanding precedents in New York are the great Morgan Library and the Frick Collection, founded in 1924 and 1935 respectively.

Solomon R. Guggenheim was the fourth of the seven Guggenheim brothers of the remarkable family which, upon arrival in the United States from Switzerland in the 19th century, had created a financial empire in mining. They supported good causes and eventually established philanthropic foundations according to their interests. In the gentlemanly tradition of empire builders, Solomon R. Guggenheim began to form an art collection of works by Old Masters. Entering rather late into this highly competitive millionaire's market, dominated by Wideners, Fricks, Baches and Altmans, he seems to have collected without strong personal taste or direction. Fifteenth century Flemish panel pieces, American landscapes, paintings of the French Barbizon School, a Joos van Cleve, a Strigel, Audubon prints and Oriental illuminations were among the works the Museum received from him and his wife. (His Old Master collection, outside the main focus of the Museum collection, was sold at auction in 1961.)

In the mid-twenties, circumstance changed the course of Mr. Guggenheim's collecting. In 1926 he met and commissioned a young German artist, Baroness Hilla Rebay von Ehrenweisen, to paint his portrait. Miss Rebay, the daughter of a Prussian military officer, had begun early to study art. Attractive, talented and dynamic, she had exhibited with avant-garde groups in Germany from 1914 to 1920, particularly the *Secession* group in Munich (1914–15) and Berlin (1915). In 1917 she exhibited at *Der Sturm* Gallery in Berlin. Here, probably through Herwarth Walden, she met other artists who exhibited in his gallery: Delaunay, Gleizes, Léger, Chagall, Kandinsky and Bauer. Her major hero was Kandinsky, later overshadowed by intense admiration for Rudolf Bauer. As their friendship developed, she introduced Mr. Guggenheim into this circle. It must have been an exciting experience for him to meet famous and often controversial painters, to participate in aesthetic discussions, and to visit studios where he viewed what must have been at first incomprehensible canvases. Converted by her enthusiasm and expertise to champion this avant-garde art, he began to buy, steadily and in increasing quantities, until the walls of his apartment at the Plaza were crowded. As the fame of his collection grew, he opened his apartment at intervals to the art world and began to lend to exhibitions. Soon it was necessary to take office space at Carnegie Hall for Miss Rebay to look after the collection. The inevitable step of converting the collection into a foundation occurred in 1937 when the Foundation was incorporated and empowered to operate a museum.

The next two years were spent in finding new quarters and preparing them for exhibition. During this time, Miss Rebay, a woman of formidable energy, organized three important loan exhibitions from the collection: to Philadelphia (1937), Charleston, South Carolina (1938) and Baltimore (1939). These shows are historical landmarks. They provided an exposure in depth to contemporary European painting: fifty works by Kandinsky, fifteen Gleizes, six Légers and five Moholy-Nagys as well as Chagalls, Delaunays, Feiningers.

When the new museum opened as the Solomon R. Guggenheim Collection of Non-Objective Paintings, in rented quarters at 24 East 54th Street on June 1, 1939, the public

discovered handsome rooms of modern design, and pure screened areas on which silver- and gold-framed Kandinskys, Bauers and Delaunays were aesthetically spaced. Exhibitions of American painting followed, as Miss Rebay attracted a circle of abstract American artists and student converts to her increasingly passionate enthusiasm for "non-objective painting."

Between 1947 and 1951, land was secured on Fifth Avenue between 88th and 89th Streets for the building of a radical museum structure, commissioned from Frank Lloyd Wright in 1943. During the interim (1948) the collection moved to a six-story mansion on the site at 1071 Fifth Avenue. Here, on gray fabric-covered walls, with music by Bach piped into the galleries, Kandinskys, Bauers and the works of young non-objective artists were shown in successive exhibitions. Retrospective loan shows were also mounted, the most important being the Kandinsky Memorial Exhibition of 1945 and the Moholy-Nagy retrospective of 1947.

In 1948 the collection was enlarged with over seven hundred items by the purchase in its entirety of the estate of Karl Nierendorf, a well-known New York dealer in German painting. From this source, into the collection came Kokoschka's historic *Knight Errant*, eighteen additional Kandinskys, one hundred and ten Klees, six Chagalls, twenty-four Feiningers, fifty-four Kirchner watercolors and prints, as well as works by lesser-known Europeans and Americans. (These additions raised the number of Kandinskys in the collection to 180 – a determining factor in a later decision to sell fifty at auction in London in 1964.)

In November 1949, Solomon Guggenheim died, leaving the remainder of the paintings in his private collection to the Foundation. Thereafter followed a period of reorientation which resolved itself in 1952 when Miss Rebay retired as director of the Museum but not as a Trustee of the Foundation, and a new director was appointed. He was

James Johnson Sweeney, internationally known art critic and former Director of the Department of Painting and Sculpture at The Museum of Modern Art, New York.

As spokesman for the family, and President of the Foundation, Harry F. Guggenheim, Solomon's nephew, encouraged the new director to fulfill even further the aspirations of his uncle and reorganize the museum along more professional lines. Draperies were taken down, walls were painted a pristine white, heavy gold frames were removed in favor of no frames at all, and the paintings were catalogued and conserved. The name of the museum was changed from The Museum of Non-Objective Painting to The Solomon R. Guggenheim Museum.

When the first exhibition in the reconditioned building on Fifth Avenue opened in February 1953, the public saw the first portion of what only a few had been privileged to see at the Plaza apartment. Mr. Sweeney proceeded to show successive selections from the collection as quickly as they could be conserved and prepared for exhibition. In addition, there were three large loan exhibitions – Delaunay, Giacometti and Brancusi – and two shows of contemporary European and American painting (1953, 1954). Mr. Sweeney also began a vigorous acquisition program, purchasing important works by established artists as well as by young talent. The most serious omission in the collection hitherto had been sculpture. When Mr. Sweeney arrived he found only four Gabo constructions. Between 1953 and 1960 sculptures were acquired by gift or purchase: eleven Brancusis, three important Cubist Archipenkos, seven Calders, *Maggy* by Duchamp-Villon, *Twinned Column* by Pevsner, Arp's marble *Growth*, Miró's ceramic *Portico, Pomona* by Maillol, Henry Moore's *Standing Figure* (commissioned by the Museum), bronzes by Max Ernst and Giacometti. The first major painting purchase was Cézanne's *Clockmaker*, widely publicized in the press as costing $ 100,000, an enormous sum for a modern painting in 1954. Mr. Sweeney also bought important Braques, Mirós, Picassos and key examples by Kline, Pollock, de Kooning, Stuart Davis and many younger artists. In 1953 the Museum received a gift from the Estate of Katherine S. Dreier. Most important among the twenty-eight objects donated were Brancusi's oak *Little French Girl*; an Archipenko bronze, 1919; a Calder string mobile, 1935; Duchamp-Villon's *Cat*, 1913; Mondrian's *Composition*, 1929; a Gris *Still Life* of 1916 and three Schwitters collages of the early twenties.

As the Korean War drew to a close and building restrictions were removed, the Foundation prepared for the building of the long-planned Frank Lloyd Wright structure. The Museum was housed in temporary quarters at 7 East 72nd Street while the Wright building was being constructed. The prolonged battles between Wright and the City building authorities were given much attention by the press, as the architect strove to override New York's antiquated building code. Well-known disputes also developed between the architect and the director, disputes that were only ended when Wright died six months before the new museum opened in October 1959. Mr. Sweeney resigned in July of the following year.

The opening of the Wright building brought the museum into world-wide recognition for which it was only partly prepared. The transition from the temporary quarters on East 72nd Street with a limited staff into the huge structure where lines of spectators waited patiently for admission, strained the Museum's resources in every respect. It became the task of a new director, Thomas M. Messer, to build a professional staff that would be equal to the increased public demands and to adjust the exhibition and acquisition programs to an unprecedented situation.

From the time of his appointment in 1961, Mr. Messer and his staff therefore proceeded with the staging of large retrospectives that surveyed the work of such "Old Masters" of modern art as: Kandinsky, Klee, Munch, Schiele, Calder, David Smith, and Brancusi, while one-man shows of lesser scope were held for more contemporary figures. These included among others: Bacon, Guston, Morris Louis, Cornell, Bissier and Lichtenstein. Variously conceived group exhibitions exposed the public to diverse aesthetic perspectives.

Acquisitions have followed the same comprehensive pattern. As in previous administrations, they were in part oriented toward historical periods to fill existing gaps. Léger's *Great Parade* of 1954, Egon Schiele's *Portrait of an Old Man*, 1916, and Kupka's *Large Nude*, 1909, might be counted in this category, which was complemented through substantial additions of work by artists already amply represented such as Miró, Calder, Klee, and Giacometti. The effort to enrich the collection with principal examples by masters of our time yielded such additions as Dubuffet's *Nunc Stans*, 1965, and the recently acquired *Bidon l'esbroufe*, 1967, by the same artist; Bacon's large triptych *Crucifixion*, 1962, David Smith's *Cubi XXVII*, 1965, and Morris Louis's *Saraband*, 1959. The works of many younger painters and sculptors from Europe, the United States, and from Latin America have also entered the collection.

Any account summarizing the developments since the Solomon R. Guggenheim Foundation began to operate the Museum in the Frank Lloyd Wright building would have to refer to the Justin K. Thannhauser Foundation and its collection. A carefully selected part from this modern art treasure is currently on permanent display from Justin K. Thannhauser who has generously designated it as a bequest to the Guggenheim Museum after his lifetime. Consisting of seventy-five paintings and sculptures, its strength lies, in the first instance, in a group of Impressionist and Neo-Impressionist masterpieces antedating the Museum's original collecting scope and therefore serving as a historical background for the collection as a whole. Beginning with

Daumier's *The Chess Players*, c. 1863, and the great Pissarro of c. 1867, *Les Côteaux de l'Hermitage, Pontoise*, works from the Impressionist period include two major Manets and three important Renoirs. In the Neo-Impressionist group are four Cézannes: two still lifes, *Portrait of Mme Cézanne* and the landscape of c. 1900, *Bibémus*. Van Gogh is represented by the *Viaduct*, c. 1887, and the *Mountains of Saint-Rémy*, 1889; Gauguin by two Tahitian landscapes of 1891; Toulouse-Lautrec and Degas by splendid pastels.

The second important group contains thirty-four Picassos dating from 1900 to 1960. Particularly famous are the *Moulin de la Galette* of 1900, *Woman Ironing* of 1904, and *Woman with Yellow Hair*, 1931–32. Nearly every period of Picasso is represented, but the group is richest in early works – fourteen dating from before the Cubist period.

Notable also are two Modiglianis, a double Vuillard cityscape, a Fauve Braque, Soutine's *The Venetian*, Rouault's *Christ and The Fisherman*, as well as bronzes by Degas and Matisse, and drawings by Matisse and van Gogh.

The Museum's collection, seen as a whole, still bears the distinct mark of its Founder, Solomon R. Guggenheim, whose original intentions are safeguarded in policies formulated by succeeding presidents – by Harry F. Guggenheim during the crucial years from 1957 to 1969, and by Peter Lawson-Johnston, the Founder's grandson, at present. Born of the maturing convictions and tastes of a private collector, the Museum's holdings were increased in the Founder's lifetime by his continual contributions and at his death by the remainder of the collection gathered by him. As briefly described above, this very substantial nucleus has been increased and enriched by subsequent purchases and donations.

Louise Averill Svendsen
Curator

Josef Albers 1888–

Josef Albers was born March 19, 1888, in Bottrop, West-phalia, Germany. Between 1913 and 1920 he studied art in Berlin, Essen and Munich, after which he entered the Bauhaus at Weimar as a student. In 1923 he became a Bauhaus professor and moved with the school to Dessau where he developed his famous "Vorkurs", an introduction to design, based on the study of color, texture, form and line.

At the closing of the Bauhaus in 1933, Albers moved to the United States, where he headed the art department at Black Mountain College in North Carolina until 1949. It was also in 1949 that the artist began elaborating his inexhaustible series *Homage to the Square*, in which he experimented with colors and the infinite variants produced through their direct interaction.

Internationally known both as a teacher and an artist, Albers was the Chairman of the art school at Yale from 1950 to 1958. He is the author of numerous poems, articles and books on art and education. He has now retired from teaching but continues to work in New Haven, Connecticut.

b And p. 1937

Oil on pressed wood, 23³/₄ x 23³/₄" (60.3 x 60.3 cm.)

Signed and dated l.r. "A37"

Provenance:

J. B. Neumann, New York
Karl Nierendorf, New York
Estate of Karl Nierendorf, 1948

Exhibitions:

NEW ART CIRCLE, New York, January 2–17, 1945, *Joseph Albers*

CINCINNATI MODERN ART SOCIETY, LORING ANDREWS GALLERY, Ohio, February 26–March 17, 1945, *From Realism to Abstraction*, ill.

CITY ART MUSEUM, St. Louis, Missouri, February 16–March 19, 1946, *American Painting, 39th Exhibition*

MUSEUM OF NON-OBJECTIVE PAINTING, New York, May 31–October 11(?), 1949, *Tenth Anniversary Exhibition*

YALE UNIVERSITY ART GALLERY, New Haven, Connecticut, April 25–June 18, 1956, *Joseph Albers, Paintings, Prints, Projects*, no.17

THE SOLOMON R. GUGGENHEIM MUSEUM, New York, October 21, 1959–June 19, 1960, *Inaugural Selection* (Checklist)

WASHINGTON GALLERY OF MODERN ART, Washington, D.C., November 5–December 31, 1965, *Joseph Albers, The American Years*

THE SOLOMON R. GUGGENHEIM MUSEUM, New York, June 28–October 1, 1967, *Museum Collection, Seven Decades, A Selection* (Checklist)

References:

ROBBINS, DANIEL and ROBBINS, EUGENIA, "Joseph Albers: Art is Looking at Us", *The Studio*, vol.CLXVII, no.850, February 1964, p.57, ill.

GOMRINGER, EUGEN, *Joseph Albers, His Work as a Contribution to Visual Articulation in the Twentieth Century*, New York, 1968, p.70, ill.

ROSENBERG, HAROLD, *Artworks and Packages*, New York, 1969, p.182, ill.

48.1172x264

In his paintings of the second half of the 1930's, Albers was concerned with establishing a basic "scale" of form and color relationships, favoring the simplest forms possible, with large 3's and 8's and L's among his preferred motifs, similar to the *b* and *p* of this painting.

In this painting, the strictness of rhythm and precise regularity attained relate to his flashed glass paintings from the Bauhaus period. These characteristics were to be more fully developed in the 1940's when he eliminated texture further and reduced form to even simpler terms. The careful adjustment of forms to the frame and the distinct isolation of his main motif in a rectangle-within-rectangle format anticipate his best-known series "Homage to the Square".

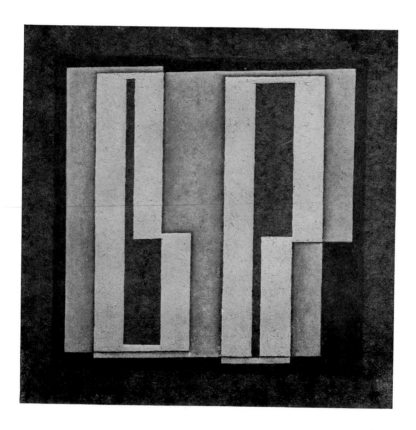

JOSEF ALBERS

Homage to the Square: Apparition. 1959

Oil on board, 47^1/$_2$ x 47^1/$_2$" (120.7 x 120.7 cm.)

Inscribed l.r. "A 59" and on reverse "Homage to the Square://'Apparition'//Albers 1959"

Provenance:
Sidney Janis Gallery, New York, 1961

Exhibitions:

THE SOLOMON R. GUGGENHEIM MUSEUM, New York, October 13, 1961–January 1, 1962, *American Abstract Expressionists and Imagists*, no.1, ill.

WORCESTER ART MUSEUM, Massachusetts, February 6–April 7, 1963, *Aspects of Twentieth Century Painting Lent by The Solomon R. Guggenheim Museum*, no.1, ill.

INDIANA UNIVERSITY, Bloomington, April 19–May 10, 1964, *American Painting 1910–1960*

THE SOLOMON R. GUGGENHEIM MUSEUM, New York, April 30–September 1, 1965, *Paintings from the Collection of The Solomon R. Guggenheim Museum*, no.80, ill.

THE SOLOMON R. GUGGENHEIM MUSEUM, New York, June 28–October 1, 1967, *Museum Collection, Seven Decades, A Selection* (Checklist)

CINCINNATI ART MUSEUM, Ohio, October 3, 1969–March 29, 1970, *Paintings from the Guggenheim Museum, A Loan Exhibition of Modern Paintings Covering the Period 1949–1965, from The Solomon R. Guggenheim Museum*, no.19

References:

ROBBINS, DANIEL and ROBBINS, EUGENIA, "Joseph Albers: Art is Looking at Us", *The Studio*, vol.CLXVII, no.850, February 1964, p.55, ill.

ARNASON, H. H., *History of Modern Art*, New York, 1968, pl.137

GOMRINGER, EUGEN, *Joseph Albers, His Work as a Contribution to Visual Articulation in the Twentieth Century*, New York, 1968, p.70, ill.

61.1590

The artist's series "Homage to the Square" was begun in the summer of 1949 and is still in progress. Although the underlying arrangement of superimposed squares remains the same, in proportion and placement each work is totally different in effect as a result of complex arrangements of color. Albers's interest in the square, which in this series functions as a container for his color, occurred at an early date in his career; in his work of the Bauhaus period the square was used in varying combinations with rectangles of different proportions.

For Albers the square is less an end in itself than a stage, "the actor and the voice which perform the endless drama of the excitements of color instrumentation". Color is for him the "structural means of the pictorial idiom". He is interested in the psychic effect caused by the interaction of color. The uniqueness of the artist's contribution resides in his ability to activate and evoke such a richness and variety of imagery through color.

Study for Homage to the Square: Closing. 1964

Oil on board, $15^{13}/_{16}$ x $15^{13}/_{16}''$ (40.2 x 40.2 cm.)

Incised l.r. "A 64" and inscribed on reverse "Albers 1964//
Closing"

Provenance:
Gift of the artist, 1969

69.1917

JOSEF ALBERS

Study for Homage to the Square: Starting. 1969

Oil on board, 15$^{13}/_{16}$ x 15$^{13}/_{16}$″ (40.2 x 40.2 cm.)

Incised l.r. "A 69" and inscribed on reverse "Albers 1969//
Starting"

Provenance:
Gift of the artist, 1969

69.1916

Pierre Alechinsky 1927–

Pierre Alechinsky was born October 19, 1927, in Brussels. In 1944 he attended the École Nationale Supérieure d'Architecture et des Arts Décoratifs in Brussels to study book illustration. In 1947 he held his first one-man exhibition in Brussels.

In 1948 a group of young artists (Appel, Corneille, Jorn and the Surrealist poet Dotremont) founded the group COBRA (COpenhagen, BRussels, Amsterdam). "Fighting calculated abstraction (the École de Paris) on the right and social realism on the left", their aim was an art somewhere between the two: expressive of vital, spontaneous and uncalculated human impulses. Their art was to be of a collective and experimental nature. To this end they drew inspiration from German Expressionism, folk art, children's art and the art of the alienated.

Alechinsky joined COBRA in 1949. He exhibited with the group that same year at the Stedelijk Museum, Amsterdam. Although the artists broke up in 1951, Alechinsky's art retains the unselfconscious vehemence of expression, the blatant color, rapid brush-stroke and automatist images characteristic of COBRA painting.

Alechinsky moved to Paris in 1951, where he studied etching with Stanley Hayter at *Atelier 17*. In 1955 he traveled to Japan. The unpredetermined images and rapidity of execution of Japanese calligraphy inspired him to make a film of Japanese masters at work. Alechinsky exhibited at the São Paulo Bienal in 1959 and represented Belgium at the Venice Biennale in 1960. The artist resides in Paris.

PIERRE ALECHINSKY

First Flight (Premier vol). 1958

Gouache, 31 3/4 x 41" (80.6 x 104.1 cm.)

Signed l. r. "Alechinsky"

Provenance:
Gift, Mrs. Leo Simon, New York, 1965

Exhibitions:

ARTS CLUB OF CHICAGO, February 26–March 27, 1965, *Pierre Alechinsky*, no.6

THE SOLOMON R. GUGGENHEIM MUSEUM, New York July 8–September 14, 1969, *Selected Sculpture and Works on Paper*, p.13, ill.

65.1778

Perhaps more than any of the original members of COBRA (who placed predominant emphasis on color), Alechinsky has consistently shown an interest in the expressive powers of line. This is supported by the profusion of etchings, lithographs and book illustrations that the artist has executed. Upon his discovery of drawing, Alechinsky made the following statement: "In drawing, everything must be written down without regret. Past time becomes legible, so does space, and thought... I started to enjoy myself. I felt I was getting somewhere. No more of this heavy painting material to drag behind me. A pen, a sheet of paper, some ink, some water. Inscribe, describe." (Interview with Jacques Putman in *L'Oeil*, no.82, Paris, 1961)

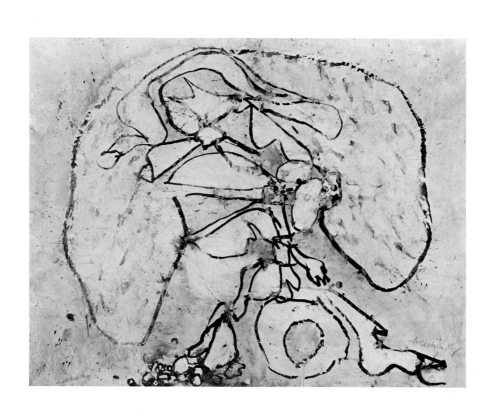

Large Black Figure. 1968.

Aquatec and charcoal on canvas with masking tape, $59^1/_4$ x $47^3/_8''$ (150.5 x 120.3 cm.)

Inscribed l.r. "Antes" and on reverse "Grosse Schwarze// Figur//Atquatec//1968"

Provenance:
Lefebre Gallery, New York, 1969

Exhibitions:
LEFEBRE GALLERY, New York, March 4–25, 1969, *Horst Antes*, no.21, ill.
X BIENAL DE SÃO PAULO, September–December 1969, p.22, no.25

69.1880

Horst Antes 1936–

Horst Antes was born October 28, 1936, in Heppenheim, Germany. He attended art school in Karlsruhe between 1957 and 1959. His first one-man exhibition was held in 1960 at the Galerie Der Spiegel in Cologne.

The painter's early work (1959–60) was abstract and gestural but it soon developed into the expressionist figural style which is characteristic of it today. In its vigorous color and primitive or archetypal imagery, it is distinctly related to the northern European expressionism typical of the COBRA group (see Alechinsky biography). Younger than the COBRA artists, Antes is usually grouped with the European trend known as "New Figuration" or "Neo-expression-ism".

Antes's paintings of the early sixties show monumental tubular figures interlocked on a closely packed surface. Compositionally reminiscent of Léger, the playful and expressionist spirit is entirely different. The colors are childlike and arbitrary and cover a broad range. In the late sixties, the artist's hues became progressively brighter and simultaneously the compositions became simpler and more compact, based on single images or figures.

Antes was awarded the UNESCO prize at the 1966 Venice Biennale. His first New York one-man exhibition was held in 1967 at the Lefebre Gallery. The artist resides near Karlsruhe where he teaches at the Karlsruhe Academy.

The mythical figure of a trunkless man which is Antes's consistent theme since approximately 1960 is a mercilessly ironic image of modern man: always physical (through the broad, thickset volumes), sometimes grotesque (at other times pathetic), and anonymously interchangeable. As the artist's style has evolved, this image has gained in impact through its progressive isolation and increasingly iconic effect. Although expressive brushstroke is still important, the flatness and precision of the image, the economy of colors, as well as the "metaphysical" spatial environment are all characteristic of the artist's work of the late sixties.

Arp began making painted wooden reliefs as early as 1914. Whereas his early reliefs are characterized by fantasy-inspired shapes, brightly contrasting colors and often a complex superimposition of flat cut-out forms, in the early thirties they attained a more homogeneous image, both in chromatic and formal relationships.

The reduction of the color scale to black or white on white emphasizes the softly rounded contours as being just what they are: the encounter of identical yet differently situated planes. The title "Constellation" is in no sense arbitrary but indicative of Arp's interest in natural forms and natural distribution as a guide-line to his creation.

There exist three numbered variations on this theme, of which the Museum's is *Variation III*. *Variation I* is in the Munson-Williams-Proctor Institute at Utica, New York.

JEAN ARP

Growth (Croissance). 1938

Marble, 31⁵/₈″ (80.4 cm.) high, marble base, 7⁷/₈″
(20 cm.) high

Not inscribed

Provenance:
Peter Watson, London, 1953

Exhibitions:
MUSÉE NATIONAL D'ART MODERNE, Paris, May–June 1952,
L'œuvre du XXe siècle, no.116; traveled to TATE GALLERY,
London, July 15–August 17, 1952, as *Twentieth Century
Masterpieces*

THE SOLOMON R. GUGGENHEIM MUSEUM, New York,
May 13–October 11, 1953, *Selection II* (Checklist)

THE SOLOMON R. GUGGENHEIM MUSEUM, New York,
October 6, 1954–February 27, 1955, *Selection IV*
(Checklist)

THE SOLOMON R. GUGGENHEIM MUSEUM, New York,
July 26–October 9, 1955, *Selection V* (Checklist)

THE SOLOMON R. GUGGENHEIM MUSEUM, New York,
January 24–May 1, 1956, *Selection VI* (Checklist)

THE SOLOMON R. GUGGENHEIM MUSEUM, New York,
October 21, 1959–June 19, 1960, *Inaugural Selection*
(Checklist)

THE SOLOMON R. GUGGENHEIM MUSEUM, New York (in
collaboration with THE UCLA ART GALLERIES, Los Angeles),
May 16–June 29, 1969, *Jean Arp (1887–1966): A Retrospective Exhibition.*

THE SOLOMON R. GUGGENHEIM MUSEUM, New York,
July 8–September 14, 1969, *Selected Sculpture and Works
on Paper,* p.95, ill.

References:
ARP, JEAN, *On My Way, Poetry and Essays, 1912–1947,*
New York, 1948, pl.15b
READ, HERBERT, *The Art of Jean Arp,* New York, 1968,
p.95, pl.104

53.1359

After his earlier torn-paper works, and string and wood
reliefs, Arp turned to free-standing sculpture in 1931.
Perhaps more than any other of the artist's varied modes
of expression, the free forms of his sculpture-in-the-round
illustrate one of his basic *credos:* "Art is a fruit which
grows within man, like a fruit on a plant, or a child in his
mother's womb." Arp's devotion to abstraction was not
due to formalist ideals; on the contrary, the artist's
commitment was to an art which was spontaneous,
sensual and irrational, like birth or growth or any other
natural process.

Arp's first sculpture of 1931 was a rhythmically deformed
human torso in marble. *Growth* of 1938, in its rhythmic
curves, writhing movement and upward thrust, could be
considered a later development of the same theme. More
exactly, it might be defined as the concrete configuration
of an organic energy with neither vegetal nor animal
distinction.

There exist several other versions of *Growth* dated 1938:
a slightly larger marble version (Sidney Janis collection)
as well as three bronze castings, one of which is in the
Philadelphia Museum of Art.

Francis Bacon 1909–

Francis Bacon was born in Dublin on October 28, 1909. He received little formal education. At the age of 16 he moved to London and then lived for about two years in Berlin and Paris. Upon his return to London he established himself as an interior decorator. Self-taught as an artist, he began to make drawings, watercolors, and then to work in oils. There followed a period inspired by Picasso's Surrealist style of the late 1920's. Bacon first exhibited in late 1929 or 1930, showing sporadically thereafter. In the mid-1940's his mature style emerged. He met Graham Sutherland who encouraged him, and he began to exhibit regularly. Among his important exhibitions were retrospectives at the Tate Gallery, London in 1962, and The Solomon R. Guggenheim Museum, New York in 1963.

A certain stylistic evolution in Bacon's work is evident. His palette was at first a limited one. He moved from a dense, stickily textured surface to more painterly works revealing a lighter touch and richer color. In his earlier work movement was indicated by blurring edges and opening planes; in more recent canvases motion is expressed by extreme foreshortening or twisting of forms, so that figures in motion become grotesquely deformed. Bacon returns again and again to the same themes, many drawn form traditional art or photographs: Velasquez's *Portrait of Pope Innocent X*, van Gogh's figures in landscape, Muybridge's nudes in motion. These themes are constantly elaborated and transformed. What is most striking in Bacon's oeuvre, despite any stylistic changes, is the consistency of his nightmare vision.

FRANCIS BACON

Three Studies for a Crucifixion. 1962

Oil with sand on canvas, 3 panels, each 78 x 57″ (198.2 x 144.8 cm.)

Not inscribed

Provenance:

from the artist through Marlborough Fine Art Ltd., London, 1964

Exhibitions:

TATE GALLERY, London, May–July 1962, *Francis Bacon*, no.90, ill.; traveled to KUNSTHALLE, Mannheim, July–August, no.79, ill.; GALLERIA CIVICA D'ARTE MODERNA, Turin, September–October, no.83, ill.; KUNSTHAUS, Zürich, October–November, no.78; STEDELIJK MUSEUM, Amsterdam, January–February 1963, no.70, ill.

TATE GALLERY, London, June 1963, *British Painting in the Sixties*, no.4, center panel ill.

THE SOLOMON R. GUGGENHEIM MUSEUM, New York, October 18, 1963–January 12, 1964, *Francis Bacon*, no.57, pp.66–67, ill; traveled to THE ART INSTITUTE OF CHICAGO, January 24–February 23, 1964

THE SOLOMON R. GUGGENHEIM MUSEUM, New York, July 1–September 13, 1964, *Van Gogh and Expressionism*

THE SOLOMON R. GUGGENHEIM MUSEUM, New York, April 30–September 1, 1965, *Paintings from the Collection of The Solomon R. Guggenheim Museum*, no.84, p.80–81, ill.

References:

ALLEY, RONALD, "Francis Bacon," *Cimaise*, 10e année, no.63, January–February 1963, p.22, ill.

HARRISON, JANE, "Dissent on Francis Bacon", *Arts*, vol.38, no.3, December 1963, p.20, ill. (left panel)

ALLEY, RONALD, *Francis Bacon*, London, 1964, pp.144–145, fig. 201

ARNASON, H. H., *History of Modern Art*, New York, 1968, p.532, pls.937–939

64.1700

Characteristically, in *Three Studies for a Crucifixion*, Bacon uses a traditional religious subject and Renaissance stylistic formulae. The triptych is associated with sacred art and the staged presentation of figures in a diorama-like space is a Renaissance convention. But these prototypes are entirely and grotesquely transformed – even parodied or blasphemed. In Renaissance painting, the figures are placed logically and obviously, conveying a sense of order and control; here all is mysterious, confused and deformed. The iconography is ambiguous. Flayed meat has been used in past art, notably by Rembrandt and Soutine, but not to convey the atmosphere of the charnel house. These are not mere sides of beef, they have human characteristics.

Bacon has offered some explanation of his iconography. He says that the undulating "figure" on the right was inspired by the Christ in Cimabue's *Crucifixion* which reminds him of a worm crawling down the cross. He says, too, that he associates slaughterhouses and meat with the Crucifixion. There is a feeling of peculiarly modern depravity and torment conveyed by the bullet holes, the mysteriously drawn windowshades and the blood-spattered bed. The topicality of imagery is increased by suggestions of tabloid newspaper photographs in the blurred gray-black faces and gestures of the ominous figures in the left panel. The screaming, clashing hot reds and oranges and the black rectangles press forward aggressively, producing an effect of choking claustrophobia. These colors and shapes force the contorted, bloody figures forward to confront the viewer at close range with a horrific image of death and decay.

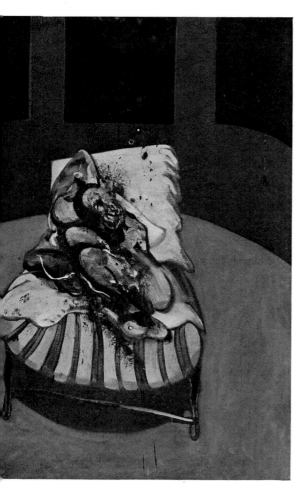 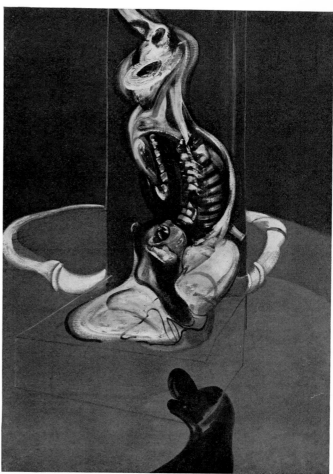

Gianfranco Baruchello 1924–

Gianfranco Baruchello was born August 29, 1924, in Livorno (Leghorn), Italy. Before becoming an artist, according to certain sources he worked as a biochemist. He had his first one-man exhibition in 1963 at the Galleria La Tartaruga, Rome and his first one-man exhibition in America at the Cordier and Ekstrom Gallery, New York in 1964.

A broad field of interests from philosophy and literature to different branches of the sciences is reflected in the artist's work. The avowed influences of Marcel Duchamp, John Cage, Joyce, Pound and Eliot are manifest in his creative technique: a technique of non-causal free association similar to the illogical sequences of dreams, into which are integrated associative symbols and images constituting verbal, visual or ideational puns. The objects of these puns often derive from a realm of traditionally irrefutable scientific authority such as mathematics, physics, astronautics, ballistics. Baruchello's preoccupations with literature, plays on words and the free functioning of the mind are definitely reminiscent of Surrealism even though the results are technically and visually different.

Baruchello has published several books, written television scripts, and made a film called *La verifica incerta (The Uncertain Verification)* which was shown in 1965 at the Festival della Nuova Musica in Palermo. The artist resides in Rome.

GIANFRANCO BARUCHELLO

Wordly Games (Les Jeux du Monde). 1965

Ink on two layers of plexiglas and paper mounted on plexiglas, 19¼ x 23⅝″ (48.9 x 60 cm.)

Inscribed on reverse "les jeux du monde à la surface de la nebuleuse des langages // 19.6 x 24 cm. 50 x 61 // Baruchello // 1965/5″

Provenance:

the artist
Cordier & Ekstrom Gallery, New York, 1966

Exhibitions:

CORDIER & EKSTROM GALLERY, New York, January 11–February 5, 1966, *Gianfranco Baruchello*

THE SOLOMON R. GUGGENHEIM MUSEUM, New York, July 8–September 14, 1969, *Selected Sculpture and Works on Paper*, p.14, ill.

References:

ASHTON, DORE, "Art-Baruchello," *Arts and Architecture*, April 1964, pp.6–7

66.1795

One could describe Baruchello's work in general as the signs and symbols of freely associated ideas incorporated in a hypothetical game structure (in other words a non-real system with its own syntactical rules). The seemingly illogical yet strictly structured system of the game is a prevalent theme in Baruchello's work. The superimposed plexiglas sheets refer to successive phases of execution of the work, thereby introducing an unusually precise temporal index of the progression of the artist's thought.

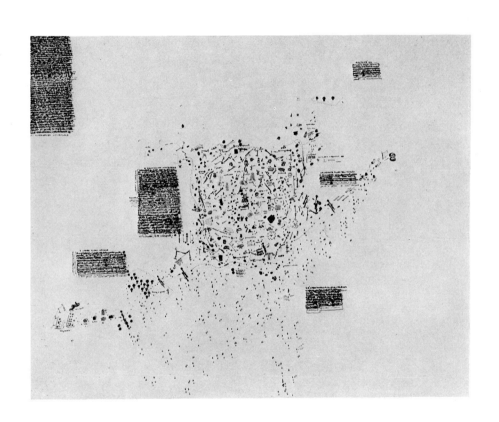

Title 1 (Lens Box). 1965

Construction, mixed media, 30 x 71^3/$_4$ x 9^1/$_2$″ (76.2 x 182.2 x 24.2 cm.)

Inscribed l.c. "Title 1"

Provenance:
from the artist through Bonino Gallery, New York, 1965

Exhibitions:
BONINO GALLERY, New York, April 13–May 8, 1965, *Mary Bauermeister, Paintings and Constructions*, no.1

THE SOLOMON R. GUGGENHEIM MUSEUM, New York, July 8–September 14, 1969, *Selected Sculpture and Works on Paper*, p.96, ill.

65.1789

Mary Bauermeister 1934–

Mary Bauermeister was born in Frankfurt, Germany, in 1934. She began painting in 1953, and participated in her first group shows in 1961 in Germany. Her first one-man exhibition was held at the Stedelijk Museum, Amsterdam, in 1962. She has subsequently shown in numerous exhibitions in the United States and Europe and has been represented in New York by the Bonino Gallery since 1964. Bauermeister now lives in New York City.

Bauermeister combines drawing, painting, relief sculpture and assemblage. She covers her surfaces with a dense accumulation of unusual materials: sand and pebbles, hollow bones and shells, torn linen, driftwood and spherical lenses which reflect light and distort the other objects. A fine calligraphic line binds these elements together. The receding and projecting surfaces undulate strangely. Shifting analogies are constantly presented: a lens distorts a stone, next to the stone may be a drawing of the stone either distorted or not, next to the drawing may be a photograph of a hand gluing down the stone, and descriptive words may be woven through the myriad objects. The effect of these works is fantastic, compulsive and ambiguous.

Bauermeister's elegant relief boxes, a mode to which she turned early in the 1960's, are comprised of variegated calligraphies, wittily cryptic or Dada phrases, and found objects. Complex magnifying lenses, the form of which is repeated in the relief objects themselves, are often interposed between surface and viewer. Such works are, stylistically, a highly personal version of the European *tachiste* sensibility.

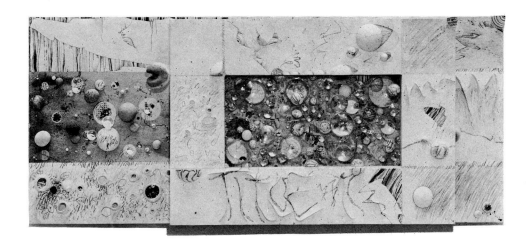

William Baziotes 1912–1963

William Baziotes was born in Pittsburgh June 11, 1912, of Greek descent, and grew up in Reading in the Pennsylvania Dutch country. For two years prior to moving to New York in 1933, he worked for a stained glass company in Reading; acquaintances there stimulated his interest in art. In New York he studied painting at the National Academy of Design (1933–36), worked as a teacher for the WPA Art Project (1936–38) and painted for the WPA Easel Painting Project (1938–40). He subsequently taught at the Brooklyn Museum Art School and New York University (1949–52), People's Art Center, The Museum of Modern Art (1950–52) and Hunter College (1952–62).

From 1939 Baziotes was engaged in a form of painting derived from Cubism, linear but expressionist. In 1941 this was subverted by the processes of automatism; he stopped painting but drew continually. When he resumed painting (1942), the influence of Matta appeared and he exhibited in André Breton's *First Papers of Surrealism* at the Whitelaw Reid Mansion. As with other artists who modified or abandoned Cubism through contact with Surrealism, the grid of Cubism remained. In 1944, the year of Baziotes's first one-man show at Peggy Guggenheim's Art of this Century Gallery, the all-over grid was inhabited by floral and faunal forms in muted color, anticipating the later work. A transition occurred at that time which led to his characteristic mature work: the compartmented structure dissolved and the remaining forms became simpler, more monumental and, at the same time, softer. In the final development of his art Baziotes painted curvilinear, quasi-biomorphic but flattened forms with deliberately drawn contours, floating in marine-like space.

After 1955 Baziotes spent each summer in Reading until his death on June 6, 1963. His work was honored with a memorial exhibition at the Guggenheim Museum in 1965.

WILLIAM BAZIOTES

Dusk. 1958

Oil on canvas, 60³/₈ x 48″ (153.4 x 121.9 cm.)

Inscribed l.r. "Baziotes", on reverse "Dusk//W. Baziotes//1958" and on vertical cross bar "Wm//Baziotes//90 La Salle//St; New York//N.Y."

Provenance:
from the artist through Samuel M. Kootz Gallery, New York, 1959

Exhibitions:

CARNEGIE INSTITUTE, Pittsburgh, December 4, 1958–February 9, 1959, *Pittsburgh International Bicentennial Exhibition of Contemporary Painting and Sculpture*, no.34, ill.

UNIVERSITY OF MICHIGAN MUSEUM OF ART, Ann Arbor, April 13–June 12, 1960, *Images at Mid-Century*

SIDNEY JANIS GALLERY, New York, March 13–April 8, 1961, *Baziotes*

PHILADELPHIA MUSEUM OF ART, November 2, 1961–January 7, 1962, *Guggenheim Museum Exhibition, A Loan Collection of Paintings, Drawings, and Prints from The Solomon R. Guggenheim Museum, New York*, no.4

WORCESTER ART MUSEUM, Massachusetts, February 6–April 7, 1963, *Aspects of Twentieth Century Painting Lent by The Solomon R. Guggenheim Museum*, no.2, ill.

MINNEAPOLIS INSTITUTE OF ARTS, November 27, 1963–January 19, 1964, *Four Centuries of American Art*

THE SOLOMON R. GUGGENHEIM MUSEUM, New York, February 5–March 21, 1965, *William Baziotes, A Memorial Exhibition*, no.38, ill.; traveled to CINCINNATI ART MUSEUM, Ohio, April 2–May 2; READING PUBLIC MUSEUM AND ART GALLERY, Pennsylvania, May 23–June 27; SANTA BARBARA MUSEUM OF ART, California, July 3–August 22; MILWAUKEE ART CENTER, September 9–October 10; ROSE

ART MUSEUM, Brandeis University, Waltham, Massachusetts, November 1–30; MUNSON-WILLIAMS-PROCTOR INSTITUTE, Utica, New York, December 11, 1965–January 11, 1966; COLUMBUS GALLERY OF FINE ARTS, Ohio, January 27–February 28; CORCORAN GALLERY OF ART, Washington, D.C., March 15–April 15; MINNEAPOLIS INSTITUTE OF ARTS, May 15–June 15; DALLAS MUSEUM OF FINE ARTS, July 4–August 4; AKRON ART INSTITUTE, Ohio, October 10–November 11, 1966

CINCINNATI ART MUSEUM, Ohio, October 3, 1969–March 29, 1970, *Paintings from the Guggenheim Museum, A Loan Exhibition of Modern Paintings Covering the Period 1949–1965, from The Solomon R. Guggenheim Museum*, no.18, ill.

References:

READ, HERBERT, *A Concise History of Modern Painting*, New York, 1959, pl.305

PELLEGRINI, ALDO, *New Tendencies in Art*, New York, 1966, p.137, ill.

ARNASON, H. H., *History of Modern Art*, New York, 1968, pl.207

59.1544

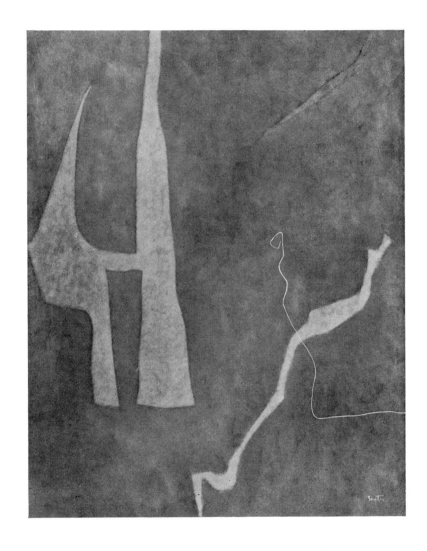

WILLIAM BAZIOTES

Aquatic. 1961

Oil on canvas, 66 x 78^1/$_8$″ (167.7 x 198.5 cm.)

Inscribed l.r. "Baziotes" and on reverse "AQUATIC//W. Baziotes 1961"

Provenance:
Saidenberg Gallery, New York, 1963
Collective Anonymous Gift, 1963

Exhibitions:
XXXII BIENNALE INTERNAZIONALE D'ARTE VENEZIA, June 20–October 18, 1964, *Today's Art in Museums: The Solomon R. Guggenheim Museum*, no.3, p.33

THE SOLOMON R. GUGGENHEIM MUSEUM, New York, February 5–March 21, 1965, *William Baziotes, A Memorial Exhibition*, no.40, ill.; traveled to CINCINNATI ART MUSEUM, Ohio, April 2–May 2; READING PUBLIC MUSEUM AND ART GALLERY, Pennsylvania, May 23–June 27; SANTA BARBARA MUSEUM OF ART, California, July 3–August 22; MILWAU-KEE ART CENTER, September 9–October 10; ROSE ART MUSEUM, Brandeis University, Waltham, Massachusetts, November 1–30; MUNSON-WILLIAMS-PROCTOR INSTITUTE, Utica, New York, December 11, 1965–January 11, 1966; COLUMBUS GALLERY OF FINE ARTS, Ohio, January 27–February 28; CORCORAN GALLERY OF ART, Washington, D.C., March 15–April 15; MINNEAPOLIS INSTITUTE OF ARTS, May 15–June 15; DALLAS MUSEUM OF FINE ARTS, July 4–August 4, 1966

63.1630

By the 1950's Abstract Expressionism had developed in two directions – gestural and chromatic abstraction. Baziotes's statements, as if issuing from Harold Rosenberg's ideal "action painter", would classify him as belonging to the gestural camp: "What happens on the canvas is unpredictable and surprising to me...", or "Whereas certain people start with a recollection or an experience, to some of us the act of doing it becomes the experience..." (quoted in *William Baziotes, A Memorial Exhibition*, New York, 1965, p.40). But Baziotes was a slow, deliberate painter. He scumbled his paint, laying color over color in soft, dry touches. This process became increasingly protracted during the course of the fifties until his output had slowed to only a few paintings a year. Any impression of motion in his paintings is checked by the sense of figure blending with ground achieved through the close-valued color and pulsating edges of his forms. This is clearly not gestural in the sense of Pollock or de Kooning. On the other hand, despite implications for placing him with the chromatic abstractionists, he did not, as did Rothko, Newman and Reinhardt, simplify and expand the areas of color into fields which relate to the canvas support. Rather he retained an essentially traditional concept of space, within which his biomorphic forms float. In this respect Baziotes's art maintains its contacts with the beginnings of Abstract Expressionism, with Gorky and especially with Miró, who combined the forms of Surrealism with flat, color painting. In *Dusk*, 1958, and *Aquatic*, 1961, the relationship to Miró is clear, in the curvilinear, flattened creatures and nervous, radiating lines. The transparent, atmospheric space and primeval shapes suggest a feeling of the oneness of nature. The titles reaffirm our response to Baziotes's imagery, alluding to the transparent atmosphere of the primordial and the watery precincts where biomorphs hover.

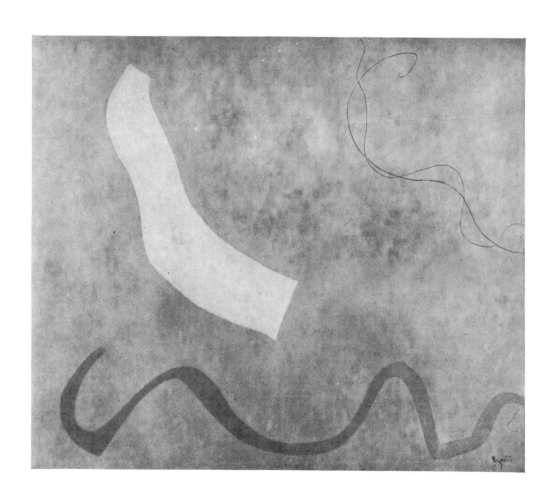

Ilya Bolotowsky 1907–

Ilya Bolotowsky was born July 1, 1907, in St. Petersburg, Russia. After studies in Caucasus and Turkey, in 1923 he immigrated with his family to America, becoming a United States citizen in 1929.

In the early thirties, when Bolotowsky turned from figurative painting to abstraction, his work showed a strong influence of Malevitch's Suprematism in his use of free floating planes on a contrasting background. However his discovery of Mondrian in 1933 was to direct the orientation of the artist's work toward Neo-Plasticism. Along with Holtzman, Diller, von Wiegand and Glarner, Bolotowsky was one of Mondrian's most faithful disciples of the forties. He remains an exponent of Neo-Plasticism today, not only in his canvases but extending the principles of this primarily pictorial idiom (based on flat tensions on a flat picture plane) to three-dimensional painted columns (since 1961).

Bolotowsky was one of the founders of the American Abstract Artists Association in 1936, a group whose aim was to make New York a center for abstract art. In the late thirties he executed several abstract mural commissions in and around New York. From 1946 to 1948 he taught at Black Mountain College, North Carolina and since then he has taught regularly throughout the United States. The artist has also written several plays and produced numerous experimental films.

ILYA BOLOTOWSKY

Blue Plane. 1963

Oil on canvas, two panels, 69^1/$_2$ x 86^1/$_2$" (176.5 x 219.7 cm.)

Signed and dated l.r. "Ilya Bolotowsky // 63"

Provenance:
from the artist, 1965

Exhibitions:

THE SOLOMON R. GUGGENHEIM MUSEUM, New York, June 28–October 1, 1967, *Museum Collection, Seven Decades, A Selection* (Checklist)

FORDHAM UNIVERSITY, New York, April 28–May 19, 1968, *Five Museums Come to Fordham*

CINCINNATI ART MUSEUM, Ohio, October 3, 1969–March 29, 1970, *Paintings from the Guggenheim Museum, A Loan Exhibition of Modern Paintings Covering the Period 1949–1965, from The Solomon R. Guggenheim Museum*, no.26

64.1724

In 1969 Bolotowsky made a general statement about his painting which is pertinent to *Blue Plane*: "More and more since the mid-forties, my work became my own version of *Neoplasticism*. Unlike Mondrian, I did not limit my palette to yellow, red and blue. Unlike Mondrian and Vantongerloo, I, generally, assign the larger areas in a painting to red, blue, yellow, sometimes to violet and, sometimes, to black which I add to achieve a pseudo-vibration through clashing with the chromatic colors like reds or blues. White areas are most often reduced in size. At times, a juxtaposition of two closely related colors is used to create an ambivalent now appearing, now disappearing contrast. I seldom find need for black lines." (quoted in *Leonardo*, Pergamon Press, vol.2, 1969, pp.225–226)

Pierre Bonnard 1867–1947

Pierre Bonnard was born October 3, 1867, at Fontenay-aux-Roses in France. After lycée studies and law school in Paris, in 1889 he decided to become a painter. He earned his first recognition as a master of poster art, lithography and illustration.

As a member of the French Nabi group (together with Sérusier, Maurice Denis, Vuillard and others) Bonnard's early work emphasized symbolic color and line and their emotional impact as decorative patterns. As a Nabi, Bonnard was influenced not only by Gauguin but by Cézanne and the Japanese print in his organization of flattened and continuous surfaces through contrasts of light and color.

Bonnard exhibited at the *Salon des Indépendants* in 1891. He had his first one-man show in 1896 (Galerie Durand-Ruel, Paris). After a trip to the south of France in 1909, his treatment of light became more vibrant and his color more arbitrary, characteristics which were to continue throughout his career. In 1925 Bonnard bought a house in Le Cannet near Cannes. There he was to spend most of his time henceforth with his wife and model Marthe Boursin. He died at Le Cannet January 23, 1947.

Dining Room on the Garden. 1934

Oil on canvas, 50 x 53³/₈″ (127 x 135.6 cm.)

Signed l.l. "Bonnard"

Provenance:

the artist, 1935
Galerie Bernheim-Jeune, Paris, 1937
Pierre Loeb, Paris, 1938

Exhibitions:

SALON D'AUTOMNE, Paris, 1935

PETIT PALAIS, Paris, June–October 1937, *Les Maîtres de l'Art Indépendant, 1895–1937,* no.25

SOLOMON R. GUGGENHEIM FOUNDATION, New York, June 1, 1939, *Art of Tomorrow* (Fifth catalogue of the Solomon R. Guggenheim Collection of Non-Objective Paintings), no.432

THE MUSEUM OF MODERN ART, New York, May 24–October 15, 1944, *Art in Progress: 15th Anniversary Exhibition, Painting, Sculpture and Prints*

THE SOLOMON R. GUGGENHEIM MUSEUM, New York, May 13–October 11, 1953, *Selection II* (Checklist)

THE SOLOMON R. GUGGENHEIM MUSEUM, New York, October 6, 1954–February 27, 1955, *Selection IV* (Checklist)

SAN FRANCISCO MUSEUM OF ART, June 17–July 10, 1955, *Art in the Twentieth Century*

WADSWORTH ATHENEUM, Hartford, Connecticut, October 19–December 4, 1955, *Twentieth Century Painting from Three Cities–New York, New Haven and Hartford*

THE SOLOMON R. GUGGENHEIM MUSEUM, New York, July 26–October 9, 1955, *Selection V* (Checklist)

THE SOLOMON R. GUGGENHEIM MUSEUM, New York, January 24–May 1, 1956, *Selection VI* (Checklist)

SOCIETY OF THE FOUR ARTS, Palm Beach, Florida, January 4–27, 1957, *Bonnard,* no.22

TATE GALLERY, London, April 16–May 26, 1957, *Paintings from The Solomon R. Guggenheim Museum,* no.2; organized by THE SOLOMON R. GUGGENHEIM MUSEUM, traveled to GEMEENTEMUSEUM, The Hague, June 25–September 1, no.2; ATENEIUMIN TAIDEKOKOELMAT, Helsinki, September 27–October 20, no.2; GALLERIA NAZIONALE D'ARTE MODERNA, Rome, December 5, 1957–January 8, 1958, no.5, ill.; WALLRAF-RICHARTZ-MUSEUM, Cologne, January 26–March 30, no.3; MUSÉE DES ARTS DÉCORATIFS, Paris, April 23–June 1, 1958, no.9, ill.

THE SOLOMON R. GUGGENHEIM MUSEUM, New York, October 21, 1959–June 19, 1960, *Inaugural Selection* (Checklist)

THE SOLOMON R. GUGGENHEIM MUSEUM, New York, August 30–October 8, 1961, *Modern Masters from the Collection of The Solomon R. Guggenheim Museum*

PHILADELPHIA MUSEUM OF ART, November 2, 1961–January 7, 1962, *Guggenheim Museum Exhibition, A Loan*

Collection of Paintings, Drawings, and Prints from The Solomon R. Guggenheim Museum, New York, no.6, ill.

THE MUSEUM OF MODERN ART, New York, September 10–December 3, 1964, *Bonnard and His Environment*, no.57, p.56, ill.

THE SOLOMON R. GUGGENHEIM MUSEUM, New York, April 30–September 1, 1965, *Paintings from the Collection of The Solomon R. Guggenheim Museum*, no.61, p.58, ill.

THE SOLOMON R. GUGGENHEIM MUSEUM, New York, June 23–October 23, 1966, *Gauguin and the Decorative Style*

THE SOLOMON R. GUGGENHEIM MUSEUM, New York, April 11–May 26, 1968, *Acquisitions of the 1930's and 1940's*, p.41, ill.

References:

Verve, vol.1, no.1, December 1937, p.87, ill.

REWALD, JOHN, *Pierre Bonnard*, New York, 1948, p.116, ill.

TERRASSE, ANTOINE, *Bonnard*, Geneva, 1964, p.74, ill.

VAILLANT, ANNETTE, *Bonnard*, Greenwich, Connecticut, 1965, p.209, ill.

RUSSOLI, FRANCO, *Bonnard*, Milan, 1966, cover ill.

TERRASSE, ANTOINE, *Pierre Bonnard*, Paris, 1967, p.146, ill.

ARNASON, H. H., *History of Modern Art*, New York, 1968, p.86, ill.

FERMIGIER, ANDRÉ, *Pierre Bonnard*, New York, 1969, p.141, ill.

38.432

Bonnard spent the summer of 1934 at Bénerville-sur-Mer on the Channel coast. Although the south of France had made him aware of the phenomenon of direct and constant sunlight, his avowed preference was for the northern coast "where the light is always changing". The scene depicts his dining room as recorded by photographic documents; the figure on the right is his wife Marthe. The theme of a laid table with figures before an open window appears frequently in Bonnard's painting. One finds it in such well-known canvases as *Dining Room in the Country* of 1913 (Minneapolis Institute of Arts) and *Breakfast* of 1930–31 (Museum of Modern Art, New York). It is a particularly prevalent theme in the 1920's and 1930's at the height of Bonnard's activity. The doors or windows in these paintings structure vertically an otherwise largely indeterminate treatment of space. They also provide a visually logical transition between the warm-toned intimacy of the interior and the cool blues outside.

Constantin Brancusi 1876–1957

Constantin Brancusi was born in 1876 in Hobitza in the foothills of the Transylvanian Mountains in Rumania. At eleven, he left home for Tirgu Jiu where he worked in a dramshop. In 1895 he entered the Craiova School of Arts and Crafts, graduating with honors in 1898. He received a diploma from the Bucharest School of Fine Arts in 1902, and the following year set out on foot for Paris, arriving in the summer of 1904. There he attended the École des Beaux-Arts, 1905–7, during which time he exhibited at the *Salon d'Automne* and met Rodin. Five works by Brancusi were included in the 1913 Armory Show, New York, and in 1914 he was given his first one-man exhibition at the Gallery of the Photo-Secession, New York, where his works were purchased by Alfred Stieglitz, Mrs. Eugene Meyer, Jr., and John Quinn. Brancusi's works have been included in hundreds of group exhibitions. In his lifetime, he was honored by one-man shows at the Brummer Gallery, New York, 1926 and 1933, and by a retrospective at the Guggenheim and Philadelphia Museums, 1955–56. The most comprehensive exhibition to this date was organized by the Guggenheim Museum in 1969–70, traveling to the Philadelphia Museum and The Art Institute of Chicago.

Brancusi died in Paris in 1957 leaving a known oeuvre of slightly over two hundred sculptures. As Sidney Geist writes, in 1907 "he abandons his studious realism and begins to develop a vision of form that will remain constant for over forty years. His process is a way of thinking the forms of the world into new structures, structures not those of nature, sculptural structures which are at once a version of the external world and the shape of the sculptor's thought." (Sidney Geist, *Constantin Brancusi 1876–1957, A Retrospective Exhibition*, New York, 1969, p.15).

The Seal (Miracle). 1936

Marble, 42³/₄ x 44⁷/₈ x 13″ (108.6 x 114 x 33 cm.)

Not inscribed

Provenance:
from the artist, 1956

Exhibitions:
THE MUSEUM OF MODERN ART, New York, May 10–September 30, 1939, *Art in Our Time*, no.316, pl.316

PHILADELPHIA MUSEUM OF ART, May 18–October 1, 1940, *Sculpture International*, no.7

PHILADELPHIA MUSEUM OF ART, October 11–December 7, 1952, *Sculpture of the Twentieth Century*; traveled to ART INSTITUTE OF CHICAGO, January 22–March 8, 1953, no.17; THE MUSEUM OF MODERN ART, New York, April 29–September 7, 1953, no.17

THE SOLOMON R. GUGGENHEIM MUSEUM, New York, October 25, 1955–January 8, 1956, *Constantin Brancusi*

THE SOLOMON R. GUGGENHEIM MUSEUM, New York, October 21, 1959–June 19, 1960, *Inaugural Selection* (Checklist), remained on exhibition through August 27, 1962

THE SOLOMON R. GUGGENHEIM MUSEUM, New York, June 28–October 1, 1967, *Museum Collection, Seven Decades, A Selection* (Checklist)

THE SOLOMON R. GUGGENHEIM MUSEUM, New York, July 8–September 14, 1969, *Selected Sculpture and Works on Paper*, p.98, ill.

THE SOLOMON R. GUGGENHEIM MUSEUM, New York, November 21, 1969–February 15, 1970, *Constantin Brancusi 1876–1957, A Retrospective Exhibition*, p.132, ill.

References:
GIEDION-WELCKER, CAROLA, *Moderne Plastik*, Zürich, 1937, p.104, ill.

CASSON, STANLEY, "Sculpture Today", *The Studio*, Spring 1939, p.129, ill.

ZERVOS, CHRISTIAN, *Cahiers d'art*, Paris, 1955, p.225, ill.

GINDERTAEL, R.V., "Brancusi, l'Inaccessible," *Cimaise*, series 3, no.3, January–February 1956, p.9, ill.

Werk, vol.6, June 1956, "Constantin Brancusi in Amerika," p.204, pl.9

POUND, EZRA, *Brancusi*, Milan, 1957, no.24, ill.

GIEDION-WELCKER, CAROLA, *Constantin Brancusi*, New York, 1959, p.119, pl.56

JIANOU, IONEL, *Brancusi*, New York, 1963, fig.60

ARNASON, H.H., *History of Modern Art*, New York, 1968, no.243, p.137, ill.

GEIST, SIDNEY, *Brancusi, A Study of the Sculpture*, New York, 1968, no.188, p.117, ill.

56.1450

The Seal is "a single continuous form whose effective feature is its bent axis. The work is symmetrical and its section is generally round except where the lower part of the body dips to produce a mass of flatter section – the tail – and at the head, where the curving form is intersected by a flat plane whose graphic function is much like that of the bevel on the famous *Bird in Space*. Sitting on its curving bottom, leaning far forward, this precarious shape needs the assistance of a wedge at its under-side to maintain balance. But the fluid image is held in space, as it were, by two vertical planes: the invisible plane of symmetry on which its axis lies, and the visible plane of the head, at a right angle to it." (Sidney Geist, *Brancusi, A Study of the Sculpture*, p.116)

The Seal is one of only two sculptures by Brancusi which were set on a base that could be turned by a concealed motor.

Georges Braque 1882–1963

Georges Braque, born in Argenteuil in 1882, began his career as an apprentice house painter. He studied at the École des Beaux Arts in Le Havre and Paris but left school in 1904. After summering in Antwerp with Othon Friesz in 1906, he made his debut as a "Fauve" in the *Salon des Indépendants* of 1907.

By 1908, the bright Fauvist palette was discarded and the pale greens and ochers of Cubism entered his geometricized landscapes. Picasso and Braque became good friends in 1909 and together they established the Cubist style. By the outbreak of World War I, Picasso and Braque had quarreled and much of the fervor had left the movement although in 1917, after recovering from a head wound received in battle, Braque returned to Synthetic Cubism. By 1922, when he showed for the first time since 1909 at the *Salon des Indépendants*, color and a painterly technique had re-entered his still lifes and figure paintings. The spatial composition was less arbitrary, indicating a return to nature although certain aspects of Cubism remained present. Braque continued to develop more or less along these lines for the rest of his career, doing some sculpture, incised plaster plaques and graphic work from the 1930's on. He died in 1963.

GEORGES BRAQUE

Violin and Palette (Violon et Palette). 1910

Oil on canvas, 36$\frac{1}{4}$ x 16$\frac{7}{8}$" (92.1 x 42.9 cm.)

Signed on reverse "BRAQUE"

Provenance:
the artist, 1910
Daniel-Henry Kahnweiler, Paris
Wilhelm Uhde
Edwin Suermondt, Burg Drove, the Eifel, Germany
Alex Vömel
Fine Arts Associates, New York, 1954

Exhibitions:
KUNSTHALLE, Bern, April 25–May 31, 1953, *Georges Braque*, no.22; traveled to KUNSTHAUS, Zürich, June 7–July 19, 1953, no.23

THE SOLOMON R. GUGGENHEIM MUSEUM, New York, July 26–October 9, 1955, *Selection V* (Checklist)

ARTS CLUB OF CHICAGO, October 3–November 4, 1955, *An Exhibition of Cubism on the Occasion of the Fortieth Anniversary of the Arts Club of Chicago*, no.2

EDINBURGH INTERNATIONAL FESTIVAL, 1956, ROYAL SCOTTISH ACADEMY, Edinburgh, August 18–September 15, 1956, no.21, pl.14b; traveled to TATE GALLERY, London, September 28–November 11, 1956

TATE GALLERY, London, April 16–May 26, 1957, *Paintings from The Solomon R. Guggenheim Museum*, no.4; organized by THE SOLOMON R. GUGGENHEIM MUSEUM, traveled to GEMEENTEMUSEUM, The Hague, June 25–September 1; ATENEIUMIN TAIDEKOKOELMAT, Helsinki, September 27–October 20; GALLERIA NAZIONALE D'ARTE MODERNA, Rome, December 5, 1957–January 8, 1958; WALLRAF–RICHARTZ-MUSEUM, Cologne, January 26–March 30; MUSÉE DES ARTS DÉCORATIFS, Paris, April 23–June 1, 1958

THE SOLOMON R. GUGGENHEIM MUSEUM, New York, October 21, 1959–June 19, 1960, *Inaugural Selection* (Checklist)

THE SOLOMON R. GUGGENHEIM MUSEUM, New York, August 30–October 8, 1961, *Modern Masters from the Collection of The Solomon R. Guggenheim Museum*

PHILADELPHIA MUSEUM OF ART, November 2, 1961–January 7, 1962, *Guggenheim Museum Exhibition, A Loan Collection of Paintings, Drawings, and Prints from The Solomon R. Guggenheim Museum, New York*, no.9

WORCESTER ART MUSEUM, Massachusetts, February 6–April 7, 1963, *Aspects of Twentieth Century Painting Lent by The Solomon R. Guggenheim Museum*, no.4, ill.

SAIDENBERG GALLERY, New York, April 7–May 2, 1964, *Braque, An American Tribute, Fauvism and Cubism*, no.14 (Organized by THE PUBLIC EDUCATION ASSOCIATION, New York)

THE SOLOMON R. GUGGENHEIM MUSEUM, New York, April 30–September 1, 1965, *Paintings from the Collection of The Solomon R. Guggenheim Museum*, no.16, p.24, ill.

THE SOLOMON R. GUGGENHEIM MUSEUM, New York, June 28–October 1, 1967, *Museum Collection, Seven Decades, A Selection* (Checklist)

References:

RICHARDSON, JOHN, *Georges Braque*, Baltimore, 1959, p.10, pl.7a

ROSENBLUM, ROBERT, *Cubism and Twentieth-Century Art*, New York, 1960, pl.30

LEYMARIE, JEAN, *Braque*, Geneva, 1961, p.42, ill.

DORRA, HENRI, *Years of Ferment, The Birth of 20th Century Art, 1886–1914*, UCLA Art Galleries, 1965, p.47, ill.

HUYGHE, RENÉ, ed., *Larousse Encyclopedia of Modern Art*, New York, 1965, no.730, p.271, ill.

HAMILTON, GEORGE HEARD, *Painting and Sculpture in Europe 1880–1940*, Harmondsworth, 1967, pl.85

ARNASON, H.H., *History of Modern Art*, New York, 1968, p.95, ill.

MULLINS, EDWIN, *The Art of Georges Braque*, New York, 1968, p.57, no.36, ill.

54.1412

GEORGES BRAQUE

Piano and Lute (Piano et Mandore; Piano and Mandola). 1910

Oil on canvas, $36^{1}/_{8}$ x $16^{7}/_{8}''$ (91.8 x 42.9 cm.)

Signed on reverse "Braque"

Provenance:
the artist, 1910
Daniel-Henry Kahnweiler, Paris
Wilhelm Uhde
Edwin Suermondt, Burg Drove, the Eifel, Germany
Alex Vömel
Fine Arts Associates, New York, 1954

Exhibitions:
KUNSTHALLE, Bern, April 25–May 31, 1953, *Georges Braque*, no.21; traveled to KUNSTHAUS, Zürich, June 7–July 19, 1953, no.22

THE SOLOMON R. GUGGENHEIM MUSEUM, New York, July 26–October 9, 1955, *Selection V* (Checklist)

ARTS CLUB OF CHICAGO, October 3–November 4, 1955, *An Exhibition of Cubism on the Occasion of the Fortieth Anniversary of the Arts Club of Chicago*, no.1

EDINBURGH INTERNATIONAL FESTIVAL, 1956, ROYAL SCOTTISH ACADEMY, Edinburgh, August 18–September 15, 1956, no.20, pl.15b; traveled to TATE GALLERY, London, September 28–November 11, 1956

TATE GALLERY, London, April 16–May 26, 1957, *Paintings from The Solomon R. Guggenheim Museum*, no.3; organized by THE SOLOMON R. GUGGENHEIM MUSEUM, traveled to GEMEENTEMUSEUM, The Hague, June 25–September 1; ATENEIUMIN TAIDEKOKOELMAT, Helsinki, September 27–October 20; GALLERIA NAZIONALE D'ARTE MODERNA, Rome, December 5, 1957–January 8, 1958; WALLRAF–RICHARTZ-MUSEUM, Cologne, January 26–March 30; MUSÉE DES ARTS DÉCORATIFS, Paris, April 23–June 1, 1958

THE SOLOMON R. GUGGENHEIM MUSEUM, New York, October 21, 1959–June 19, 1960, *Inaugural Selection* (Checklist)

THE SOLOMON R. GUGGENHEIM MUSEUM, New York, August 30–October 8, 1961, *Modern Masters from the Collection of The Solomon R. Guggenheim Museum*

PHILADELPHIA MUSEUM OF ART, November 2, 1961–January 7, 1962, *Guggenheim Museum Exhibition, A Loan Collection of Paintings, Drawings, and Prints from The Solomon R. Guggenheim Museum, New York*, no.8

WORCESTER ART MUSEUM, Massachusetts, February 6–April 7, 1963, *Aspects of Twentieth Century Painting Lent by The Solomon R. Guggenheim Museum*, no.3, ill.

SAIDENBERG GALLERY, New York, April 7–May 2, 1964, *Braque, An American Tribute, Fauvism and Cubism*, no.15 (Organized by THE PUBLIC EDUCATION ASSOCIATION, New York)

THE SOLOMON R. GUGGENHEIM MUSEUM, New York, April 30–September 1, 1965, *Paintings from the Collection of The Solomon R. Guggenheim Museum*, no.15, p.24, ill.

THE SOLOMON R. GUGGENHEIM MUSEUM, New York, June 28–October 1, 1967, *Museum Collection, Seven Decades, A Selection* (Checklist)

References:
RICHARDSON, JOHN, *Georges Braque*, Baltimore, 1959, p.10, pl.7b

RUSSELL, JOHN. G., *Braque*, New York, 1959, pl.10 (as *Piano and Guitar*)

LEYMARIE, JEAN, *Braque*, Geneva, 1961, p.43, ill.

MULLINS, EDWIN, *The Art of Georges Braque*, New York, 1968, p.57, no.37, ill.

54.1411

The companion paintings of *Piano and Lute* and *Violin and Palette* painted by Braque in 1910 are classic examples of the early phase of Cubism. The term Analytical Cubism is applied to the works of Picasso and Braque during the years 1910 to 1912 in reference to the dissection and fragmentation of natural forms into abstract movements and space. This departure from the world of appearances is further enhanced by the almost exclusive use of muted greens and browns. The denial of color allowed the artist to work out his complex formal ideas without the added complications which arise from color.

Although the objects are still recognizable, the nail in *trompe-l'œil* at the top of the canvas in *Violin and Palette* creates a plastic tension between the palpably real and the illusionary world, a pictorial concept which is further explored in Braque's later collages.

Victor Brauner 1903–1966

Victor Brauner was born June 15, 1903, in Piatra Neamt, Rumania. He grew up in Bucharest and had his first one-man exhibition there in 1924 (Galerie Mozart). That same year he founded an avant-garde magazine *75 HP* to which he contributed articles including a manifesto on "Picto-poetry", a combination of painting and poetry which was to be his ultimate pictorial aim.

In 1930 Brauner moved to Paris, where he participated actively in the Surrealist group. He showed regularly in Surrealist exhibitions from 1930 to 1949. The catalogue of his first Parisian one-man exhibition (Galerie Pierre, 1934) was prefaced by André Breton.

Brauner's personal form of Surrealism is characterized by fantastic mythological figures (chimeras, androgynous personages, imaginary fauna and flora) usually portrayed in hieratic stances. Often erotic, sometimes cruelly humorous, in the Surrealist sense they are images of "inner models": subconscious sentiments projected in symbolic or archetypal forms.

Brauner died March 12, 1966, in Paris. His work was exhibited posthumously in the French pavilion of the 1966 Venice Biennale.

VICTOR BRAUNER

Spread of Thought (L'Étendue de la Pensée). July 1956

Oil on canvas, 28³/₄ x 23¹/₂ " (73.1 x 59.7 cm.)

Provenance:
the artist
Alexandre Iolas Gallery, New York
Gift, Dominique and John de Menil, Houston, Texas, 1959

Exhibitions:
THE SOLOMON R. GUGGENHEIM MUSEUM, New York, October 21, 1959–June 19, 1960, *Inaugural Selection* (Checklist)
THE SOLOMON R. GUGGENHEIM MUSEUM, New York, October 3–November 12, 1961; January 9–February 25, 1962, *Elements of Modern Painting,* circulated by
THE AMERICAN FEDERATION OF ARTS, July 1962–September 1963 as *Elements of Modern Art*

59.1517

Titles referring to abstract concepts, inner states of mind, or imaginary faculties are found throughout Brauner's work. Not interested in depicting objects per se, the artist concentrated on psychological states, usually endowed with a totemic, iconic or magical morphology.

Spread of Thought is a rather unusual painting in Brauner's mature production, which is more commonly characterized by an organically flowing composition on a flat, single-toned ground. The angular simplification of the figure as well as the repetitive hatched motifs of the background are distinctly reminiscent of primitive art (New Guinean Tapa art for example). Such static and hieratic frontality of a figure and the decorative hatching recur intermittently in other drawings and paintings of 1956–60.

Alberto Burri 1915–

Alberto Burri was born March 12, 1915, in Città di Castello (Perugia), Italy. He studied medicine in Perugia where he earned his degree in 1940. He practiced as a doctor until World War II. During the war he was imprisoned first in North Africa by the British, 1944, and then in Texas by the Americans in 1945. It was then that he began to paint.

Upon his liberation, Burri settled in Rome, devoting all his activity to painting. His first canvases were in oil; it was not until 1949 that he undertook collage, which was to become his characteristic mode of creation. Influenced by Malevitch and Neo-Plasticism in his strict organization of the surface plane, he was equally influenced by Kandinsky's spatial concepts and Miró's curvilinear, organic forms.

Between 1950 and 1951 Burri executed paintings using pitch and mould; after 1952 he worked primarily in burlap. 1956–1957 is the period of his combustions (charred wood or paper on canvas) whereas in 1958 he composed with metal sheets, seared and shaded with an acetylene torch. In 1961 he explored the effects of layers of transparent plastic over varied grounds which ultimately led to his white paintings of 1966 in canvas and vinyl.

Through its seams, scars, tears and gaping holes, Burri's art is an aggressive, sensual idiom. The emphasis on raw materials and textures is characteristic of the movement of *art informel* predominant in Europe primarily during the fifties. The artist had his first one-man exhibition in 1947 (Galleria La Margherita, Rome) and has shown widely, both nationally and internationally since (Pittsburgh, São Paolo, Venice, Kassel). Burri resides in Rome.

Composition. 1953

Oil, gold and glue on canvas and burlap, 34 x 39³/₈″ (87.6 x 100 cm.)

Signed on reverse "Burri"

Provenance:
from the artist, Rome, 1953

Exhibitions:
THE SOLOMON R. GUGGENHEIM MUSEUM, New York, December 2, 1953–May 2, 1954, *Younger European Painters,* no.5, ill.; traveled to WALKER ART CENTER, Minneapolis, August 8–September 24; PORTLAND ART MUSEUM, Oregon, October 8–November 14; SAN FRANCISCO MUSEUM OF ART, November 26, 1954–January 25, 1955; DALLAS MUSEUM OF FINE ARTS, February 1–March 1; UNIVERSITY OF ARKANSAS, Fayetteville, March 7–April 9; DAYTON ART INSTITUTE, Ohio, April 15–May 13; ADDISON GALLERY OF AMERICAN ART, Phillips Academy, Andover, Massachusetts, October 1–31; CARPENTER ART GALLERIES, Dartmouth College, Hanover, New Hampshire, November 5–December 31, 1955; DWIGHT ART MEMORIAL, Mount Holyoke College, South Hadley, Massachusetts, January 3–31, 1956; DAVISON ART CENTER, Wesleyan University, Middletown, Connecticut, February 6–March 18, 1956

UNIVERSITY OF MICHIGAN MUSEUM OF ART, Ann Arbor, April 13–June 12, 1960, *Images at Mid-Century*

WADSWORTH ATHENEUM, Hartford, Connecticut, April 21–May 28, 1961, *Salute to Italy,* p.14, ill.

PHILADELPHIA MUSEUM OF ART, November 2, 1961–January 7, 1962, *Guggenheim Museum Exhibition, A Loan Collection of Paintings, Drawings, and Prints from The Solomon R. Guggenheim Museum, New York,* no.8

WORCESTER ART MUSEUM, Massachusetts, February 6–April 7, 1963, *Aspects of Twentieth Century Painting Lent by The Solomon R. Guggenheim Museum,* no.5, p.11, ill.

MARTHA JACKSON GALLERY, New York, April 6–May 3, 1965, *International 4-Collages and Constructions*

THE MUSEUM OF MODERN ART, New York, September 1966–February 1968, circulating exhibition, *Burri-Fontana,* no.4

CINCINNATI ART MUSEUM, Ohio, October 3, 1969–March 29, 1970, *Paintings from the Guggenheim Museum, A Loan Exhibition of Modern Paintings Covering the Period 1949–1965, from The Solomon R. Guggenheim Museum,* no.4

References:
SWEENEY, JAMES JOHNSON, *Burri,* Rome, 1955, pl.15
BRANDI, CESARE, *Burri,* Rome, 1963, pl.20

53.1364

In this *Composition* of 1953 one can see the dominant characteristics of Burri's art: an architectonic surface structure, a sensuality of texture and a viscerality achieved through the tears, seams, spots of red (evoking blood) and other surface "accidents".

Burri was one of the first to appropriate burlap as an artistic medium, respecting and emphasizing its intrinsic characteristics. Modest and unpretentious in its associations, burlap nonetheless has an assertive natural texture and lends itself to infinite variations in tone, shading, contrasts, pattern and compositional effects. This explains the artist's predilection for this material for a period spanning from 1952 to 1956.

Alexander Calder 1898–

Alexander Calder was born July 22, 1898, in Philadelphia. In 1919 he graduated as a mechanical engineer from the Stevens Institute of Technology in Hoboken. He worked as an engineer until 1922, when he began to study at the Art Students League in New York and took a job as a freelance illustrator for the *National Police Gazette*. Calder has continued to draw throughout his entire career, including many book illustrations. In later years, when he rejected representation in sculpture, drawing remained the outlet for his naturalistic style.

In 1926 Calder traveled to Paris, where he began his miniature circus, consisting of tiny, movable toys fashioned from scraps of random materials and wire. His first animated toys and representational wire sculpture also date from 1926 and were shown in his first one-man exhibition at the Weyhe Gallery, New York in 1927. Subsequently, the artist began to divide his time between France and the United States, a practice he continues to this day. Calder's visit to Mondrian's studio in 1930 in Paris marked a turning point in his career: he renounced representational sculpture for abstraction, and began to paint his sculpture in primary colors. These new geometric works were christened "stabiles" by Arp. Soon afterwards, the artist began to incorporate motion into his abstract style; first he included single moving objects, then he devised more complex arrangements in which two or more elements moved at varying rates of speed. These works were driven by simple motors or operated by hand cranks. Marcel Duchamp named them "mobiles". Calder has developed many variations of the mobile: wall, standing, hanging and tower. Although he concentrated more and more on the mobile, he never abandoned the stabile, which also changed in style and scale. The stabiles range in size from tiny objects to gigantic outdoor constructions. Calder lives in Roxbury, Connecticut and Saché, France.

ALEXANDER CALDER

Romulus and Remus. 1928

Wire and wood, 31 x 112 x 30" (78.8 x 284.5 x 76.2 cm.)

Signed in wire on tail "Calder"

Provenance:
from the artist, 1965

Exhibitions:
THE SOLOMON R. GUGGENHEIM MUSEUM, New York, November 5, 1964–January 31, 1965, *Alexander Calder: A Retrospective Exhibition*, no.52, ill.; traveled to WASHINGTON UNIVERSITY GALLERY OF ART, St. Louis, February 21–March 26; ART GALLERY OF TORONTO, April 30–May 30; MUSÉE NATIONAL D'ART MODERNE, Paris, July 8–October 12, 1965, no.8, ill.

THE SOLOMON R. GUGGENHEIM MUSEUM, New York, July 8–September 14, 1969, *Selected Sculpture and Works on Paper*, p.100, ill.

References:
ARNASON, H. H., *Calder*, Princeton, New Jersey, 1966, pp.30, 31, ill.
ARNASON, H. H., *History of Modern Art*, New York, 1968, pl.640

65.1738

Spring (Le Printemps). 1929

Wire and wood, 94^1/$_2$″ (240 cm.) high

Signed in wire "Calder"

Provenance:
from the artist, 1965

Exhibitions:
THE SOLOMON R. GUGGENHEIM MUSEUM, New York,
November 5, 1964–January 31, 1965, *Alexander Calder: A
Retrospective Exhibition*, no.73, ill.; traveled to MILWAUKEE
ART CENTER, February 25–March 28; DES MOINES ART
CENTER, Iowa, April 28–May 30; MUSÉE NATIONAL D'ART
MODERNE, Paris, July 8–October 12, 1965

THE SOLOMON R. GUGGENHEIM MUSEUM, New York,
July 8–September 14, 1969, *Selected Sculpture and Works
on Paper*, p.99, ill.

References:
ARNASON, H. H., *Calder*, Princeton, New Jersey, 1966,
p.29, ill.

65.1739

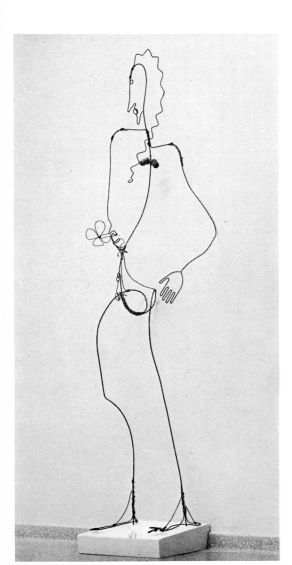

Calder's earliest artistic efforts were humorous line
drawings made when he was an illustrator for the *National
Police Gazette*; these drawings were followed by the tiny
figures of the Circus and small mechanical toys. His large
wire sculptures, of which *Romulus and Remus* and *Spring*
are two examples, grew directly out of these
predecessors. Indeed, *Romulus and Remus* and *Spring* are
line drawings in space – the ink has been translated into
wire. Despite their size (both measure over eight feet),
they retain all the freshness and spontaneity of the rapidly
executed drawings as well as the delightful humor present
in all Calder's work. The use of the material itself is
witty: wooden door-stops used to represent genitals and
nipples, the squiggles of *Spring*'s hair in contrast to the
sweeping lines of her body. Here, as in much of Calder's
drawing, the humor is a trifle risqué. The normally lofty
subject matter – *Spring* is allegorical, *Romulus and Remus*
mythological – is, to say the least, treated lightly.

ALEXANDER CALDER

Mobile. 1934?

Sheet metal, rods, cord, 9 x 16″ (22.8 x 40.6 cm.)

Not inscribed

Provenance:
Collection Mary Reynolds, Gift of her brother, 1953

Exhibitions:
THE SOLOMON R. GUGGENHEIM MUSEUM, New York, November 5, 1964–January 31, 1965, *Alexander Calder:*

A Retrospective Exhibition, no.143; traveled to MILWAUKEE ART CENTER, February 25–March 28; DES MOINES ART CENTER, Iowa, April 28–May 30; MUSÉE NATIONAL D'ART MODERNE, Paris, July 8–October 12, 1965, no.93

FONDATION MAEGHT, St. Paul-de-Vence, April 2–May 30, 1969, *Alexander Calder*

References:
ARNASON, H. H., *Calder*, Princeton, New Jersey, 1966, p.46, ill.

53.1388

ALEXANDER CALDER

Mobile. 1936?

Sheet metal, metal rods, glass, pottery, wood, cord,
49 x 50″ (124.5 x 127 cm.)

Not inscribed

Provenance:
Collection Mary Reynolds, Gift of her brother, 1953

Exhibitions:
THE SOLOMON R. GUGGENHEIM MUSEUM, New York,
March 30–May 5, 1954, *Selection III* (Checklist)

VANCOUVER ART GALLERY, November 16–December 12,
1954, *The Solomon R. Guggenheim Museum,
A Selection from the Museum Collection,* no.2, ill.

THE SOLOMON R. GUGGENHEIM MUSEUM, New York,
November 5, 1964–January 31, 1965, *Alexander Calder:
A Retrospective Exhibition,* no.147; traveled to MILWAUKEE
ART CENTER, February 25–March 28; DES MOINES ART
CENTER, Iowa, April 28–May 30; MUSÉE NATIONAL D'ART
MODERNE, Paris, July 8–October 12, 1965, no.98

THE SOLOMON R. GUGGENHEIM MUSEUM, New York,
July 8–September 14, 1969, *Selected Sculpture and Works
on Paper,* p.102, ill.

53.1391

ALEXANDER CALDER

Mobile. 1936?

Wood, metal rods, cord, 39 x 36″ (99 x 91.5 cm.)

Not inscribed

Provenance:
Collection Mary Reynolds, Gift of her brother, 1953

Exhibitions:
THE SOLOMON R. GUGGENHEIM MUSEUM, New York, March 30–May 5, 1954, *Selection III* (Checklist)

ARTS CLUB OF CHICAGO, April 19–May 19, 1960, *Sculpture and Drawings by Sculptors from The Solomon R. Guggenheim Museum*, no.7

THE SOLOMON R. GUGGENHEIM MUSEUM, New York, November 5, 1964–January 31, 1965, *Alexander Calder: A Retrospective Exhibition*, no.148, ill.; traveled to MILWAUKEE ART CENTER, February 25–March 28; DES MOINES ART CENTER, Iowa, April 23–May 30; MUSÉE NATIONAL D'ART MODERNE, Paris, July 8–October 12, 1965, no.99

FONDATION MAEGHT, St. Paul-de-Vence, April 2–May 30, 1969, *Alexander Calder*

THE SOLOMON R. GUGGENHEIM MUSEUM, New York, July 8–September 14, 1969, *Selected Sculpture and Works on Paper*, p.103; ill.

53.1392

ALEXANDER CALDER

Mobile. 1936?

Wood, metal, cord, 67 x 65″ (170.2 x 165.1 cm.)

Not inscribed

Provenance:

Collection Mary Reynolds, Gift of her brother, 1953

Exhibitions:

THE SOLOMON R. GUGGENHEIM MUSEUM, New York,
March 30–May 5, 1954, *Selection III* (Checklist)

VANCOUVER ART GALLERY, November 16–December 12,
1954, *The Solomon R. Guggenheim Museum, A Selection
from the Museum Collection*, no.1

THE SOLOMON R. GUGGENHEIM MUSEUM, New York,
October 21, 1959–June 19, 1960, *Inaugural Selection*
(Checklist)

CLEVELAND MUSEUM OF ART, Ohio, October 4–
November 13, 1960, *Paths of Abstract Art*, no.11, ill.

SOLOMON R. GUGGENHEIM MUSEUM, New York,
November 5, 1964–January 31, 1965, *Alexander Calder: A
Retrospective Exhibition*, no.146; traveled to WASHINGTON
UNIVERSITY GALLERY OF ART, St. Louis, February 21–
March 26; ART GALLERY OF TORONTO, April 30–May 30;
MUSÉE NATIONAL D'ART MODERNE, Paris, July 8–October 12,
1965, no.97

THE SOLOMON R. GUGGENHEIM MUSEUM, New York,
July 8–September 14, 1969, *Selected Sculpture and Works
on Paper*, p.104

References:

ARNASON, H. H., *Calder*, Princeton, New Jersey, 1966,
p.48, ill.

53.1390

Although Calder has worked in many mediums and created many forms of sculpture, he is most closely identified with the mobile – as the artist who made sculpture move. There are diverse types of mobiles, but the most characteristic form is the hanging mobile, like the five shown here. Composed of abstract forms suspended by string or wire from metal rods, the elements are propelled by air currents. The mobile's ever-changing profile moves spontaneously and unpredictably, different elements traveling in different directions at varying rates of speed. While all the hanging mobiles follow this general pattern, within the basic framework they vary greatly in color, material, size and emotional content. The abstract shapes are made of many different materials: painted sheet metal in *Red Lily Pads* and *Mobile*, 1934?; smooth, rounded wood in one *Mobile*, 1936?; broken bits of pottery and glass in another *Mobile*, 1936? The mobiles range in size from small and fragile – *Mobile*, 1934? is 16 inches at its fullest extension – to monumental – *Red Lily Pads* is 201 inches at its widest point. Color range is usually restricted, most characteristically to primary colors, black, white and sometimes orange, but there are many exceptions to this rule. *Mobile*, 1934?, with its dull off-shades, is a most unusual example, and in *Mobile*, 1936?, made of found objects, Calder has used a particularly wide range of colors. Although the mobiles are abstract, they evoke natural processes, because the forms, as well as the motion, are organic and free. Thus, *Red Lily Pads* is at once an abstract composition of red-painted discs and wire, and a giant emblem of leaves floating in water.

ALEXANDER CALDER

Constellation. 1943

Wood, metal rods, 22 x 44 1/2″ (55.9 x 113 cm.)

Not inscribed

Provenance:
Collection Mary Reynolds, Gift of her brother, 1953

Exhibitions:
THE SOLOMON R. GUGGENHEIM MUSEUM, New York, March 30–May 5, 1954, *Selection III* (Checklist)

THE SOLOMON R. GUGGENHEIM MUSEUM, New York, October 6, 1954–February 27, 1955, *Selection IV* (Checklist)

MONTREAL MUSEUM OF FINE ARTS, June 4–July 3, 1955, *A Selection from The Solomon R. Guggenheim Museum, New York,* no.2

THE SOLOMON R. GUGGENHEIM MUSEUM, New York, January 24–May 1, 1956, *Selection VI* (Checklist)

THE SOLOMON R. GUGGENHEIM MUSEUM, New York, October 21, 1959–June 19, 1960, *Inaugural Selection* (Checklist)

THE SOLOMON R. GUGGENHEIM MUSEUM, New York, November 5, 1964–January 31, 1965, *Alexander Calder: A Retrospective Exhibition,* no.203, ill; traveled to

MILWAUKEE ART CENTER, February 25–March 28; DES MOINES ART CENTER, Iowa, April 28–May 30; MUSÉE NATIONAL D'ART MODERNE, Paris, July 8–October 12, 1965, no.120, ill.

AKADEMIE DER KÜNSTE, Berlin, May 21–July 16, 1967, *Alexander Calder,* no.68, p.56, ill.

THE SOLOMON R. GUGGENHEIM MUSEUM, New York, July 8–September 14, 1969, *Selected Sculpture and Works on Paper,* p.106, ill.

References:
ARNASON, H. H., *Calder,* Princeton, New Jersey, 1966, p.56, ill.

53.1393

The typical stabile is made of sheets of metal. During the war, when metal was scarce, Calder developed the constellation, a special variety of stabile constructed of pieces of wood and thin metal rods. *Constellation,* 1943, like the other works of this type, is intimate in scale. Attached to the wall, it is like a crawling, spindly creature. Characteristically, the color range is reduced. The abstract wooden forms, lovingly carved and smoothed, reveal Calder's feeling for a medium he rarely used after the 1920's. These wooden elements contrast in color, shape and texture with the spiky black rods.

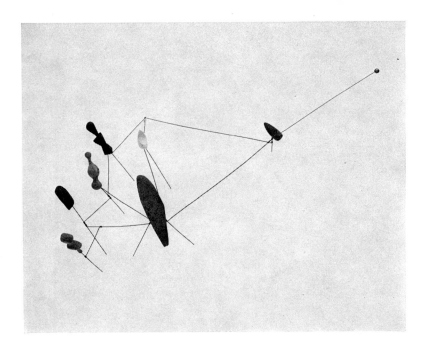

ALEXANDER CALDER

Red Lily Pads. (Nénuphars Rouges). c.1956

Painted sheet metal, metal rods, wire, 42 x 201 x 109″
(106.6 x 510.5 x 278.8 cm.)

Signed and dated on largest lily pad "CA//56"

Provenance:

from the artist through Perls Galleries, New York, 1965

Exhibitions:

THE SOLOMON R. GUGGENHEIM MUSEUM, New York,
November 5, 1964–January 31, 1965, *Alexander Calder:
A Retrospective Exhibition*, no.160, ill.; traveled to
WASHINGTON UNIVERSITY GALLERY OF ART, St. Louis,
February 21–March 26; ART GALLERY OF TORONTO,
April 30–May 30, 1965

THE SOLOMON R. GUGGENHEIM MUSEUM, New York,
July 8–September 14, 1969, *Selected Sculpture and Works
on Paper*, p.109, ill.

References:

ARNASON, H. H., *Calder*, Princeton, New Jersey, p.81,
p.135, ill.

65.1737

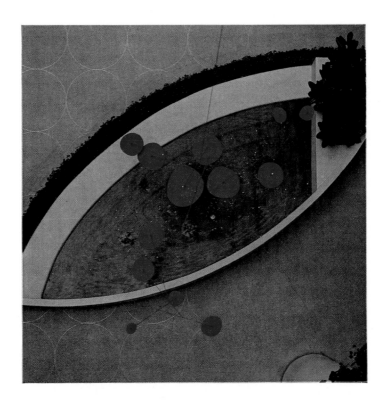

Paul Cézanne 1839–1906

Paul Cézanne was born January 19, 1839, at Aix-en-Pro-vence. He studied at the Aix School of Drawing from 1856 to 1861 and at the Aix Law School from 1859 to 1861. In 1862 he devoted his entire activity to painting.

From 1861 to the end of his life, the artist made frequent prolonged trips to Paris where he visited the Louvre exten-sively and frequented Impressionist circles. In 1874 he participated in the first Impressionist group exhibition. He began showing regularly in group exhibitions after 1889 and in 1895 held his first one-man show at Ambrose Vol-lard's Gallery, Paris.

Cézanne's emphasis on the reality of perception, in which volumes are perceived as a succession of planes existing at equal level, as well as his rejection of Renaissance single-vanishing-point perspective in favor of a composite image of multiple vanishing points, were to have a great influence on Braque and Picasso in their elaboration of Cubism. Cézanne died October 22, 1906 in Aix-en-Provence.

The Clockmaker (L'Horloger: L'Homme aux Bras Croisés). 1895–1900

Oil on canvas, 36¹/₄ x 28³/₄″ (92.1 x 73 cm.)

Not inscribed

Provenance:
Mrs. Martha Reuther, Heidelberg
M. Knoedler & Co., Inc., New York, 1954

Exhibitions:
THE SOLOMON R. GUGGENHEIM MUSEUM, New York, March 30–May 5, 1954, *Selection III* (Checklist)
THE SOLOMON R. GUGGENHEIM MUSEUM, New York, October 6, 1954–February 27, 1955, *Selection IV* (Checklist)
THE SOLOMON R. GUGGENHEIM MUSEUM, New York, July 26–October 9, 1955, *Selection V* (Checklist)
THE SOLOMON R. GUGGENHEIM MUSEUM, New York, January 24–May 1, 1956, *Selection VI* (Checklist)
GEMEENTEMUSEUM, The Hague, June–July 1956, *Paul Cézanne*, no.43, ill.
TATE GALLERY, London, April 16–May 26, 1957, *Paintings from The Solomon R. Guggenheim Museum*, no.6; organized by THE SOLOMON R. GUGGENHEIM MUSEUM, traveled to GEMEENTEMUSEUM, The Hague, June 25–September 1; ATENEIUMIN TAIDEKOKOELMAT, Helsinki, September 27–October 20; GALLERIA NAZIONALE D'ARTE MODERNA, Rome, December 5, 1957–January 8, 1958; WALLRAF-RICHARTZ-MUSEUM, Cologne, January 26–March 30; MUSÉE DES ARTS DÉCORATIFS, Paris, April 23–June 1, 1958
THE SOLOMON R. GUGGENHEIM MUSEUM, New York, October 21, 1959–June 19, 1960, *Inaugural Selection* (Checklist)
THE SOLOMON R. GUGGENHEIM MUSEUM, New York, August 30–October 8, 1961, *Modern Masters from the Collection of The Solomon R. Guggenheim Museum*
THE SOLOMON R. GUGGENHEIM MUSEUM, New York, June 5–October 13, 1963, *Cézanne and Structure in Modern Painting*, ill.
THE SOLOMON R. GUGGENHEIM MUSEUM, New York, April 30–September 1, 1965, *Paintings from the Collection of The Solomon R. Guggenheim Museum*, no.6, ill.
THE SOLOMON R. GUGGENHEIM MUSEUM, New York, June 28–October 1, 1967, *Museum Collection, Seven Decades, A Selection* (Checklist)

References:
BERNARD, ÉMILE, "La technique de Paul Cézanne", *L'Amour de l'Art,* 1920, Supplement, p.271, ill.
KLINGSOR, TRISTAN L., *Cézanne*, Paris, 1923, p.55
VENTURI, LIONELLO, *Cézanne, son art, son œuvre*, Paris, 1936, vol.1, p.213, no.689; vol.2, pl.224
Art Digest, no.28, April 15, 1954, p.20, cover ill.
Werk, no.41, July 1954, Supplement, p.157, ill.

MURPHY, RICHARD W., *The World of Cézanne*, New York, 1968, p.88, ill.

54.1387

Painted a few years after the artist's celebrated *Cardplayers* (1890–92), *The Clockmaker* is an example of Cézanne's mature style. Although a portrait, it is the formal breakdown of the sitter's morphology which interested Cézanne and from which all expression of character was to come. The strongly determined and contrasting masses, the simplification of volumes into their essential planes, the close-valued yet pulsating application of color, the arbitrary use of light and the flatness of the modeling endow the figure with a presence which is not only physical but psychological and spiritual.

A painting similar to the Museum's, *Man with Crossed Arms* (1895–1900), exists in a private collection in Annapolis, Maryland.

Marc Chagall 1887–

Marc Chagall was born July 7, 1887, in Vitebsk, Russia. He began art school in St. Petersburg in 1907, and entered the studio of Leon Bakst, the painter and scenarist, in 1908, where he discovered the powers of color and the expressively deformed line. Chagall's earliest paintings were inspired by familiar subjects and universal themes such as birth, marriage and death.

In 1910 Chagall moved to Paris, where he was exposed to Cubism and Orphism. The years 1911–12 show a marked liberation from the traditional pictorial conventions which had governed his work. His palette became lighter and his spatial organization more personal through the gradual flattening of the image, the extreme disparities in the scale of the figures, and the latters' increased mobility.

Chagall's first one-man exhibition was held in 1914 at the Gallery *Der Sturm* in Berlin. On a trip to Russia later that year, he was caught by the war. After the October Revolution, he was appointed Commissar for Art for Vitebsk and Director of the Vitebsk Academy. Forced to resign in 1920, he moved to Moscow where he designed sets, costumes and decorative murals for the Kamerny State Jewish Theater.

Chagall left Russia in 1922 and returned to France the next year. A retrospective exhibition of his work was held in 1924 in Paris, and in 1926, he had his first New York one-man show. His painting grew progressively loose in structure, symbolic in meaning and poetic in feeling. Motifs of his Russian homeland recur throughout.

World War II forced Chagall to flee France. Between 1941 and 1947 he lived in New York. Since that time he has made several trips to Israel and executed monumental paintings and stained-glass windows both there and in France. The artist resides in Paris and Vence.

The Soldier Drinks. 1912

Oil on canvas, 43¼ x 37¼" (109.9 x 94.6 cm.)

Signed l.r. "Chagall"

Provenance:
Herwarth Walden, Berlin
Nell Urech-Walden, Schinznach-Bad, Switzerland, 1949

Exhibitions:
THE MUSEUM OF MODERN ART, New York, April 9–June 23, 1946, *Marc Chagall*, p.22, ill.; traveled to ART INSTITUTE OF CHICAGO, October 24–December 15, 1946

STEDELIJK MUSEUM, Amsterdam, December 1947–January 1948, *Chagall*

THE SOLOMON R. GUGGENHEIM MUSEUM, New York, February 3–May 3, 1953, *A Selection* (Checklist)

WALKER ART CENTER, Minneapolis, May–July 1954, *Reality and Fantasy 1900–1954*

TATE GALLERY, London, April 16–May 26, 1957, *Paintings from The Solomon R. Guggenheim Museum*, no.7; organized by THE SOLOMON R. GUGGENHEIM MUSEUM, traveled to GEMEENTEMUSEUM, The Hague, June 25–September 1, no.7; ATENEIUMIN TAIDEKOKOELMAT, Helsinki, September 27–October 20, no.7; GALLERIA NAZIONALE D'ARTE MODERNA, Rome, December 5, 1957–January 8, 1958, no.34, ill.; WALLRAF-RICHARTZ-MUSEUM, Cologne, January 26–March 30, no.8, ill.; MUSÉE DES ARTS DÉCORATIFS, Paris, April 23–June 1, 1958, no.45, ill.

THE SOLOMON R. GUGGENHEIM MUSEUM, New York, August 30–October 8, 1961, *Modern Masters from the Collection of The Solomon R. Guggenheim Museum*

PHILADELPHIA MUSEUM OF ART, November 2, 1961–January 7, 1962, *Guggenheim Museum Exhibition, A Loan Collection of Paintings, Drawings, and Prints from The Solomon R. Guggenheim Museum, New York*, no.13

WORCESTER ART MUSEUM, Massachusetts, February 6–April 14, 1963, *Aspects of Twentieth Century Painting Lent by The Solomon R. Guggenheim Museum*, no.6, p.12, ill.

NATIONAL MUSEUM OF EUROPEAN ART, Tokyo, October 1–November 10, 1963, *Marc Chagall*, p.43, pl.18; traveled to MUNICIPAL MUSEUM, Kyoto, November 20–December 10, 1963

KUNSTHAUS, Zürich, May 6–July 30, 1967, *Marc Chagall*, no.10, ill.; traveled to WALLRAF-RICHARTZ-MUSEUM, Cologne, September 1–November 5, 1967

THE SOLOMON R. GUGGENHEIM MUSEUM, New York, April 11–May 26, 1968, *Acquisitions of the 1930's and 1940's*, p.120, ill.

GRAND PALAIS, Paris, December 13, 1969–March 8, 1970, *Marc Chagall*

References:

WALDEN, HERWARTH, *Expressionismus*, Berlin, 1918, p.23, ill.

Sturm-Bilderbücher 1, Marc Chagall, Berlin, 1923, p.9, ill.

SWEENEY, JAMES JOHNSON, *Marc Chagall*, New York, 1946, p.22, ill.

MARITAIN, RAISSA, *Chagall ou l'orage enchanté*, Geneva-Paris, 1948, p.69, ill.

ESTIENNE, CHARLES, *Chagall*, Paris, 1951, p.16, ill.

VENTURI, LIONELLO, *Chagall*, Geneva, 1956, p.40, ill.

MEYER, FRANZ, *Marc Chagall*, New York, 1963, pp.179, 184, ill.

CASSOU, JEAN, *Chagall*, New York, 1965, p.102, pl.71

ERBEN, WALTER, *Marc Chagall*, New York, rev. ed., 1966, p.16, ill.

TROELS, ANDERSON, *Moderne Russisk Kunst, 1910–1925*, Copenhagen, 1967, ill.

49.1211

The Soldier Drinks is characteristic of Chagall's painting of 1912. It shows a definite Cubist influence in the artist's translation of volumes into planes and the subsequent shallowness of the image. Chagall's paintings of 1911 were generally more modeled and maintained a more traditional recession in depth. Further characteristics of the artist's work in 1912 are the large-scale human figure and its assertive rhythmic gestures.

Chagall's exposure to Cubism afforded him greater freedom from the norms of representation and provided him with a formal discipline with which to organize his highly imaginative pictorial metaphors. Although this canvas was painted in Paris, the artist's native Russia is recalled through the samovar and the small dancing figures in the lower central portion of the painting.

A small gouache study for the painting is in a private collection in London.

MARC CHAGALL

Paris Through the Window. 1913

Oil on canvas, 52³/₈ x 54″ (133 x 137.2 cm.)

Signed l.l. "Chagall//1913"

Provenance:

Collection Kluxen
Solomon R. Guggenheim, New York
Gift, Solomon R. Guggenheim, 1937

Exhibitions:

GIBBES MEMORIAL ART GALLERY, Charleston, South
Carolina, March 1–April 12, 1936, *Solomon R. Guggenheim Collection of Non-Objective Paintings*, no.110

THE MUSEUM OF MODERN ART, New York, December 7,
1936–January 17, 1937, *Fantastic Art, Dada, and Surrealism*,
p.115

PHILADELPHIA ART ALLIANCE, February 8–28, 1937,
*Solomon R. Guggenheim Collection of Non-Objective
Paintings*, no.142

GIBBES MEMORIAL ART GALLERY, Charleston, South
Carolina, March 7–April 7, 1938, *Solomon R. Guggenheim Collection of Non-Objective Paintings*, no.213

SOLOMON R. GUGGENHEIM FOUNDATION, New York,
June 1, 1939, *Art of Tomorrow* (Fifth catalogue of the
Solomon R. Guggenheim Collection of Non-Objective
Paintings), no.438

THE MUSEUM OF MODERN ART, New York, April 9–June 23,
1946, *Marc Chagall;* traveled to ART INSTITUTE OF CHICAGO,
October 24–December 15, 1946

MUSÉE NATIONAL D'ART MODERNE, Paris, October 17–
December 22, 1947, *Exposition Marc Chagall: Peintures
1908–1947*, no.14

STEDELIJK MUSEUM, Amsterdam, December 1947–
January 1948, *Chagall*

THE SOLOMON R. GUGGENHEIM MUSEUM, New York,
February 3–May 3, 1953, *A Selection* (Checklist)

ART GALLERY OF TORONTO, April 2–May 9, 1954, *A Loan
Exhibition of Paintings from The Solomon R. Guggenheim
Museum*, no.3

ALBRIGHT ART GALLERY, Buffalo, New York, May 14–
June 12, 1955, *Fifty Paintings, 1905–1913*

THE SOLOMON R. GUGGENHEIM MUSEUM, New York,
July 26–October 9, 1955, *Selection V* (Checklist)

THE SOLOMON R. GUGGENHEIM MUSEUM, New York,
January 24–May 1, 1956, *Selection VI* (Checklist)

TATE GALLERY, London, April 16–May 26, 1957, *Paintings
from The Solomon R. Guggenheim Museum*, no.9; organized by THE SOLOMON R. GUGGENHEIM MUSEUM, traveled
to GEMEENTEMUSEUM, The Hague, June 25–September 1,
no.9; ATENEIUMIN TAIDEKOKOELMAT, Helsinki, September 27–October 20, no.9; GALLERIA NAZIONALE D'ARTE
MODERNA, Rome, December 5, 1957–January 8, 1958,
no.35, ill.; WALLRAF-RICHARTZ-MUSEUM, Cologne,
January 26–March 30, no.10, ill.; MUSÉE DES ARTS
DÉCORATIFS, Paris, April 23–June 1, 1958, no.46, ill.

THE SOLOMON R. GUGGENHEIM MUSEUM, New York,
October 21, 1959–June 19, 1960, *Inaugural Selection*

THE SOLOMON R. GUGGENHEIM MUSEUM, New York,
August 30–October 8, 1961, *Modern Masters from the
Collection of The Solomon R. Guggenheim Museum*

THE SOLOMON R. GUGGENHEIM MUSEUM, New York,
June 5–October 13, 1963, *Cézanne and Structure in Modern
Painting*

THE SOLOMON R. GUGGENHEIM MUSEUM, New York,
April 30–September 1, 1965, *Paintings from the Collection
of The Solomon R. Guggenheim Museum*, no.28, p.33, ill.

THE SOLOMON R. GUGGENHEIM MUSEUM, New York,
April 11–May 26, 1968, *Acquisitions of the 1930's and 1940's*,
p.21, ill.

THE SOLOMON R. GUGGENHEIM MUSEUM, New York,
May 30–September 2, 1968, *Rousseau, Redon, and Fantasy*,
ill.

References:

WALDEN, HERWARTH, *Expressionismus*, Berlin, 1918, p.24,
ill.

WITH, KARL, *Marc Chagall*, Leipzig, 1923, ill.

Sturm Bilderbücher 1, Marc Chagall, Berlin, 1923, p.10, ill.

SWEENEY, JAMES JOHNSON, *Marc Chagall*, New York, 1946,
p.28, ill.

MARITAIN, RAISSA, *Chagall ou l'orage enchanté*,
Geneva-Paris, 1948, p.76, ill.

ESTIENNE, CHARLES, *Chagall*, Paris, 1951, p.22, ill.

ROSENBLUM, ROBERT, *Cubism and Twentieth-Century Art*,
New York, 1960, p.248, pl.177

MEYER, FRANZ, *Marc Chagall*, New York, 1963, p.204,
pp.2–7, ill.

CASSOU, JEAN, *Chagall*, New York, 1965, p.36, ill.

ERBEN, WALTER, *Marc Chagall*, New York, rev. ed., 1966,
p.12, ill.

GREENFELD, HOWARD, *Marc Chagall*, New York, 1967, ill.
opp. p.72

37.438

In his authoritative volume on Chagall, Franz Meyer describes this painting as "the major work of his last Paris period... It commemorates the sensuous-spiritual experience of the city. The indoor and outdoor views are closely linked, like the two faces of Janus, and the experience can, in reality, only be rendered by constant movement from one to the other. The discontinuity in the direction of the spectator's gaze is most obvious in the contrasting motifs – the human-headed cat, the houses and railway train, the promenaders, the tower and parachutist, the two-faced man. They admit the spectator, one might say, to both domains. He is at once within and without: in the light and traffic of Paris, and close to the images that flash up mysteriously from the depths of the soul." (Franz Meyer, *Marc Chagall*, New York, 1963, p.205.)

MARC CHAGALL

Burning House (La Calêche Volante). 1913

Oil on canvas, 41⁷/₈ x 47¹/₄″ (106.4 x 120 cm.)

Signed l.r. "Chagall Paris 13"

Provenance:

Herwarth Walden, Berlin
Nell Urech-Walden, Schinznach-Bad, Switzerland, 1949

Exhibitions:

THE MUSEUM OF MODERN ART, New York, April 9–June 23, 1946, *Marc Chagall*, p.30, ill.; traveled to ART INSTITUTE OF CHICAGO, October 24–December 15, 1946

MUSÉE NATIONAL D'ART MODERNE, Paris, October 17–December 22, 1947, *Exposition Marc Chagall: Peintures 1908–1947*, no.16

STEDELIJK MUSEUM, Amsterdam, December 1947–January 1948, *Chagall*

THE SOLOMON R. GUGGENHEIM MUSEUM, New York, February 3–May 3, 1953, *A Selection* (Checklist)

ART GALLERY OF TORONTO, April 2–May 9, 1954, *A Loan Exhibition of Paintings from The Solomon R. Guggenheim Museum*, no.2

THE SOLOMON R. GUGGENHEIM MUSEUM, New York, October 6, 1954–February 27, 1955, *Selection IV* (Checklist)

MONTREAL MUSEUM OF FINE ARTS, June 4–July 3, 1955, *A Selection from The Solomon R. Guggenheim Museum, New York*, no.5, p.56, ill.

THE SOLOMON R. GUGGENHEIM MUSEUM, New York, January 24–May 1, 1956, *Selection VI* (Checklist)

TATE GALLERY, London, April 16–May 26, 1957, *Paintings from The Solomon R. Guggenheim Museum*, no.8; organized by THE SOLOMON R. GUGGENHEIM MUSEUM, traveled to GEMEENTEMUSEUM, The Hague, June 25–September 1, no.8; ATENEIUMIN TAIDEKOKOELMAT, Helsinki, September 27–October 20, no.8; GALLERIA NAZIONALE D'ARTE MODERNA, Rome, December 5, 1957–January 8, 1958, no.36, ill.; WALLRAF-RICHARTZ-MUSEUM, Cologne, January 26–March 30, no.9; MUSÉE DES ARTS DÉCORATIFS, Paris, April 23–June 1, 1958, no.47, ill.

BRANDEIS UNIVERSITY, Waltham, Massachusetts, May 15–June 15, 1960, *Marc Chagall*

THE SOLOMON R. GUGGENHEIM MUSEUM, New York, August 30–October 8, 1961, *Modern Masters from the Collection of The Solomon R. Guggenheim Museum*

THE SOLOMON R. GUGGENHEIM MUSEUM, New York, October 3, 1961–January 9, 1962, *Elements of Modern Painting;* circulated by THE AMERICAN FEDERATION OF ARTS, July 1962–September 1963, as *Elements of Modern Art*

NATIONAL MUSEUM OF EUROPEAN ART, Tokyo, October 1–November 10, 1963, *Marc Chagall*, p.44, pl.19; traveled to MUNICIPAL MUSEUM, Kyoto, November 20–December 10, 1963

THE SOLOMON R. GUGGENHEIM MUSEUM, New York, April 30–September 1, 1965, *Paintings from the Collection of The Solomon R. Guggenheim Museum*, no.27, p.33, ill.

THE SOLOMON R. GUGGENHEIM MUSEUM, New York, June 23–October 23, 1966, *Gauguin and the Decorative Style*

KUNSTHAUS, Zürich, May 6–July 30, 1967, *Marc Chagall*, no.38, ill.

THE SOLOMON R. GUGGENHEIM MUSEUM, New York, April 11–May 26, 1968, *Acquisitions of the 1930's and 1940's*, p.123, ill.

GRAND PALAIS, Paris, December 13, 1969–March 8, 1970, *Marc Chagall*

References:

Sturm Bilderbücher 1, Marc Chagall, Berlin, 1923, p.11, ill.
SWEENEY, JAMES JOHNSON, *Marc Chagall*, New York, 1946, p.30, ill.
MARITAIN, RAISSA, *Chagall ou l'orage enchanté*, Geneva–Paris, 1948, p.11, ill.
MEYER, FRANZ, *Marc Chagall*, New York, 1963, pp.200, 204, ill.
CASSOU, JEAN, *Chagall*, New York, 1965, p.55, pl.39
GREENFELD, HOWARD, *Marc Chagall*, New York, 1967, ill. opp. p.32

49.1212

By 1913 Chagall had developed a more dynamic, fluid and subtly symbolic pictorial idiom, compared to his earlier work of 1912. *Burning House* shows not only an expressionist sensuality – through its vibrant color – but it has definite symbolic overtones. As Franz Meyer has described it: "The cool and flaming zones are emblems of night and day. On the left, the fire cart ascends into the solar region; on the right, the woman stands before the dark sky, her arms bent in a great S – a form that symbolizes the calm circles of moon and stars, in contrast to the open scissors of the man's arms that may be linked with the sun. The astral powers, sun and moon, appear in opposition, as in Romanesque representations of the Crucifixion. Between them stands the house of man, forever burning yet never consumed." (Franz Meyer, *Marc Chagall*, New York, 1963, p.204)

MARC CHAGALL

Green Violinist. 1924–25 (previously dated 1918)

Oil on canvas, 77³/₄ x 42³/₄" (197.5 x 108.6 cm.)

Signed l.r. "Chagall//Marc"; inscribed on trouser cuff in Hebrew "Oh! Daddy"

Provenance:
the artist, 1936
Solomon R. Guggenheim, New York
Gift, Solomon R. Guggenheim, 1937

Exhibitions:

PHILADELPHIA ART ALLIANCE, February 8–28, 1937, *Solomon R. Guggenheim Collection of Non-Objective Paintings,* no.149

GIBBES MEMORIAL ART GALLERY, Charleston, South Carolina, March 7–April 7, 1938, *Solomon R. Guggenheim Collection of Non-Objective Paintings,* no.220

SOLOMON R. GUGGENHEIM FOUNDATION, New York, June 1, 1939, *Art of Tomorrow* (Fifth catalogue of the Solomon R. Guggenheim Collection of Non-Objective Paintings), no.446

THE MUSEUM OF MODERN ART, New York, April 9–June 23, 1946, *Marc Chagall,* no.25, p.43, ill.

THE SOLOMON R. GUGGENHEIM MUSEUM, New York, February 3–May 3, 1953, *A Selection* (Checklist)

THE SOLOMON R. GUGGENHEIM MUSEUM, New York, May 13–October 11, 1953, *Selection II* (Checklist)

ART GALLERY OF TORONTO, April 2–May 9, 1954, *A Loan Exhibition of Paintings from The Solomon R. Guggenheim Museum,* no.4

THE SOLOMON R. GUGGENHEIM MUSEUM, New York, October 6, 1954–February 27, 1955, *Selection IV* (Checklist)

MONTREAL MUSEUM OF FINE ARTS, June 4–July 3, 1955, *A Selection from The Solomon R. Guggenheim Museum, New York,* no.6

THE SOLOMON R. GUGGENHEIM MUSEUM, New York, September 12–October 9, 1955, *Selection V* (Checklist)

TATE GALLERY, London, April 16–May 26, 1957, *Paintings from The Solomon R. Guggenheim Museum,* no.11, ill.; organized by THE SOLOMON R. GUGGENHEIM MUSEUM, traveled to GEMEENTEMUSEUM, The Hague, June 25–September 1, no.11, ill.; ATENEIUMIN TAIDEKOKOELMAT, Helsinki, September 27–October 20, no.11, ill.; GALLERIA NAZIONALE D'ARTE MODERNA, Rome, December 5, 1957–January 8, 1958, no.38, ill.; WALLRAF–RICHARTZ–MUSEUM, Cologne, January 26–March 30, no.12, ill.; MUSÉE DES ARTS DÉCORATIFS, Paris, April 23–June 1, 1958, no.49, ill.

THE SOLOMON R. GUGGENHEIM MUSEUM, New York, October 21, 1959–June 19, 1960, *Inaugural Selection* (Checklist)

THE SOLOMON R. GUGGENHEIM MUSEUM, New York, August 30–October 8, 1961, *Modern Masters from the Collection of The Solomon R. Guggenheim Museum*

THE SOLOMON R. GUGGENHEIM MUSEUM, New York, June 5–October 13, 1963, *Cézanne and Structure in Modern Painting*

THE SOLOMON R. GUGGENHEIM MUSEUM, New York, April 30–September 1, 1965, *Paintings from the Collection of The Solomon R. Guggenheim Museum,* no.46, ill.

THE SOLOMON R. GUGGENHEIM MUSEUM, New York, April 11–May 26, 1968, *Acquisitions of the 1930's and 1940's,* pp.22–23, ill.

References:

BASLER, ADOLPHE and KUNSTLER, CHARLES, *La Peinture Indépendante en France,* Paris, 1929, vol.II, no.55 (as "Le Musicien, 1920")

FIERENS, PAUL, *Marc Chagall,* Paris, 1929, p.14, ill. (as "Le Musicien")

VENTURI, LIONELLO, *Marc Chagall,* New York, 1945, pl.XXII

SWEENEY, JAMES JOHNSON, *Marc Chagall,* New York, 1946, p.43, ill.

MARITAIN, RAISSA, *Chagall ou l'orage enchanté,* Geneva-Paris, 1948, p.89, ill.

ESTIENNE, CHARLES, *Chagall,* Paris, 1951, p.34, ill.

LASSAIGNE, JACQUES, *Chagall,* Paris, 1957, p.96, ill.

MEYER, FRANZ, *Marc Chagall,* New York, 1963, p.33, p.295, ill.

GREENFELD, HOWARD, *Marc Chagall,* New York, 1965, cover ill.

37.446

When Chagall returned from Russia to Paris in 1923, he began to recreate many of the important paintings he had lost in Germany and Paris during the war or had had to leave behind in Russia. These versions were painted from memory, photographs and, in some cases, from originals; they vary from very free re-interpretations to near replicas. The earlier rendering of this theme is *Music,* one of the murals Chagall painted in 1920 for the auditorium of the Kamerny State Jewish Theater in Moscow (now in the Tretyakov Gallery, Moscow).

MARC CHAGALL

I and the Village. c.1925

Gouache and watercolor, $15^1/_4$ x $11^3/_4$" (38.7 x 29.9 cm.)

Inscribed l.l. "A Hilla Rebay//Marc Chagall" and l.
margin "A Madame Hilla Rebay sympathiquement//
Marc Chagall//Paris, 1934"

Provenance:

Hilla Rebay, Greens Farms, Connecticut, 1938
Solomon R. Guggenheim, New York
Gift, Solomon R. Guggenheim, 1941

Exhibitions:

THE MUSEUM OF MODERN ART, New York, 1934, *Modern
Works of Art*, no.54

GIBBES MEMORIAL ART GALLERY, Charleston, South
Carolina, March 1–April 12, 1936, *Solomon R. Guggenheim Collection of Non-Objebtive Paintings*, no.109

TOLEDO MUSEUM OF ART, Ohio, November 6–
December 11, 1938, *Contemporary Movements in European
Painting*, no.12

THE SOLOMON R. GUGGENHEIM MUSEUM, New York,
April 11–May 26, 1968, *Acquisitions of the 1930's and 1940's*,
p.61, ill.

THE SOLOMON R. GUGGENHEIM MUSEUM, New York,
July 8–September 14, 1969, *Selected Sculpture and Works
on Paper*, p.17, ill.

41.435

Chagall's first painting called *I and the Village* dates from 1911 (oil, The Museum of Modern Art, New York). The title was invented by the French poet Blaise Cendrars, who supplied titles for many of Chagall's canvases of 1911–12.

Chagall executed many replicas of this theme between 1924 and 1926. By 1925 – the conjectured date of this gouache – the compositional structure of the initial version, based on taut diagonals and circular forms, has become looser, but the motifs and their articulation remain identical.

The date of 1934 visible on the lower margin refers to the date of the artist's inscription to Miss Rebay upon her acquisition of the gouache.

Eduardo Chillida 1924–

Eduardo Chillida was born January 10, 1924, in San Sebastian, Spain. He studied architecture in Madrid from 1943 to 1947, after which he attended art school briefly. In 1947 he executed his first sculpture.

Chillida's earliest work was in clay and plaster. In 1950 the artist began working in iron, which led him to a more abstract sculptural idiom. His works incarnate the directness and simplicity of iron as a working medium, emphasizing sober mottled surfaces and an organic flow of interrelating parts. They give an impression of being both architectonic – in their sound structural integrity – and graphic – in the rhythmic, dynamic gestures which they describe in space.

In 1960–61 Chillida undertook the first of a series of monumental sculptures in wood and granite. One of these, *Abesti Gogora I*, in granite, was commissioned by the Museum of Fine Arts of Houston, Texas. After these works, even smaller pieces by the artist became more monumental in scale and more explicitly architectonic.

Chillida had his first one-man exhibition in 1954 (Clan Gallery, Madrid). Since then his work has been shown nationally and internationally and has been awarded several important international prizes (Venice Biennale, 1958; Carnegie International, 1964).

EDUARDO CHILLIDA

From Within (Desde Dentro). March 1953

Forged iron, $38^3/4''$ (98.4 cm.) high

Inscribed with insignia on top of hanging ring

Provenance:
from the artist through Galerie Maeght, Paris, 1958

Exhibitions:

GALERIE MAEGHT, Paris, October–November 1956, *Chillida*, no.5 (Catalogue published as *Derrière le Miroir*, nos.90–91, October–November 1956)

THE SOLOMON R. GUGGENHEIM MUSEUM, New York, February 11–April 27, 1958, *Sculptures and Drawings by Seven Sculptors*

THE SOLOMON R. GUGGENHEIM MUSEUM, New York, October 21, 1959–June 19, 1960, *Inaugural Selection* (Checklist)

AMERICAN FEDERATION OF ARTS, New York, March 1964–March 1965, *Elements of Modern Art II* (circulated in the United States)

MUSEUM OF FINE ARTS OF HOUSTON, October 4–November 20, 1966, *Eduardo Chillida: Retrospective Exhibition*, no.4, ill.

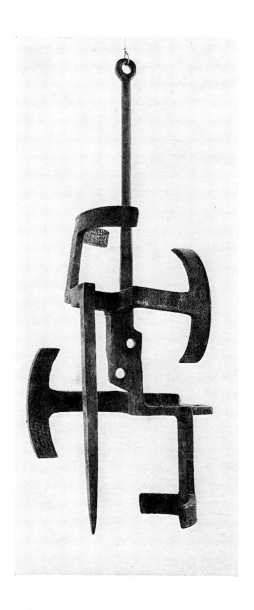

KUNSTHAUS, Zürich, March 8–April 13, 1969, *Eduardo Chillida: Plastik, Zeichnungen, Graphik*, no.2; traveled to STEDELIJK MUSEUM, Amsterdam, April 25–June 8, 1969

THE SOLOMON R. GUGGENHEIM MUSEUM, New York, July 8–September 14, 1969, *Selected Sculpture and Works on Paper*, p.111, ill.

References:

GEIST, SIDNEY, "Month in Review," *Arts*, vol.32, no.6, March 1958, p.51, ill.

NETTER, MARIA, "Der Baskische Bildhauer Eduardo Chillida," *Werk*, vol.49, no.6, p.214, ill.

VOLBOUDT, PIERRE, *Chillida*, New York, 1967, no.8, ill.

58.1504

Working within the Spanish tradition of wrought iron craftsmanship, during the 1950's Chillida developed a sculptural style – ultimately Cubist in derivation – of linear gestures in space. Chillida's open avowal of the craft and process of making his sculptures, of which this work is among the earlier examples, identifies him as an exponent of the *tachiste* or Abstract Expressionist sensibility of the late 1940's and 1950's.

Corneille 1922–

Corneille was born Cornelis van Beverloo on July 3, 1922, in Luik, Belgium, of Dutch parents. Although he studied drawing briefly at the State Academy of Fine Arts, Amsterdam, he is largely self-taught as a painter. Corneille had his first one-man exhibition in 1946 at the Het Beerenhuis, Groningen.

Co-founder of the Dutch "Reflex" group and avant-garde magazine, Corneille was also a co-founder of COBRA in 1948 (see Alechinsky). Although Corneille's early work shows the influence of Klee and Miró, true to the COBRA aesthetic, it was to be increasingly inspired by Surrealism, children's art and folk art. Corneille's canvases are generally more ordered and less gestural than those of other COBRA members such as Alechinsky, Appel or Jorn. The emphasis is on brilliance of color and the primary appeal of a simple, flat, and organic assemblage of forms.

Corneille moved to Paris in 1950, where he studied etching with Stanley Hayter in 1953. In 1956 he won the Guggenheim International Award for the Netherlands. His work has been widely exhibited and, in 1962, he represented Holland at the Venice Biennale. The artist resides in Paris.

The Spell of the Island (Sortilège d'une Ile). 1965

Oil on canvas, 63 $^1/_2$ x 51" (161.3 x 129.5 cm.)

Signed l.c. "Corneille '65"

Provenance:
Lefebre Gallery, New York, 1965

Exhibitions:
LEFEBRE GALLERY, New York, October 12–November 6, 1965, *Corneille,* ill.

STEDELIJK MUSEUM, Amsterdam, October 21–December 11, 1966, *Corneille,* no.72, ill.; traveled to KUNSTHALLE, Düsseldorf, January 27–March 5, 1967, no.40, ill.

THE SOLOMON R. GUGGENHEIM MUSEUM, New York, June 28–October 1, 1967, *Museum Collection, Seven Decades, A Selection* (Checklist)

CINCINNATI ART MUSEUM, Ohio, October 3, 1969– March 29, 1970, *Paintings from the Guggenheim Museum, A Loan Exhibition of Modern Paintings Covering the Period 1949–1965, from The Solomon R. Guggenheim Museum,* no.30, ill.

65.1781

Apparently inspired by the artist's summer sojourns on the Mediterranean coast, Corneille's paintings of 1965 are particularly brilliant and pure in color and mosaic-like in their cellular organization of distinctly defined forms. Although entirely abstract, his irregular imagery evokes associations with nature through its amoeba-like shapes, patches of vegetation, and rhythmic contrasts of colors and textures.

Space Object Box. late 1950's

Construction and collage, 11 x 17⅝ x 5⅜″ (28 x 44.8 x 13.7 cm.)

Signed on reverse "Joseph Cornell"

Provenance:
from the artist, 1968

Exhibitions:
THE SOLOMON R. GUGGENHEIM MUSEUM, New York, May 4–June 25, 1967, *Joseph Cornell*, p.25

THE SOLOMON R. GUGGENHEIM MUSEUM, New York, July 8–September 14, 1969, *Selected Sculpture and Works on Paper*, p.114, ill.

68.1878

Joseph Cornell 1903–

Born on Christmas Eve, 1903, in Nyack, New York, Cornell attended the Phillips Academy at Andover, Massachusetts. In 1929, he and his family moved to Flushing, Queens, to the house in which he still lives. Largely self-taught, Cornell absorbed much of his schooling from the lively artistic climate that existed in New York during the 1930's, and from contacts with the Surrealist painters and writers who were in the United States prior to and during World War II.

Shortly after Cornell first saw Max Ernst's album, *La Femme 100 Têtes*, he showed his own initial efforts at collage to Julien Levy, who included them in a Surrealist group show in January 1932. In 1936 Cornell was included in a major exhibition, "Fantastic Art, Dada, Surrealism" at the Museum of Modern Art. Although many well-known Surrealists had produced objects and boxes, Cornell's use of the box was a major innovation; his particular sensibility brought to his constructions the quality of both a real and an imagined existence. His early boxes incorporated objects with explicit literary connotations; but by 1942, with the well-known *Medici Slot Machine*, he was dealing more directly with his objects as forms that transcended their literary associations.

The "Aviary", "Dovecote", and "Observatory" series were the next themes that he explored. During the early fifties, he concentrated on series of "Observatories", "Night Skies," and "Hotels". During the sixties he returned to the collage, a natural outgrowth of his growing concern with flatness and frontality in his work. Cornell's unique contribution is that he has managed to create the illusionistic space of a painting in terms of an equally resolute three-dimensionality.

Cornell was honored by two museum retrospective exhibitions in 1967, one at the Pasadena Art Museum in California, and the other at The Solomon R. Guggenheim Museum.

Characteristic of Cornell's constructions during the late 1950's, *Space-Object Box* is a continuation of the "Night Skies" series of astrological constellations. The purity of the pale blue cork ball and the ring, combined with the simplicity of the whitewashed board and the dust-green and white child's block, forms a serenely harmonious, almost classical, composition. However, tensions do exist within the box: the space enclosed by the frame is literal, objective space, while the space evoked by the sky chart is imaginary and subjective. Not only does the actual construction conjure up a timeless world of cosmic mystery, past existences, and unspoken, delicate memories, but it is also a real world unto itself.

Much of one's enjoyment is derived from peering through the glass partition to catch a glimpse of the intimate interior stage of the box. Many movie directors also use the device of indirectly viewing an action through a window; it has moreover been noted that Cornell frequently incorporates filmic techniques into his work. In addition to the function of the glass, the nature of the box demands that the images be viewed frontally, like a painting; but, at the same time, the construction is composed of three-dimensional objects, thus situating Cornell and his art outside of any specific medium, time, or school.

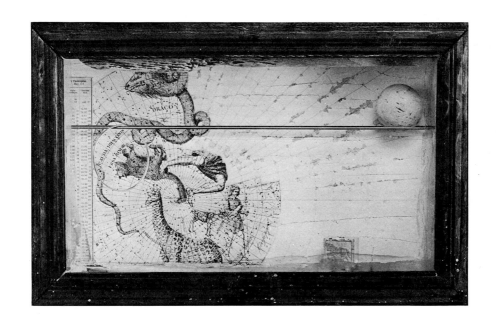

Interplanetary Navigation. 1964

Collage with watercolor, 11 $^1/_2$ x 8$^5/_8$″ (29.2 x 21.9 cm.)

Signed on reverse "Joseph Cornell"

Provenance:
Rose Fried Gallery, New York
Gift, Mr. and Mrs. Walter N. Pharr, New York, 1965

Exhibitions:
THE SOLOMON R. GUGGENHEIM MUSEUM, New York, May 4–June 25, 1967, *Joseph Cornell*, p.51, ill.

THE SOLOMON R. GUGGENHEIM MUSEUM, New York, July 8–September 14, 1969, *Selected Sculpture and Works on Paper*, p.18, ill.

References:
ROSENBERG, HAROLD, *Artworks and Packages*, New York, 1969, pp.82–83, ill.

65.1741

It is as if we are observing a microscopic glimpse of a Vermeer-like reality, although the Vermeer analogy does not extend beyond a general sensation, which is one of delicacy, grace, and purity in both form and content. Cornell, as always, has created a work entirely of his own imaginative vision, through which he controls and charts our route. In the foreground one encounters the figure of a milkmaid, precariously balanced on the edge of the photograph; is she inside or outside the opening? Since she seems to be in front of the drawn circle, she must be outside, just as we are. We can follow her "gaze" and reach, via an unseen diagonal, a second figure of an angel playing on a horn, proportionately scaled down in size to depict distance. Our eye then recedes further into the deep space of the photographic clouds and sky, only to be brought back abruptly by the presence of the iridescent doves descending toward the first figure which, at second glance, might well be encircled by a halo. Cornell takes the viewer on a complex journey, only to bring him back to where he started.

José Luis Cuevas 1933–

José Luis Cuevas was born in 1933 in Mexico City. He began drawing seriously during a long illness: "Drawing was the best vehicle for expressing my daily struggle with death." His drawings and prints generally reflect his views of the evil, sinister and ugly aspects of humanity.

Cuevas's only art training was one year at the School of Painting and Sculpture of La Esmerelda, Mexico City, when he was ten years old. Early in the 1950's Cuevas and several other young Mexican artists opened the Prisse Gallery in Mexico where he had his first one-man exhibition in 1953. He has since been widely exhibited in the United States and Latin America, winning the First International Drawing Prize at the Bienal de São Paulo in 1959. He has also illustrated numerous books. Cuevas now teaches art at the Universidad Iberoamericana, Mexico City.

The Printmaker Désandré Working on a Self Portrait. 1965

Ink and watercolor, 17⅝ x 22¼" (44.8 x 56.5 cm.)

Inscribed l.r. "Cuevas//El grabada Désandré//trabajando en su aut artoretrato"

Provenance:
from the artist through Grace Borgenicht Gallery, New York, 1965

Exhibitions:
GRACE BORGENICHT GALLERY, New York, May 18–June 5, 1965, *Recent Drawings by José Luis Cuevas*

ANDREW D. WHITE MUSEUM, Cornell University, Ithaca, New York, October 8–November 8, 1965, *The Emergent Decade;* organized by THE SOLOMON R. GUGGENHEIM MUSEUM; traveled to DALLAS MUSEUM OF FINE ARTS, December 18, 1965–January 18, 1966; NATIONAL GALLERY OF CANADA, Ottawa, April 1–May 1; THE SOLOMON R. GUGGENHEIM MUSEUM, New York, May 20–June 19; KRANNERT ART MUSEUM, University of Illinois, Champaign, September 16–October 9; DECORDOVA MUSEUM, Lincoln, Massachusetts, November 6–December 4, 1966; JOHN AND MABLE RINGLING MUSEUM OF ART, Sarasota, Florida, April 9–May 7, 1967

DELAWARE ART CENTER, Wilmington, March 9–April 7, 1968, *Contemporary Latin American Artists*

ART GALLERY/CENTER FOR INTER-AMERICAN RELATIONS, New York, July 2–September 14, 1969, *Latin American Paintings from the Collection of The Solomon R. Guggenheim Museum*, pp.12–13, ill.

65.1774

"I hate accident, improvisation, play with new material[s] for their own sake. I believe in originality only when it comes from the very essence of tradition. I believe an artist is original only when he shows his own accent or his full voice through materials given by his predecessors... Today my main interest is the work of great artists of the past: van Eyck, Hals, Velasquez, Zurbarán, etc. and above all, the great Chinese draftsmen of the XVI and XVII centuries." (José Luis Cuevas, statement to The Museum of Modern Art, New York, January 1960)

Robert Delaunay 1885–1941

Robert Delaunay was born in Paris on April 12, 1885. After lycée studies and an apprenticeship to the set-designer Ronsin, in 1904 he turned entirely to painting, exhibiting at the *Salon d'Automne* and the *Salon des Indépendants* that same year.

Early influences on the artist included Impressionism, Neo-Impressionist "pointillisme" and Cézanne. Finally in 1912 Delaunay entered what he called his "constructive" period, characterized by an attempt to "construct" a new kind of pictorial experience through the juxtaposition of colored planes and their "simultaneous contrasts". In 1912, he inaugurated a series of chromatically dissected circular forms, which, through the elaboration of contrasts and rhythms, became one of the artist's better known themes. In these endeavors, the artist was encouraged and seconded by his artist-wife Sonia Terck Delaunay.

Delaunay's visible rejection of the Cubist idiom as well as his emphasis on color, light and motion earned him praise from Guillaume Apollinaire – who coined the term *Orphisme* in 1912 on his account – and an invitation from Kandinsky to exhibit at the first *Blaue Reiter* exhibition in Berlin. His work of this period made a lasting impression on Franz Marc and Paul Klee.

From then to his death, Delaunay developed his study of the potential of color as a rhythmic formal constituent in relationship to both figurative (1920's) and abstract (1930's) themes, murals (Paris World's Fairs, 1925 and 1937) and wall reliefs (1930's). The artist died in Montpellier on October 25, 1941.

St. Séverin. 1909

Oil on canvas, 44⁷/₈ x 35¹/₈″ (114 x 89.2 cm.)

Signed l.r. "r. delaunay"

Provenance:
Mannheim Museum, Germany
Gutekunst & Klipstein, Bern, 1939
Solomon R. Guggenheim, New York
Gift, Solomon R. Guggenheim, 1941

Exhibitions:
MUSEUM OF NON-OBJECTIVE PAINTING, New York, opening April 29, 1952, *Evolution to Non-Objectivity,* no.45 (Checklist)

THE SOLOMON R. GUGGENHEIM MUSEUM, New York, February 3–May 3, 1953, *A Selection* (Checklist)

THE SOLOMON R. GUGGENHEIM MUSEUM, New York, May 13–October 11, 1953, *Selection II* (Checklist)

THE SOLOMON R. GUGGENHEIM MUSEUM, New York, October 6, 1954–February 27, 1955, *Selection IV* (Checklist)

THE SOLOMON R. GUGGENHEIM MUSEUM, New York, March 23–May 22, 1955, *Robert Delaunay;* traveled to INSTITUTE OF CONTEMPORARY ART, Boston, June 2–30,1955

THE SOLOMON R. GUGGENHEIM MUSEUM, New York, July 26–October 9, 1955, *Selection V* (Checklist)

THE SOLOMON R. GUGGENHEIM MUSEUM, New York, January 24–May 1, 1956, *Selection VI* (Checklist)

MUSÉE NATIONAL D'ART MODERNE, Paris, May 25–September 30, 1957, *Robert Delaunay,* no.15; traveled in part to STEDELIJK MUSEUM, Amsterdam, October 18–December 1, 1957, no.9; STEDELIJK VAN ABBE MUSEUM, Eindhoven, December 6–January 11, 1958; THE ARTS COUNCIL OF GREAT BRITAIN, 1958, ill.

THE SOLOMON R. GUGGENHEIM MUSEUM, New York, October 21, 1959–June 19, 1960, *Inaugural Selection* (Checklist)

THE SOLOMON R. GUGGENHEIM MUSEUM, New York, August 30–October 8, 1961, *Modern Masters from the Collection of The Solomon R. Guggenheim Museum*

KUNSTVEREIN, Hamburg, January 26–March 11, 1962, *Robert Delaunay,* no.8, ill.; traveled to WALLRAF-RICHARTZ-MUSEUM, Cologne, March 24–May 6, 1962; KUNSTVEREIN, Frankfurt, May 18–June 24, 1962

SOLOMON R. GUGGENHEIM MUSEUM, New York, June 5–October 13, 1963, *Cézanne and Structure in Modern Painting*

NATIONAL GALLERY OF CANADA, Ottawa, April 1965, *Robert and Sonia Delaunay,* no.9, ill; traveled to MONTREAL MUSEUM OF FINE ARTS, October–December 5, 1965

THE SOLOMON R. GUGGENHEIM MUSEUM, New York, April 30–September 1, 1965, *Paintings from the Collection of The Solomon R. Guggenheim Museum,* no.14, ill.

Eiffel Tower. 1910

Oil on canvas, 79³/₄ x 54⁵/₈″ (202 x 138.8 cm.)

Inscribed l.l. "la Tour 1910" and l.r. "r. delaunay 1910"; on reverse "la tour 1910 // Salle 41 indépendants // 1911// r. delaunay 19 B1 Malesherbes"

Provenance:

Solomon R. Guggenheim, New York
Gift, Solomon R. Guggenheim, 1937

Exhibitions:

XXVIIth SALON DES INDÉPENDANTS, Paris, April 21–June 13, 1911, Salle 41

VIIIth SALON DES INDÉPENDANTS, Brussels, June 10–July 3, 1911, *Les Indépendants*, no.54

GRAND PALAIS, Paris, February 20–March 21, 1926, *Trente Ans d' Art Indépendant, 1884–1914*

KUNSTHAUS, Zürich, October 6–November 3, 1929, *Abstrakte und Surrealistische Malerei und Plastik*, no.21

THE SOLOMON R. GUGGENHEIM MUSEUM, New York, February 3–May 3, 1953, *A Selection* (Checklist)

THE SOLOMON R. GUGGENHEIM MUSEUM, New York, October 6, 1954–February 27, 1955, *Selection IV* (Checklist)

THE SOLOMON R. GUGGENHEIM MUSEUM, New York, March 23–May 22, 1955, *Robert Delaunay;* traveled to INSTITUTE OF CONTEMPORARY ART, Boston, June 2–30, 1955

MUSÉE NATIONAL D'ART MODERNE, Paris, May 25–September 30, 1957, *Robert Delaunay*, no.22, ill.; traveled in part to STEDELIJK MUSEUM, Amsterdam, October 18–December 1, 1957; STEDELIJK VAN ABBE MUSEUM, Eindhoven, December 6–January 11, 1958; THE ARTS COUNCIL OF GREAT BRITAIN, 1958

PALAIS DES BEAUX-ARTS, Brussels, April 17–July 21, 1958, *50 Ans d' Art Moderne*

THE SOLOMON R. GUGGENHEIM MUSEUM, New York, October 21, 1959–June 19, 1960, *Inaugural Selection* (Checklist)

THE SOLOMON R. GUGGENHEIM MUSEUM, New York, August 30–October 8, 1961, *Modern Masters from the Collection l of The Solomon R. Guggenheim Museum*

References:

WALDEN, HERWARTH, *Expressionismus*, Berlin, 1918, p.60, ill.

DE LA TOURETTE, F. GILLES, *Robert Delaunay*, Paris, 1950, pl.9

FRANCASTEL, PIERRE and HABASQUE, GUY, *Robert Delaunay: du Cubisme à l' art abstrait*, Paris, 1957, no.78

READ, HERBERT, *A Concise History of Modern Painting*, New York, 1959, p.292, pl.15

GOLDING, JOHN, *Cubism*, London, 1959, pl.56 (French edition, *Le cubisme*, Paris, 1965, pl.96)

HAMILTON, GEORGE HEARD, *Painting and Sculpture in Europe 1880–1940*, Harmondsworth, 1967, pl.97

THE SOLOMON R. GUGGENHEIM MUSEUM, New York, June 28–October 1, 1967, *Museum Collection, Seven Decades, A Selection* (Checklist)

THE SOLOMON R. GUGGENHEIM MUSEUM, New York, April 11–May 26, 1968, *Acquisitions of the 1930's and 1940's*, p.63, ill.

References:

RAYNAL, MAURICE, *Modern French Painters* (American edition), New York, 1928, p.196

GLEIZES, ALBERT, *Kubismus, Bauhausbücher 13*, Munich, 1928, pl.5

HAFTMANN, WERNER, *Malerei im 20. Jahrhundert*, Munich, 1955, p.134, ill.

FRANCASTEL, PIERRE and HABASQUE, GUY, *Robert Delaunay: du Cubisme à l' art abstrait*, Paris, 1957, no.45

ROSENBLUM, ROBERT, *Cubism and Twentieth-Century Art*, New York, 1960, pl.94

VRIESEN, GUSTAV and IMDAHL, MAX, *Robert Delaunay – Licht und Farbe*, Cologne, 1967, p.26, pl.10

41.462

"*Saint-Séverin*, a period of transition from Cézanne to Cubism, or rather from Cézanne to the *Windows*… In *Saint-Séverin*, whereas there is a will to structure, the forms remain traditional. The broken lines and planes appear only timidly. Color is still *clair-obscur* in spite of the decision not to copy nature literally; there is still a rendering of perspective. Like Cézanne, contrasts are binary, not simultaneous; the chromatic variations lead to a linear articulation… The general orientation of this painting is pursued in my later work." (Delaunay, quoted from Francastel and Habasque, p.87)

There exist eight oil versions of Saint-Séverin of which the Guggenheim's is the third. The second and fourth are in the Minneapolis Institute of Arts and the Philadelphia Museum of Art respectively, the others in private collections.

MARTIN, MARIANNE W., *Futurist Art and Theory*, Oxford, 1968, pl.74a

37.463

The Eiffel Tower was a favorite theme of Delaunay's, not only as a symbol of modernism, progress, the future, but of Paris, the City of Light.

Visually, the tower lent itself to a fragmented rendering as its monumentality, seen from close by, was impossible to grasp by the human eye except as an agglomerate of diverging lines, planes and perspectives. Furthermore the angularity and openwork of the edifice engendered a complex play of shadows.

The choice of subject, its expressive treatment, the bright colors and elliptical perspective declare Delaunay's independence from Analytical Cubism as do the introduction of moving circular forms in the cloud formations.

The theme of the Eiffel Tower appears intermittently in the artist's work from 1909 to his last paintings of 1937. The Museum owns two other Eiffel Tower oils, dated 1909 and 1911.

ROBERT DELAUNAY

The City (La ville). 1911

Oil on canvas, 57¹/₈ x 44¹/₈" (145.1 x 112.1 c.m.)

Inscribed l.l. "la ville 1911 r. delaunay"

Provenance:
from the artist, 1938

Exhibitions:

XXVIIth SALON DES INDÉPENDANTS, Paris, April 21–June 13, 1911, Salle 41

GALERIE THANNHAUSER, Munich, December 19, 1911–January 1912, *Der Blaue Reiter,* no.18

GALERIE BARBAZANGES, Paris, February 28–March 13, 1912, *Robert Delaunay – Marie Laurencin,* no.8

LES EXPOSITIONS DES "BEAUX ARTS", Paris, March–April 1935, *Les créateurs du cubisme,* no.27

THE SOLOMON R. GUGGENHEIM MUSEUM, New York, February 3–May 3, 1953, *A Selection* (Checklist)

THE SOLOMON R. GUGGENHEIM MUSEUM, New York, October 6, 1954–February 27, 1955, *Selection IV* (Checklist)

THE SOLOMON R. GUGGENHEIM MUSEUM, New York, July 26–October 9, 1955, *Selection V* (Checklist)

THE SOLOMON R. GUGGENHEIM MUSEUM, New York, March 23–May 22, 1955, *Robert Delaunay;* traveled to INSTITUTE OF CONTEMPORARY ART, Boston, June 2–30, 1955

MUSÉE NATIONAL D'ART MODERNE, Paris, May 25–September 30, 1957, *Robert Delaunay,* no.26; traveled in part to STEDELIJK MUSEUM, Amsterdam, October 18–December 1, 1957; STEDELIJK VAN ABBE MUSEUM, Eindhoven, December 6–January 11, 1958; THE ARTS COUNCIL OF GREAT BRITAIN, 1958

THE SOLOMON R. GUGGENHEIM MUSEUM, New York, August 30–October 8, 1961, *Modern Masters from the Collection of The Solomon R. Guggenheim Museum*

KUNSTVEREIN, Hamburg, January 26–March 11, 1962, *Robert Delaunay;* traveled to WALLRAF-RICHARTZ-MUSEUM, Cologne, March 24–May 6, 1962; KUNSTVEREIN, Frankfurt, May 18–June 24, 1962, no.14, ill.

LEONARD HUTTON GALLERIES, New York, February 19–March 30, 1963, *Der Blaue Reiter,* no.26, ill.

NATIONAL GALLERY OF CANADA, Ottawa, April 1965, *Robert and Sonia Delaunay,* no.14, ill; traveled to MONTREAL MUSEUM OF FINE ARTS, October–December 5, 1965

THE SOLOMON R. GUGGENHEIM MUSEUM, New York, June 28–October 1, 1967, *Museum Collection, Seven Decades, A Selection* (Checklist)

MUSEO NATIONAL DE BELLAS ARTES, Buenos Aires, May 15–June 5, 1968, *De Cézanne à Miró,* p.30, ill.; organized by The International Council of THE MUSEUM OF MODERN ART, traveled to MUSEO DE ARTE CONTEMPORANEO DE LA UNIVERSIDAD DE CHILE, Santiago, June 26–July 17; MUSEO DE BELLAS ARTES, Caracas, August 4–25, 1968

References:

FRANCASTEL, PIERRE and HABASQUE, GUY, *Robert Delaunay: du Cubisme a l'art abstrait,* Paris, 1957, no.87

GOLDING, JOHN, *Cubism,* London, 1959, pl.57 (French edition, *Le cubisme,* Paris, 1965, pl.104)

VRIESEN, GUSTAV and IMDAHL, MAX, *Robert Delaunay–Licht und Farbe,* Cologne, 1967, pl.16

38.464

This cityscape viewed from a window is one of Delaunay's more strictly Cubist paintings. Aside from the curtain folds which frame the window on either side, the rest of the painting is of slight but undefined depth. The close-valued color scheme is reminiscent not only of Cézanne but of Cubist chromatic austerity.

Unlike Braque's and Picasso's Cubism – an essentially graphic form of expression – drawing is nonexistent here. Furthermore, light and its effect on color is a determining compositional factor. In order to achieve the splintered modulation of the field, Delaunay used a mosaic-like pointilliste technique he had practiced earlier (1906–7) under the influence of the Neo-Impressionists Signac and Henri-Edmond Cross.

The artist's earliest painting of *The City* series dates from 1910. A 1910 version closely resembling the Museum's is in the Musée National d'Art Moderne, Paris.

ROBERT DELAUNAY

Windows (simultaneous composition, 2nd motif, 1st part).
(Les fenêtres simultanées, 2e motif, 1ère partie).

Oil on canvas, 21 3/4 x 18 3/8" (55.3 x 46.7 cm.)

Inscribed l.l. "les fenêtres simultané//r. delaunay 12"; on reverse, "les fenêtres 2m motif 1r partie (1912) r.d. Paris".

Provenance:

Hilla Rebay, Greens Farms, Connecticut, 1938
Solomon R. Guggenheim, New York
Gift, Solomon R. Guggenheim, 1941

Exhibitions:

ARTS CLUB OF CHICAGO, October 24–November 21, 1952, *Robert Delaunay*, no.12

THE SOLOMON R. GUGGENHEIM MUSEUM, New York, May 13–October 11, 1953, *Selection II* (Checklist)

THE SOLOMON R. GUGGENHEIM MUSEUM, New York, March 23–May 22, 1955, *Robert Delaunay*; traveled to INSTITUTE OF CONTEMPORARY ART, Boston, June 2–30, 1955

THE SOLOMON R. GUGGENHEIM MUSEUM, New York, July 26–October 9, 1955, *Selection V* (Checklist)

THE SOLOMON R. GUGGENHEIM MUSEUM, New York, January 24–May 1, 1956, *Selection VI* (Checklist)

TATE GALLERY, London, April 16–May 26, 1957, *Paintings from The Solomon R. Guggenheim Museum*, no.37; organized by THE SOLOMON R. GUGGENHEIM MUSEUM, traveled to GEMEENTEMUSEUM, The Hague, June 25–September 1; ATENEIUMIN TAIDEKOKOELMAT, Helsinki, September 27–October 20; GALLERIA NAZIONALE D'ARTE MODERNA, Rome, December 5, 1957–January 8, 1958; WALLRAF-RICHARTZ-MUSEUM, Cologne, January 26–March 30; MUSÉE DES ARTS DÉCORATIFS, Paris, April 23–June 1, 1958

THE SOLOMON R. GUGGENHEIM MUSEUM, New York, October 21, 1959–June 19, 1960, *Inaugural Selection* (Checklist)

THE SOLOMON R. GUGGENHEIM MUSEUM, New York, August 30–October 8, 1961, *Modern Masters from the Collection of The Solomon R. Guggenheim Museum*

PHILADELPHIA MUSEUM OF ART, November 2, 1961–January 7, 1962, *Guggenheim Museum Exhibition, A Loan Collection of Paintings, Drawings, and Prints from The Solomon R. Guggenheim Museum, New York*, no.21

69TH REGIMENT ARMORY, New York, April 6–28, 1963, *The Armory Show in Retrospect, 50th Anniversary Exhibition*, no.256

THE SOLOMON R. GUGGENHEIM MUSEUM, New York, April 30–September 1, 1965, *Paintings from the Collection of The Solomon R. Guggenheim Museum*, no.25, ill.

THE SOLOMON R. GUGGENHEIM MUSEUM, New York, June 23–October 23, 1966, *Gauguin and the Decorative Style*

THE SOLOMON R. GUGGENHEIM MUSEUM, New York, June 28–October 1, 1967, *Museum Collection, Seven Decades, A Selection* (Checklist)

THE SOLOMON R. GUGGENHEIM MUSEUM, New York, April 11–May 26, 1968, *Acquisitions of the 1930's and 1940's*, p.64, ill.

MUSEO NACIONAL DE BELLAS ARTES, Buenos Aires, May 15–June 5, 1968, *De Cézanne à Miró*; organized by the International Council of THE MUSEUM OF MODERN ART, traveled to MUSEO DE ARTE CONTEMPORANEO DE LA UNIVERSIDAD DE CHILE, Santiago, June 26–July 17; MUSEO DE BELLAS ARTES, Caracas, August 4–25, 1968

References:

SEUPHOR, MICHEL, *L'art abstrait*, Paris, 1949, p.210

SUTTON, DENYS, "Robert Delaunay", *Magazine of Art*, vol.42, no.6, October 1949, p.210

FRANCASTEL, PIERRE and HABASQUE, GUY, *Robert Delaunay: du Cubisme à l'art abstrait*, Paris, 1957, no.106

OERI, GEORGINE, "Delaunay in Search of Himself", *Arts*, vol.33, no.6, March 1959, pp.32–38, ill.

GOLDING, JOHN, *Cubism*, London, 1959, pp.172–176, pl.59 (French edition, *Le cubisme*, Paris, 1965, pl.125)

41.464A

It was in 1912 that Delaunay finally found his mature style and entered what he called the "constructive" phase of his career. "At this time, I had ideas about a kind of painting which would exist only through color – chromatic contrasts developing in temporal sequence yet simultaneously visible. I borrowed Chevreuil's scientific term: 'simultaneous contrasts'." (Robert Delaunay in his notebook, 1912; quoted by G. de la Tourelle, *Robert Delaunay*, Paris, 1950, p.37)

The "simultaneous contrasts" of *Windows* of 1912 – the
unprecedented emphasis on light and color – were
considered not only by the artist but by sympathetic
observers as the creation of a radically new pictorial
idiom. Although a triangular articulation recalls the
organization of the earlier Eiffel Tower series, undeniably
the painting's structure is created through the rhythmic
alternation between warm and cool (lit and shaded) zones
of equal value and intensity. They do not succeed each
other in time but are perceived simultaneously.

ROBERT DELAUNAY

Circular Forms. 1912?

Oil on canvas, 50⁷/₈ x 76⁷/₈" (129.2 x 195.3 cm.)

Signed l.c. "r. delaunay"

Provenance:
Sonia Delaunay, Paris, 1949

Exhibitions:

ARTS CLUB OF CHICAGO, October 24–November 21, 1952, *Robert Delaunay*, no.13

THE SOLOMON R. GUGGENHEIM MUSEUM, New York, February 3–May 3, 1953, *A Selection* (Checklist)

THE SOLOMON R. GUGGENHEIM MUSEUM, New York, March 23–May 22, 1955, *Robert Delaunay*; traveled to INSTITUTE OF CONTEMPORARY ART, Boston, June 2–30, 1955

STÄDTISCHES MUSEUM MORSBROICH, Leverkusen, June 7–July 15, 1956, *Robert Delaunay*, no.37, pl.5; traveled to KUNSTVEREIN, Freiburg, July 22–August 19, 1956

TATE GALLERY, London, April 16–May 26, 1957, *Paintings from The Solomon R. Guggenheim Museum*, no.37; organized by THE SOLOMON R. GUGGENHEIM MUSEUM, traveled to GEMEENTEMUSEUM, The Hague, June 25–September 1; ATENEIUMIN TAIDEKOKOELMAT, Helsinki, September 27–October 20; GALLERIA NAZIONALE D'ARTE MODERNA, Rome, December 5, 1957–January 8, 1958; WALLRAF-RICHARTZ-MUSEUM, Cologne, January 26–March 30; MUSÉE DES ARTS DÉCORATIFS, Paris, April 23–June 1, 1958

THE SOLOMON R. GUGGENHEIM MUSEUM, New York, October 21, 1959–June 19, 1960, *Inaugural Selection* (Checklist)

THE SOLOMON R. GUGGENHEIM MUSEUM, New York, August 30–October 8, 1961, *Modern Masters from the Collection of The Solomon R. Guggenheim Museum*

PHILADELPHIA MUSEUM OF ART, November 2, 1961–January 7, 1962, *Guggenheim Museum Exhibition, A Loan Collection of Paintings, Drawings, and Prints from The Solomon R. Guggenheim Museum, New York*, no.22

THE SOLOMON R. GUGGENHEIM MUSEUM, New York, April 30–September 1, 1965, *Paintings from the Collection of The Solomon R. Guggenheim Museum*, no.26, ill.

THE SOLOMON R. GUGGENHEIM MUSEUM, New York, June 23–October 23, 1966, *Gauguin and the Decorative Style*

THE SOLOMON R. GUGGENHEIM MUSEUM, New York, June 28–October 1, 1967, *Museum Collection, Seven Decades, A Selection* (Checklist)

References:

ARP, HANS, *Onze peintres*, Zürich, 1949, p.23, ill.

FRANCASTEL, PIERRE and HABASQUE, GUY, *Robert Delaunay: du Cubisme à l'art abstrait*, Paris, 1957, no.270 (misdated 1930)

The Baltimore Museum of Art News, Baltimore, vol.xxv, no.3, Spring, 1962, p.11, pl.1

MULLER, JOSEPH ÉMILE, *L'Art au XXe siècle*, Paris, 1967, p.97, pl.40

49.1184

In the winter of 1912–13, Delaunay started developing *Circular Forms*. Some paintings have a single form, others (such as this) have two forms which apparently symbolized the sun and moon and their rotational cosmic cycles.

In these paintings the artist attains a physical luminosity of color as never before. The thick bright colors, their studied "crossed contrasts" and their application with a wide, flat, divided stroke not only seal the canvas from the penetration of light but throw it back in a swift rotary movement. Color and light exist concretely, no longer as illusions of light and shade. Furthermore they provide both the form and structure of the rhythmic development.

Considered a heretic formal digression by the Cubists, the rhythmic flux of circular forms will be a major theme in Delaunay's work throughout his career, especially dominant in his large wall reliefs of the 1930's.

At least five other versions of this painting are known, dated either 1912 or 1912–13.

PEARLS

Pearls. 1961

Oil and collage on canvas, 70 x 69″ (177.8 x 175.2 cm.)

Inscribed l.c. "PEARLS"

Provenance:
the artist, February 1962
Martha Jackson Gallery, New York
Leon A. Mnuchin, New York
Gift, Leon A. Mnuchin, 1963

Exhibitions:
MARTHA JACKSON GALLERY, New York, January 9–
February 3, 1962, *Jim Dine*
THE SOLOMON R. GUGGENHEIM MUSEUM, New York,
April 19–May 15, 1966, *The Solomon R. Guggenheim
Museum Collection*

References:
GORDON, JOHN, *Jim Dine*, New York, 1970, no.27

63.1681

Jim Dine 1935–

Born on June 16, 1935, in Cincinnati, Ohio, Jim Dine
received his B.F.A. from Ohio University. His first group
exhibition after he came to New York occurred in 1958 at
the Judson Gallery. He showed there again in 1959 and in
1960 with Oldenburg. In 1960 he had his first one-man
show at the Reuben Gallery.

Although Dine has been considered one of the founders of
Pop art, his work grew out of, and strongly reflects, Abstract Expressionism. Along with Oldenburg and Kaprow,
Dine was instrumental in the pioneering of Happenings;
his *Car Crash* of 1960 is one of his best known works. His
work on canvas is an interchange between theater and
painting, with the objects projected away from the canvas
in such a way as to become almost literally independent.
From the beginning, Dine indicated a propensity for attach-
ing objects to his canvases, many of which were his own
possessions. Therefore, in contrast to other Pop artists who
commented on the outside world, Dine's art is fundamen-
tally introverted and autobiographical.

Among the early works are his "Crash" series, dating from
the death of a friend, and several works featuring a single
object, of which *Pearls* is one. These were followed by his
"Bathroom" series of 1962, and his "Palette" and "Hat-
chet" series of 1963–64, which evolved into his "Bathrobe"
and "Self-Portrait" themes. During the mid-to-late 60's,
Dine produced watercolors and prints and began to work
in aluminum. As a result, he created many three-dimensional works, as well as some environments.

In March of 1970, Dine had his first major retrospective
exhibition in the United States at the Whitney Museum
of American Art.

In Dine's *Pearls*, a facsimile necklace placed just off-center
at the top of the canvas, is paralled by the unfinished
word "pearls", placed more clearly off-center at the
bottom edge. By presenting the word and image in
opposing positions, Dine appears to consider them as
equals, an equation that he disrupts by the manner in
which they are rendered. Dine establishes quite clearly
the object status of the image and de-emphasizes, just
as explicitly, the sign quality of the word.

The multiple references that Dine creates in *Pearls* is
characteristic of his style, a play on illusion and reality
(which is more real – the object or the word?) that has
much in common with the work of Jasper Johns.
Although Dine has been associated most frequently with
Pop art, his work has a greater affinity with the painter-
liness of Johns and Rauschenberg than it does with the
crisp, logical style of such artists as Lichtenstein or
Warhol, and the recent work of Oldenburg.

Composition 11. 1918

Oil on canvas, 22 1/4 x 40" (56.5 x 101.6 cm.)

Signed with monogram and dated l.r. "19[monogram]18"

Provenance:
the artist
Mme. Pétro van Doesburg, Meudon, 1954

Exhibitions:
STEDELIJK MUSEUM, Amsterdam, July 6–September 25, 1951, *de Stijl*

XXVI BIENNALE INTERNAZIONALE D'ARTE VENEZIA, summer 1952, *de Stijl*, no.26, p.384

THE MUSEUM OF MODERN ART, New York, December 16, 1952–February 15, 1953, *de Stijl, 1917–1928* (Catalogue published as *The Museum of Modern Art Bulletin*, vol. XX, no.2, Winter, 1952–1953)

THE SOLOMON R. GUGGENHEIM MUSEUM, New York, March 30–May 5, 1954, *Selection III* (Checklist)

THE SOLOMON R. GUGGENHEIM MUSEUM, New York, October 6, 1954–February 27, 1955, *Selection IV* (Checklist)

MONTREAL MUSEUM OF FINE ARTS, June 4–July 3, 1955, *A Selection from The Solomon R. Guggenheim Museum, New York*, no.7

THE SOLOMON R. GUGGENHEIM MUSEUM, New York, July 26–October 9, 1955, *Selection V* (Checklist)

THE SOLOMON R. GUGGENHEIM MUSEUM, New York, June 28–October 1, 1967, *Museum Collection, Seven Decades, A Selection* (Checklist)

STEDELIJK VAN ABBE MUSEUM, Eindhoven, December 13, 1968–January 26, 1969, *Theo van Doesburg 1883–1931*, no.A17, ill.; traveled to GEMEENTEMUSEUM, The Hague, February 7–March 23; KUNSTHALLE, Nürnburg, April 6–May 15; KUNSTHALLE, Basel, August 9–September 7, 1969

References:
JAFFÉ, H. L. C., *De Stijl/1917–1931, the Dutch Contribution to Modern Art*, Amsterdam, 1956, pl.13

54.1360

Theo van Doesburg 1883–1931

Theo van Doesburg was born C. E. M. Küpper on August 30, 1883, in Utrecht. He began painting in 1899; by 1908, when his work was first shown at The Hague, he was painting in an Impressionist technique. During his military service (1914–16), van Doesburg, influenced by Kandinsky's *On the Spiritual in Art*, experimented with Cubism and abstraction.

In 1916 he collaborated with the architects Jan Wils and J. J. P. Oud and, with the latter, formed the *De Sphinx* group. The following year he founded *De Stijl*, a monthly periodical whose contributors, Mondrian, Oud, Wils, Bart van der Leck, Vantongerloo, became the leaders of the *De Stijl* movement. Working closely together, the group stressed the need for abstraction and simplification. Subject matter was excluded from their works; composition was constructed on the principle of the straight line, rectangle or cube; the palette was reduced to the primary colors, black, gray, and white. They extended these principles to all of the arts – architecture, graphic and industrial design as well as painting and sculpture.

After 1917, van Doesburg became a propagandist for *De Stijl,* traveling to Belgium, France (where he organized a *De Stijl* exhibition in Paris in 1923), Italy, Spain, Czechoslovakia and Germany. His lectures at the Bauhaus strongly influenced both masters and students. His friendship with Kurt Schwitters led to an interest in Dada (poems written under the pseudonym, I.K. Bonset). In 1926, after working with Jean Arp, van Doesburg published his manifesto of Elementarism, which broadened the principles of *De Stijl*. When, on March 7, 1931, van Doesburg died, *De Stijl* ceased publication, but the movement survived with the foundation of *Abstraction-Création* in the same year.

Nunc Stans. May 16–June 5, 1965

Vinyl on canvas, three sections, each 63$\frac{3}{4}$ x 107$\frac{7}{8}$"
(161.9 x 274 cm.)

Signed and dated on third panel l.l. "j. Dubuffet 65"

Provenance:

the artist
Galerie Beyeler, Basel, and Galerie Jeanne Bucher, Paris,
1966

Exhibitions:

GALERIE JEANNE BUCHER, Paris, April–May 1966, *Nunc
Stans, Épokhê, cycle de l'Hourloupe, Dubuffet*, ill.

THE SOLOMON R. GUGGENHEIM MUSEUM, New York,
October 27, 1966–February 5, 1967, *Jean Dubuffet
1962–66*, no.70, ill.

THE SOLOMON R. GUGGENHEIM MUSEUM, New York,
June 28–October 1, 1967, *Museum Collection, Seven
Decades, A Selection* (Checklist)

References:

JOLLEY, DAVID, "Recent Museum Acquisitions, Jean
Dubuffet: Nunc Stans (Solomon R. Guggenheim
Museum, New York)", *Burlington Magazine*, vol.109,
September 1967, p.534, pl.51

LOREAU, MAX, *Catalogue des Travaux de Jean Dubuffet,
Fascicule XXI: L'Hourloupe II*, cat. no.143, pp.82–4, ill.

66.1818

This recent orientation of Dubuffet's art is characterized
by a reintroduction of color (restricted to the primary
colors, black and white) and the abolition of the traditional figure/ground relationship, replaced by a synthetic
all-over pattern of interlocking pictographs. Although
typically equivocal both in imagery and meaning, the
Hourloupe series (1962–64) and its subsequent variations
such as this are distinguished from Dubuffet's earlier
production through the emphasis on two-dimensional
plane, the precision and clarity of the puzzle-like patterns
and the smooth surfaces.

Nunc Stans was originally intended as a mural for the
University of Paris at Nanterre.

JEAN DUBUFFET

Bidon l'Esbroufe. December 11, 1967

Acrylic on fiberglass-reinforced polyester resin, 65³/₄″ (167 cm.) high

Signed and dated on side of left foot "J.D. 67"

Provenance:
the artist
Gift to the Guggenheim Museum in honor of Mr. and Mrs. Thomas M. Messer, 1970

References:
XXe Siècle, no. XXXII, June 1969, p.28, ill.

70.1920

In November and December of 1967, Dubuffet executed a series of six three-dimensional standing personages, of which *Bidon l'Esbroufe* is the final one. Typical of the artist's fantasy and invention, all are endowed with names which defy not only translation but any attempts to paraphrase them: *Canotin Mache-œil, Papa Loustic, Bêniquet Trompette, Brûle Savate, Fiston la Filoche, Bidon l'Esbroufe*. These titles are humorous, poetic, and onomatopoeic. They are comparable to children's freely concocted nicknames, in their irrational juxtapositions of words and images and their rhythmic resonance.

Characteristic of Dubuffet's sculpture is its particular form of three-dimensionality which can be generally described as an assemblage of predominantly two-dimensional elements. The colors moreover accentuate this impression, flattening the forms rather than modeling them.

Raymond Duchamp-Villon 1876–1918

Raymond Duchamp-Villon was born November 5, 1876, at Damville, France, the brother of Jacques Villon (1875–1963) and Marcel Duchamp (1887–1968). After secondary schooling in Rouen, he entered the University of Paris as a medical student. In 1898, rheumatic fever forced him to abandon medicine and allowed him to devote all his time to sculpture. He exhibited for the first time at the *Salon de la Société Nationale des Beaux-Arts* in 1901, and from 1905 to 1913 he exhibited annually at the *Salon d'Automne*. During this same period Duchamp-Villon participated in the formation of the *Section d'or* group at Puteaux. This group included Marcel Duchamp, Jacques Villon, Léger, Delaunay, Gleizes, Metzinger, Gris, Picabia, Kupka, Le Fauconnier, La Fresnaye, Lhote and Archipenko, and differed from the Cubism of Picasso and Braque through their interest in the formal dynamics of color, light and movement.

In 1913, Duchamp-Villon sent five sculptures to the Armory Show (New York, Chicago, Boston). In 1914 he enlisted in the army as a medical officer and, stationed in St. Germain until September 1915, he was able to continue work on his major sculpture and the culmination of his short artistic career, *Horse*. In 1915, he was sent to the front where, one year later, he became ill and died in an army hospital in Cannes on October 7, 1918.

Maggy (Tête de Femme, portrait de Mme. Georges Ribemont-Dessaignes). 1912

Bronze, third of eight casts executed November 1954, by Georges Rudier, Paris, 29 1/8″ (74 cm.) high

Inscribed on rear shoulder "Duchamp-Villon//1911", rear l.l. "Louis Carré. Editeur paris." and l.r. "Rudier// Fondeur. Paris."

Provenance:

Galerie Louis Carré & Cie., Paris, 1957

Exhibitions:

THE SOLOMON R. GUGGENHEIM MUSEUM, New York, February 19–March 10, 1957, *Jacques Villon, Raymond Duchamp-Villon, Marcel Duchamp*, ill.; traveled to MUSEUM OF FINE ARTS OF HOUSTON, March 22–April 21, 1957

THE SOLOMON R. GUGGENHEIM MUSEUM, New York, October 21, 1959–June 19, 1960, *Inaugural Selection* (Checklist)

M. KNOEDLER & CO., INC., New York, October 11–November 4, 1967, *Raymond Duchamp-Villon 1876–1918*, no.17, fig.4

THE SOLOMON R. GUGGENHEIM MUSEUM, New York, July 8–September 14, 1969, *Selected Sculpture and Works on Paper*, p.116, ill.

References:

GIEDION-WELCKER, CAROLA, *Contemporary Sculpture*, New York, 1955, p.20, ill.

ROSENBLUM, ROBERT, "The Duchamp Family," *Arts*, vol.31, no.7, April 1957, pp.20–23, ill.

SELZ, JEAN, *Modern Sculpture*, New York, 1963, pl.XIII

HAMILTON, GEORGE HEARD, *Painting and Sculpture in Europe 1880–1940*, Harmondsworth, 1967, p.175, pl.102(B)

HAMILTON, GEORGE HEARD, "Raymond-Duchamp-Villon", *L'Oeil*, nos.151–153, September 1967, pp.46–55, no.5, ill.

ARNASON, H. H., *History of Modern Art*, New York, 1968, pl.186

57.1464

This is the third of eight casts executed November 1954 by Georges Rudier, Paris. Another unsigned and undated cast exists in the Musée National d'Art Moderne in Paris and a third in the collection of Louis Carré, Paris.

Although Duchamp-Villon's early sculpture was influenced by Rodin and Art Nouveau, *Maggy* is representative of his more mature work. Characteristic of this later style is the absence of any attempt at realism. There is no modeling, texture, surface incident, nor is there any interest in psychological interpretation.

Instead, emphasis is on the expressiveness of elementary volumes and their formal relationships within what remains a unified whole. The even black patina which Duchamp-Villon used regularly after 1907 accentuates not only the turn away from realism but from the principle of "truth to materials" of his predecessors. It sets off the volumes as closed, dense and unequivocal, making this a masterpiece in the history of Cubist sculpture.

Max Ernst 1891–

Max Ernst was born April 2, 1891, in Bruehl near Cologne, Germany. After studying at the University of Bonn and serving in the army, he went to Cologne where, with Arp and Baargeld, he launched the Cologne Dada movement in 1919. In 1922, he moved to Paris where he collaborated in the founding of Surrealism.

The experiences of Dada and Surrealism had a lasting effect on the formulation of Max Ernst's art. Since his earliest Dada collages, the artist's work has been infused with a whimsical and blasphemous quality. During his Surrealist period (1922–1938), he was a prolific inventor of techniques for provoking "automatist" or irrational imagery *(frottage, décalcomanie, oscillation)*. Irrational, symbolic and mythical imagery are the constant themes of his creative activity. Primarily a painter, the artist began working in sculpture in 1935, his most important three-dimensional work – executed in the United States – dating from 1944. This series of bronze mythical personages was extended and developed at intervals into the sixties.

In 1941 Ernst came to New York with the aid of Peggy Guggenheim, whom he married that year. After 1945 he spent most of his time in Sedona, Arizona, with his second wife, the American Surrealist Dorothea Tanning. He returned to Paris, where he now resides, in 1952, and became a French citizen in 1958. In 1959 his work was honored by a major retrospective exhibition at the Musée National d'Art Moderne, Paris.

MAX ERNST

Anxious Friend. 1944

Bronze, fifth of nine casts executed by Modern Art Foundry, Long Island, 1957, from plaster original (now destroyed), Collection Julien Levy, Bridgewater, Connecticut, 26³/₈″ (67 cm.) high

Incised on right face of base "1944 Max Ernst"

Provenance:

the artist, 1957
Alexandre Iolas Gallery, New York
Gift, Dominique and John de Menil, 1959

Exhibitions:

ALEXANDRE IOLAS GALLERY, New York, April – May 1957, *Max Ernst*

ARTS CLUB OF CHICAGO, April 19–May 19, 1960, *Sculpture and Drawings by Sculptors from The Solomon R. Guggenheim Museum*, no.9, ill.

PHILBROOK ART CENTER, Tulsa, Oklahoma, October 1–23, 1962, *Twentieth Century Sculpture*, no.21, ill.

THE SOLOMON R. GUGGENHEIM MUSEUM, New York, July 8–September 14, 1969, *Selected Sculpture and Works on Paper*, p.118

References:

BOSQUET, ALAIN, *Max Ernst, Oeuvre Sculpté 1913–1961,* Paris, 1961, no.26, ill.

RUSSELL, JOHN, *Max Ernst, Life and Work,* New York, 1967, pl.130

59.1521

Anxious Friend is one of an important group of sculptures which Ernst executed in the United States in 1944. Like others in this group, the work was originally made in plaster, for which the artist used found objects. Bronze casts were subsequently made from the original plaster. Such accidental or chance points of departure have always been essential to Ernst, but here this method is combined with both his knowledge of primitive art and his mastery of visual wit and surprise.

Etienne Martin 1913–

Etienne Martin was born February 4, 1913, in Loriol (Drôme), France. In 1929 he entered the Académie des Beaux-Arts at Lyon where he remained until 1933.

In 1933 Etienne Martin moved to Paris where he began independent work as a sculptor. His early work contains certain indications of the characteristics of his mature style: a predilection for wood and symbolic forms and archaic allusions recalling Gauguin and the early Henry Moore.
In 1942, after World War II, during which Etienne Martin was drafted and subsequently imprisoned, the sculptor settled in Dieulefit. In 1947 he returned to Paris, where his sculptures evolved from organic tent-like structures, based on experimentations with fabrics, to rough-hewn labyrinthine "Dwellings" of human, habitable scale. Symbolic of man's subconscious wish to return to the primeval womb, Etienne Martin's wooden "Dwellings" *(Demeures)* have become his most constant and characteristic creative form.

The artist was awarded the Grand Prize for Sculpture at the 1966 Venice Biennale. He resides in Paris.

ETIENNE MARTIN

Anemone. 1955

Elmwood, 43$^1/_2''$ (110.5 cm.) high

Not inscribed

Provenance:
from the artist, 1957

Exhibitions:
THE SOLOMON R. GUGGENHEIM MUSEUM, New York, February 11–April 27, 1958, *Sculptures and Drawings by Seven Sculptors*, ill.

THE SOLOMON R. GUGGENHEIM MUSEUM, New York, October 21, 1959–June 19, 1960, *Inaugural Selection* (Checklist; withdrawn from exhibition April 4, 1960)

ARTS CLUB OF CHICAGO, April 19–May 19, 1960, *Sculpture and Drawings by Sculptors from The Solomon R. Guggenheim Museum*, no.10, ill.

THE SOLOMON R. GUGGENHEIM MUSEUM, New York, July 8–September 14, 1969, *Selected Sculpture and Works on Paper*, p.137, ill.

References:
Werk, vol.45, no.5, May 1958, p.103, ill.

57.1486

Beginning with a massive tree root which he treats partially as an *objet trouvé*, Etienne Martin has completed a process which nature began. In so doing he demonstrates his faithfulness to the artisanal woodworking traditions of his native *département*, the Ardèche, in Central France; and he also situates himself in a twentieth-century European tradition of vitalist art. Just as in his later, monumental *Demeure Soleil* of 1963 (Stedelijk Museum, Amsterdam), which he fashioned from a single huge tree bole, Etienne Martin in this work has used organic material and forms borrowed directly from nature in order to impart a sense of life to his image.

Wojciech Fangor 1922–

Wojciech Fangor was born November 15, 1922, in Warsaw, Poland. He graduated from the Warsaw Academy of Fine Arts in 1946 and taught there, as an Assistant Professor, between 1953 and 1961. His first one-man exhibition was held in Warsaw in 1949. During the years 1958-9, Fangor collaborated on architectural designs; at about this time he began hanging his paintings as environmental situations, and experimenting with free-standing sculptures as extensions of color in space.

Fangor's dominant subject matter is color, its elusive qualities of change and movement, and the varied effects of interaction and vibration on the viewer's eye. An "optical" art that is intuitive rather than systematic, it suggests organic movements of expansion and contraction, projection and recession.

The artist had his first American one-man exhibition in 1960 at the Gres Gallery in Washington. He participated in "15 Polish Painters" (1961) and "The Responsive Eye" (1965), both at The Museum of Modern Art, New York, and the Guggenheim International Award Exhibition in 1965. He has lived in Paris, Berlin and London. Since 1966, Fangor has been teaching at Fairleigh Dickinson University in Madison, New Jersey.

WOJCIECH FANGOR

New Jersey 5, 1965. 1965

Oil on canvas, 56 x 56" (142.2 x 142.2 cm.)

Signed on reverse "Fangor//NJ 5 1965"

Provenance:
Fairleigh Dickinson University, Madison, New Jersey
Gift, Mrs. Alfred J. Teer, Shorthills, New Jersey, in memory of Alfred J. Teer, 1965

Exhibitions:
RIVERSIDE MUSEUM, New York, 1965

GALERIE CHALETTE, New York, March 3–May 1967, *Fangor Retrospective*

THE SOLOMON R. GUGGENHEIM MUSEUM, New York, June 28–October 1, 1967, *Museum Collection, Seven Decades, A Selection* (Checklist)

CINCINNATI ART MUSEUM, Ohio, October 3, 1969–March 29, 1970, *Paintings from the Guggenheim Museum, A Loan Exhibition of Modern Paintings Covering the Period 1949–1965, from The Solomon R. Guggenheim Museum,* no.31

65.1783

Fangor's prime concern is color, with which he experiments in simple, modular patterns. One of his frequent themes is the circle, a motif which, through its radial symmetry and rotational movement, allows infinite effects of contraction and expansion. Form is dissolved into an immaterial color experience as the brilliant concentric circles bleed into one another.

Paul Feeley 1910–1966

Paul Feeley was born July 27, 1910, in Des Moines, Iowa. In 1922, his family moved to Palo Alto, California where he finished secondary school and began to study painting. He moved to New York in 1931, where he attended the Art Students League for portrait and figure classes. In 1935 he joined the Mural Painters Society of New York and supported himself by decorating restaurants, hotels and night clubs. That same year he began teaching painting and drawing at the Cooper Union Art School, an activity he continued until 1939. In the meantime he was an associate of a commercial display studio which designed displays for New York department stores and the 1939 New York World's Fair. In 1939 he went to Bennington College in Vermont as a teacher of painting, a post he held until his death except for three years of military service with the Marines in the Pacific (1943–46).

Feeley's early work was figurative and expressionist. Introduced to the American avant-garde (Pollock, de Kooning) in 1951, around 1953–4 his style began to move toward a more abstract and color-oriented idiom. His forms of the late fifties are fluid. Recalling in some instances the biomorphism of artists like Baziotes, they are nonetheless simpler and create highly equivocal relationships between figure and ground. The modular character of his shapes, their symmetry and spatial tensions are accentuated in his work of 1962–3, the colors becoming brighter and more contrasted, and the paint more smoothly applied. In 1964, Feeley achieved the classic phase of his mature style, marked by economy of form, clarity of image and luminosity of color.

Feeley had his first major New York exhibition in 1955 (Tibor de Nagy Gallery), after which his work was shown regularly. He died June 10, 1966, in New York.

PAUL FEELEY

Formal Haut. 1965

Acrylic on canvas, 60 x 60″ (152.4 x 152.4 cm.)

Inscribed on reverse on stretcher "Formal Haut Paul Feeley 1965"

Provenance:
Betty Parsons Gallery, New York, 1966

Exhibitions:
THE SOLOMON R. GUGGENHEIM MUSEUM, New York, June 28–October 1, 1967, *Museum Collection, Seven Decades, A Selection* (Checklist)
THE SOLOMON R. GUGGENHEIM MUSEUM, New York, April 11– May 26, 1968, *Paul Feeley 1910–1966, A Retrospective Exhibition,* p.51, ill.
CINCINNATI ART MUSEUM, Ohio, October 3, 1969–March 2 1970, *Paintings from the Guggenheim Museum, A Loan Exhibition of Modern Paintings Covering the Period 1949–1965, from The Solomon R. Guggenheim Museum,* no.32

66.1832

Formal Haut is an excellent example of Feeley s classic style. Discreet in its symmetrical repetition of one or two shapes on a white (raw canvas) ground, the hues are pure and buoyant. Through the contrasts of colors as well as that of convex and concave contours, the artist has created a pattern of rhythmic tensions which relates to the square area of the canvas.

The two modular forms – one described as a "jack" (as in the game of jacks), the other as a "baluster" – are constant in Feeley's painting of 1964–5. They also provide the basic structural motifs for many of the assembled planar sculptures in painted wood which the artist undertook after 1965.

Gelmeroda IV. 1915

Oil on canvas, 39¹/₈ x 31¹/₄″ (99.4 x 79.4 cm.)

Inscribed l.r. "Feininger//15" and on reverse "GELMERODA" and "Gelmeroda"

Provenance:
the artist, Weimar, 1920
Eric Mendelsohn, San Francisco,
Mrs. Eric Mendelsohn, San Francisco, 1954

Exhibitions:
THE MUSEUM OF MODERN ART, New York, October 24, 1944–January 14, 1945, *Lyonel Feininger/Marsden Hartley*, p.24, ill.
THE SOLOMON R. GUGGENHEIM MUSEUM, New York, October 6, 1954–February 27, 1955, *Selection IV* (Checklist)
MONTREAL MUSEUM OF FINE ARTS, June 4–July 3, 1955, *A Selection from The Solomon R. Guggenheim Museum, New York*, no.8
THE SOLOMON R. GUGGENHEIM MUSEUM, New York, July 26–October 9, 1955, *Selection V* (Checklist; withdrawn August 26, 1955)
THE SOLOMON R. GUGGENHEIM MUSEUM, New York, January 24–May 1, 1956, *Selection VI* (Checklist)
TATE GALLERY, London, April 16–May 26, 1957, *Paintings from The Solomon R. Guggenheim Museum*, no.19; organized by THE SOLOMON R. GUGGENHEIM MUSEUM, traveled to GEMEENTEMUSEUM, The Hague, June 25–September 1; ATENEIUMIN TAIDEKOKOELMAT, Helsinki, September 27–October 20; GALLERIA NAZIONALE D'ARTE MODERNA, Rome, December 5, 1957–January 8, 1958; WALLRAF-RICHARTZ-MUSEUM, Cologne, January 26–March 30; MUSÉE DES ARTS DÉCORATIFS, Paris, April 23–June 1, 1958
THE SOLOMON R. GUGGENHEIM MUSEUM, New York, October 21, 1959–June 19, 1960, *Inaugural Selection* (Checklist)
THE SOLOMON R. GUGGENHEIM MUSEUM, New York, August 30–October 8, 1961, *Modern Masters from the Collection of The Solomon R. Guggenheim Museum*
PHILADELPHIA MUSEUM OF ART, November 2, 1961–January 7, 1962, *Guggenheim Museum Exhibition, A Loan Collection of Paintings, Drawings, and Prints from The Solomon R. Guggenheim Museum, New York*, no.24, ill.
WORCESTER ART MUSEUM, Massachusetts, February 6–April 7, 1963, *Aspects of Twentieth Century Painting Lent by The Solomon R. Guggenheim Museum*, no.10, ill.
DETROIT INSTITUTE OF ARTS, September 8–27, 1964, *Lyonel Feininger: The Formative Years*, no.137
PASADENA ART MUSEUM, April 26–May 29, 1966, *Lyonel Feininger 1871–1956, A Memorial Exhibition*, no.13, ill.; traveled to MILWAUKEE ART CENTER, July 10–August 11; BALTIMORE MUSEUM OF ART, September 7–October 23, 1966

Lyonel Feininger 1871–1956

Born of German parents, both accomplished musicians, in New York on July 17, 1871, Charles Léonell Feininger spent his youth studying the violin and observing the burgeoning mechanization of Manhattan. The ships on the East and Hudson Rivers, the skyscrapers, and romantic paintings of Gothic ruins in the Metropolitan Museum were to be continuing influences on his art.

At the age of 17, Feininger sailed to Hamburg to study music. Once there, his interest shifted from music to painting, which he studied at the *Kunstgewerbeschule* in Hamburg, the Berlin Academy and, from 1892–93, in the Colarossi Studio in Paris.

Until 1907, when he began to paint, Feininger made his reputation as a political and satirical cartoonist for German, French and American newspapers. His early mature style was shaped by what he observed in Paris in 1911: "…in that Spring I had gone to Paris for 2 weeks and found the art world agog with Cubism – a thing I had never heard even mentioned before, but which I had already, entirely intuitively, striven after *for years*." In 1913 he exhibited with the *Blaue Reiter* group in Munich and in 1917 had his first one-man show at *Der Sturm*.

In 1919, Feininger became a professor at the newly-formed Bauhaus in Weimar. When the Bauhaus moved to Dessau in 1926, he stopped teaching, but remained with the Bauhaus as artist in residence until it was closed in 1933.

He returned to New York in 1937 where his work was less well known, although it had been shown occasionally, notably with Galka Scheyer's Blue Four group (composed also of Kandinsky, Klee and Jawlensky) in New York, Chicago and on the West Coast. During the forties and fifties, color became more important to Feininger's painting, but formally and thematically it took no new course. He died in New York on January 13, 1956.

References:

WHITTICK, ARNOLD, *Eric Mendelsohn*, London, 1956, p.90

ELIOT, ALEXANDER, *Three Hundred Years of American Painting*, New York, 1957, p.175, ill.

HESS, HANS, *Lyonel Feininger*, New York, 1961, p.74, pl.12, cat. no.146

54.1410

Feininger's creative output, although prolific, covers few themes and often, within these limits, numerous variations on specific subjects. The church at Gelmeroda, a medieval village near Feininger's beloved Weimar, pre-occupied him from 1906, when he first sketched it, until the end of his career (his final lithograph is of the church at Gelmeroda).

Gelmeroda I (Collection Stefan Pauson, Glasgow), painted in 1915, shows the church from the apse end with a large pine tree on the left. It is stylistically close to Franz Marc, who invited Feininger to join the *Blaue Reiter* artists in the *Erste Deutsche Herbstsalon* exhibition of that year.

Gelmeroda IV shows the church from the same viewpoint, but shifts the two dominant verticals, the steeple and the pine, toward the center of the composition. In this painting the slashing diagonal lines of *Gelmeroda I* have given way to geometric planes, much less an analysis of space (as in Cubist painting) or of time (as in Futurist painting) than a device with which to unify the picture plane.

LYONEL FEININGER

Gelmeroda. August 26, 1927

Watercolor and ink, $15^1/_2$ x $11^1/_8$" (39.4 x 28.3 cm.)

Inscribed l.l. "Feininger", l.c. "Gelmeroda", l.r. "26 8 27"

Provenance:
Karl Nierendorf, New York
Estate of Karl Nierendorf, 1948

Exhibitions:
THE SOLOMON R. GUGGENHEIM MUSEUM, New York,
May 13–October 11, 1953, *Selection II* (Checklist)

ART GALLERY OF TORONTO, April 2–May 9, 1954, *A Loan
Exhibition of Paintings from The Solomon R. Guggenheim
Museum,* no.10

VANCOUVER ART GALLERY, November 16–December 12,
1954, *The Solomon R. Guggenheim Museum, A Selection
from the Museum Collection,* no.6

MONTREAL MUSEUM OF FINE ARTS, June 4–July 3, 1955,
*A Selection from The Solomon R. Guggenheim Museum,
New York,* no.9

PHILADELPHIA MUSEUM OF ART, November 2, 1961–
January 7, 1962, *Guggenheim Museum Exhibition, A Loan
Collection of Paintings, Drawings, and Prints from The
Solomon R. Guggenheim Museum, New York,* no.27

THE SOLOMON R. GUGGENHEIM MUSEUM, New York,
April 11–May 26, 1968, *Acquisitions of the 1930's and 1940's,*
p.111, ill.

48.1172X507

Gelmeroda was executed during the Dessau Bauhaus years,
but was probably done at Deep (Pomerania), where
Feininger spent the summer. Compositionally it is very
close to *Gelmeroda XI* of 1928 (Hess, cat. no.295)
for which it is perhaps a study.

Lüneburg II. 1933

Watercolor and ink, 17 x 14″ (43.2 x 35.6 cm.)

Inscribed l.l. "Feininger", l.c. "Lüneburg II", l.r. "1933"

Provenance:

Karl Nierendorf, New York
Estate of Karl Nierendorf, 1948

Exhibitions:

THE SOLOMON R. GUGGENHEIM MUSEUM, New York,
May 13–October 11, 1953, *Selection II* (Checklist)

ART GALLERY OF TORONTO, April 2–May 9, 1954, *A Loan
Exhibition of Paintings from The Solomon R. Guggenheim
Museum,* no.12

THE SOLOMON R. GUGGENHEIM MUSEUM, New York,
October 6, 1954–February 27, 1955, *Selection IV*
(Checklist)

THE SOLOMON R. GUGGENHEIM MUSEUM, New York,
January 24–May 1, 1956, *Selection VI* (Checklist)

THE SOLOMON R. GUGGENHEIM MUSEUM, New York,
August 30–October 8, 1961, *Modern Masters from the
Collection of The Solomon R. Guggenheim Museum*

PHILADELPHIA MUSEUM OF ART, November 2, 1961–
January 7, 1962, *Guggenheim Museum Exhibition, A Loan
Collection of Paintings, Drawings, and Prints from The
Solomon R. Guggenheim Museum, New York,* no.28

THE SOLOMON R. GUGGENHEIM MUSEUM, New York,
April 11–May 26, 1968, *Acquisitions of the 1930's and 1940's,*
p.110, ill.

THE SOLOMON R. GUGGENHEIM MUSEUM, New York,
July 8–September 14, 1969, *Selected Sculpture and Works
on Paper,* p.21, ill.

References:

WERNER, ALFRED, "A Painter of Space and Dimension –
Lyonel Feininger, 1871–1956", *American Artist,* vol.24,
no.26, October 1960, p.30, ill.

48.1172x473

In the late summer of 1921, Feininger visited Lüneburg
near Hamburg. There he observed an architecture very
different from that of Gelmeroda and the other towns of
Thuringia- an architecture reminiscent of the Belgian
towns which were his first view of old Europe. In his
student days at Liège, Feininger had written, "Then the
quaint old houses, three and four centuries old, some of
them, with their huge chimneys and quaint gables, give
existence in their darker recesses to monstrous shadows."
The difference in space and structure of Lüneburg's
architecture as compared with that of Gelmeroda is
represented in this watercolor through a greater opaqueness
and tautness of composition.

José Antonio Fernández-Muro 1920–

José Antonio Fernández-Muro was born in Madrid in 1920. In 1938 he moved to Argentina, becoming a citizen of that country in 1940. He studied drawing, engraving and painting in Buenos Aires, but is primarily a self-taught artist. From 1948 to 1950 he lived in Madrid and Paris where he studied museology. In 1957–58 he traveled again to Europe and to the United States on a UNESCO fellowship to pursue his studies in museology. His first one-man exhibition was held at Galeria Witcomb, Buenos Aires, 1944, followed by others including Galeria Bucholz, Madrid, 1948, Pan American Union, Washington, D.C., 1957, Galeria Bonino, Buenos Aires, 1958 and 1962, the Andrew-Morris Gallery, New York, 1963, and Galleria Pogliani, Rome, 1964. He has participated in numerous group exhibitions among which are the II Bienal de São Paulo, 1953, XXVIII Biennale, Venice, 1956, Pittsburgh International, 1958, World's Fair, Brussels, 1958, and the Guggenheim International Exhibitions of 1960 and 1964. Fernández-Muro and his wife, the painter Sarah Grilo, live in New York.

Fernández-Muro's early work depends on a highly reasoned pointillisme which, suppressing gesture and color, projects a subtle but expressive abstract imagery. In 1962, a texture of metallic appearance, as if embossed, replaced the painted surface of earlier works. In his more recent work, the minor key of the metallic monochromes gives way to daring statements in clear tonalites, his abstract images are sharpened but are not affected by hard-edge concepts, and the structured flat surface has become pictorial relief.

JOSÉ ANTONIO FERNÁNDEZ-MURO

Tangential Red. 1966

Latex and embossed foil on canvas, $59^7/_8$ x 48″ (151.7 x 121.9 cm.)

Inscribed on reverse "Tangential red//J. A. Fernandez Muro//1966 New York"

Provenance:
from the artist through Galeria Bonino, New York; Gift, Fundación Neumann, Caracas, 1966

Exhibitions:
THE SOLOMON R. GUGGENHEIM MUSEUM, New York, May 20–June 19, 1966, *The Emergent Decade*
ART GALLERY/CENTER FOR INTER-AMERICAN RELATIONS, New York, July 2–September 14, 1969, *Latin American Paintings from the Collection of The Solomon R. Guggenheim Museum*, p.17, ill.

66.1819

Fernández-Muro has always been interested in surface texture. Whereas in his earlier work he used broad areas of contrasting textures to define monolithic shapes, here the subtle imagery has been replaced by an all-over grid pattern, thus emphasizing the priority of the shimmering surface. A modification of the artist's pointilliste technique reinforces the surface interest. Originally the artist applied oil glazes to a field of stencilled dots. In *Tangential Red* a similar effect is attained yet heightened by the underlying relief of dots embossed in metallic foil.

Sam Francis 1923–

Sam Francis was born June 25, 1923, in San Mateo, California. Between 1941 and 1943 he studied medicine at the University of California at Berkeley. He joined the United States Air Force in 1943. A plane crash sent him to the hospital where he began to paint, continuing at the California School of Fine Arts upon his release. From 1948 to 1950, he studied Art History at Berkeley, acquiring a Master of Arts degree. In 1950, he settled in Paris.

Francis had his first important one-man exhibition in Paris in 1952 (Galerie Nina Dausset). His canvases impressed the European public through their vast scale and the closely knit surfaces of deep-keyed or brilliant clots of color and interstices of light. By 1954 the density of all-over pattern began to loosen until – through a consistent development – by 1956, the canvas was predominantly bare, punctuated by isolated splashes of brilliant color. Simultaneously, his color gradually changed in key: from the mellowness of blacks, roses, pale greens, grays and violets, it shifted to more primary hues. The importance of the void or empty field, inflected by incidental bursts of color becoming more strictly defined, was reinforced by the artist's first trip to Japan in 1957 and has grown steadily since that time. In his recent work, color is relegated to the outermost edges, leaving the central area untouched.

The artist lived in Paris until 1961. He made several trips around the world, exhibiting frequently and executing murals in Tokyo, Basel and New York. In 1961, Francis returned to the United States. He resides in Santa Monica, California.

SAM FRANCIS

Shining Back. 1958

Oil on canvas, $79^3/_8$ x 53" (201.6 x 134.6 cm.)

Not inscribed

Provenance:
from the artist through Martha Jackson Gallery, New York, 1959

Exhibitions:
DUNCAN PHILLIPS GALLERY, Washington, D.C., October 19–November 20, 1958, *Sam Francis*

MARTHA JACKSON GALLERY, New York, November 25–December 20, 1958, *Sam Francis*

SAN FRANCISCO MUSEUM OF ART, December 1958, *Sam Francis*; traveled to SEATTLE ART MUSEUM, April 24–May 17, 1959, no.7

UNIVERSITY OF MICHIGAN MUSEUM OF ART, Ann Arbor, April 13–June 12, 1960, *Images at Mid-Century*

THE SOLOMON R. GUGGENHEIM MUSEUM, New York, April 18–May 21, 1961, *Acquisitions 1953–1961*

PHILADELPHIA MUSEUM OF ART, November 2, 1961–January 7, 1962, *Guggenheim Museum Exhibition, A Loan Collection of Paintings, Drawings, and Prints from The Solomon R. Guggenheim Museum, New York*, no.34

XXXII BIENNALE INTERNAZIONALE D'ARTE VENEZIA, June 20–October 18, 1964, *Today's Art in Museums: The Solomon R. Guggenheim Museum*, no.7, p.34

THE SOLOMON R. GUGGENHEIM MUSEUM, New York, April 30–September 1, 1965, *Paintings from the Collection of The Solomon R. Guggenheim Museum*, no.78, ill.

COLUMBUS GALLERY OF FINE ARTS, Ohio, October 5, 1968–September 7, 1969, *Paintings from The Solomon R. Guggenheim Museum*, p.41, ill.

References:

ARNASON, H. H., *History of Modern Art*, New York, 1968, pl.1110

59.1560

As an artist living in Europe, Sam Francis developed his mature style somewhat outside the mainstream of the New York Abstract Expressionist School. Some critics situate him as a "Second Generation" Abstract Expressionist (along with artists like Frankenthaler). Others see influences of a European tradition in his painting, evoking Monet's *Waterlilies* as an artistic reference. Francis is quoted moreover as saying, "I make the late Monet pure." (Letter from Bernhard Schultze to Anneliese Hoyer, reproduced in *Sam Francis*: *Exhibition of Drawings and Lithographs*, San Francisco Museum of Art, 1967).

Shining Back illustrates the artist's style of the late 1950's, where sensual blots of vibrant color accentuate the open, airy and diaphanous quality of the empty field.

Naum Gabo 1890–

Naum Gabo was born Naum Pevsner, the younger brother of Antoine, in 1890 in Briansk, Russia. In 1910 he graduated from the Gymnasium at Kursk and went to Munich, where he studied medicine and engineering and also attended Wölfflin's art lectures. He visited Paris for the first time in 1912–13, where he saw Cubist painting and sculpture. At the start of World War I in 1914, he went to Copenhagen, Stockholm and then Oslo with his younger brother Alexei. Here Gabo began to emerge as a sculptor and develop his theories; in 1915 he made his first constructions using the name Gabo. With the outbreak of the Revolution in 1917, Gabo returned to Russia. Amid the revolutionary turmoil and fervor infecting the arts, Gabo and Pevsner published the *Realistic Manifesto* in Moscow in 1920.

Although Gabo had read and was influenced by Worringer's *Abstraction and Empathy* and Kandinsky's *On the Spiritual in Art*, he rejected Cubist abstraction as unsystematic. In the *Realistic Manifesto*, he proposed Constructivism, a revolutionary new aesthetic. Central to this new aesthetic was a concept of space as a continuum, rather than a monolithic volume. Sculpture of mass was rejected in favor of flat planes and continuous rhythms expressive of continuous depth. Unlike much other abstraction, Constructivism does not refer to the real object as a point of departure: naturalistic content and inspiration are foreign to its conception. Gabo also emphasized specifically contemporary materials such as plastic.

In 1922 Gabo left Moscow for Berlin, where he lived until 1932 when he went to Paris, and became a member of the *Abstraction-Création* group. He settled in England in 1935. There he edited, with J. L. Martin and Ben Nicholson, *Circle: International Survey of Constructive Art*. Gabo emigrated to the United States in 1946 and became a United States citizen in 1952. He lives in Middlebury, Connecticut.

Column. 1923

Plastic, wood, metal, 41″ (104.2 cm.) high

Not inscribed

Provenance:
the artist, 1949
Addison Gallery of American Art, Phillips Academy, Andover, Massachusetts, (later exchanged to the artist for *Linear Construction No.2, Variation No.1*), 1952
the artist, 1955

Exhibitions:
THE MUSEUM OF MODERN ART, New York, March 2–April 19, 1936, *Cubism and Abstract Art*, no.72, ill.
THE MUSEUM OF MODERN ART, New York, May 10–September 30, 1939, *Art in Our Time*, no.314, ill.
THE MUSEUM OF MODERN ART, New York, January 12–March 3, 1940, *Painting and Sculpture from the Museum Collection*
THE MUSEUM OF MODERN ART, New York, December 27, 1940–January 12, 1941, *We Like Modern Art*
THE MUSEUM OF MODERN ART, New York, May 6–April 30, 1944, *Paintings and Sculpture from the Museum Collection*
THE MUSEUM OF MODERN ART, New York, May 24–October 15, 1944, *Art in Progress*, p.140, ill.
THE MUSEUM OF MODERN ART, New York, February 10–April 25, 1948, *Naum Gabo/Antoine Pevsner*, p.26, ill.
THE MUSEUM OF MODERN ART, New York, October 5–December 4, 1949, *Modern Art in Your Life*
ADDISON GALLERY OF AMERICAN ART, Phillips Academy, Andover, Massachusetts, Winter 1949–50, *Material and the Immaterial*
THE MUSEUM OF MODERN ART, New York, April 28–September 7, 1953, *Sculpture of the Twentieth Century*, p.151, ill.
THE SOLOMON R. GUGGENHEIM MUSEUM, New York, July 26–October 9, 1955, *Selection V* (Checklist)
THE SOLOMON R. GUGGENHEIM MUSEUM, New York, January 24–May 1, 1956, *Selection VI* (Checklist)
THE SOLOMON R. GUGGENHEIM MUSEUM, New York, July 8–September 14, 1969, *Selected Sculpture and Works on Paper*, pp.120–121, ill.

References:
SEUPHOR, MICHEL, *L'Art abstrait, ses origines, ses premiers maîtres*, Paris, 1950, p.58, ill.
RITCHIE, ANDREW CARDUFF, *Sculpture of the Twentieth Century*, New York, 1952, p.151, ill.
READ, HERBERT and MARTIN, LESLIE, *Gabo: Constructions, Sculpture, Paintings, Drawings, Engravings*, Cambridge, Massachusetts, 1957, pl.26
SELZ, JEAN, *Modern Sculpture, Origins and Evolution*, New York, 1963, pl.xv

READ, HERBERT, *A Concise History of Modern Sculpture*, New York, 1964, pl.103

MARTIN, LESLIE, "Constructie en intuïtie", in Stedelijk Museum, Amsterdam, April 23–June 8, 1965, *Naum Gabo*, pl.B

ERNEST, JOHN, "Constructivism and Content", *Studio International*, vol.171, no.876, April 1966, p.150, ill.

ARNASON, H. H., *History of Modern Art*, New York, 1968, pl.497

55.1429

The *Column* is one of the most important surviving works of Russian Constructivism, and it occupies a position of comparable importance in the evolution of Gabo's art and thought. It was begun, as the artist wrote in an unpublished letter of 1949, "in the winter of 1920–21, as a tiny model, and executed in the winter of 1922–23 in its big form – when it was first shown in Germany and then in Holland, in France, and in America."

There are three small versions of the *Column*, all approximately 11 inches high, in the following collections: the artist; Yale University, Collection of the Société Anonyme; Professor Sir Leslie Martin, C.B.E. One of these three is presumably the model to which Gabo refers in the above letter. The *Column* itself was probably included in the important exhibition of Gabo and Pevsner held in Paris at the Galerie Percier, June 19–July 5, 1924.

The rigorously geometrical, logical and virtually symmetrical structure of this work, as well as its use of modern, industrially produced materials are indications of the exemplary role of the *Column* in the history of Constructivism. Among Gabo's early works this sculpture has a further significance as one of his projects or models for large-scale monuments and architecture, none of which were carried out. Gabo's efforts in this direction were paralleled by others, including Tatlin with his great project for a tower to the Third International, during the heroic 1920–22 period in Russian modern art when "fine" artists offered their services to the building of a new, post-revolutionary society.

Alberto Giacometti 1901–1966

Alberto Giacometti was born October 10, 1901, in Stampa (Grisons), Switzerland near the Italian border, the son of the Neo-Impressionist painter Augusto Giacometti. Although he began drawing and painting slightly earlier, his first sculpture – a bust of his brother Diego – dates from 1914. In 1919, Giacometti entered the École des Arts et Métiers in Geneva to study sculpture. Subsequently he traveled and lived in Italy for nine months and in 1922 he settled in Paris.

After studying with the French sculptor Bourdelle (1922–25), Giacometti began working on his own. His first sculptures, in their compactness and simplicity, show a Cubist influence as well as that of primitive sculpture. In 1928, Giacometti's experiments led him to more open structures. By 1929 he was making "cage sculptures" and had joined the Surrealist group. During these years, the Surrealist ideal of "interior models" provided his major source of inspiration.

Giacometti returned to the figure in the mid-thirties. In the early forties he concentrated on a series of minuscule statuettes which eventually led to the tall, slender and eroded human silhouettes of his mature style. A simultaneous activity in painting and drawing helped him resolve problems of formal structure.

The artist had his first one-man exhibition in 1932 in Paris (Galerie Pierre Colle). Retrospective exhibitions of his work were held in 1955 at The Solomon R. Guggenheim Museum and, in 1965, at The Museum of Modern Art, New York. Giacometti died January 11, 1966, in Coiro (Grisons), Switzerland.

ALBERTO GIACOMETTI

Standing Woman (Femme Cuiller). 1926

Bronze, 57″ (144.8 cm.) high

Inscribed on rear "Alberto Giacometti" and base "A. Giacometti 3/6"

Third of six casts made in 1954 from original plaster of 1926

Provenance:
from the artist through Pierre Matisse Gallery, New York, 1955

Exhibitions:
THE SOLOMON R. GUGGENHEIM MUSEUM, New York, June 7–July 17, 1955, *Alberto Giacometti* (Checklist)

THE SOLOMON R. GUGGENHEIM MUSEUM, New York, January 24–May 1, 1956, *Selection VI* (Checklist)

ARTS CLUB OF CHICAGO, April 19–May 19, 1960, *Sculpture and Drawings by Sculptors from The Solomon R. Guggenheim Museum*, no.13, ill.

MUSEUM DES 20. JAHRHUNDERTS, Vienna, September 21–November 4, 1962, *Kunst von 1900 bis heute, Eröffnungs-ausstellung*, no.137, ill.

PHILLIPS COLLECTION, Washington, D.C., February 2–March 4, 1963, *Alberto Giacometti, A Loan Exhibition*, no.2

THE SOLOMON R. GUGGENHEIM MUSEUM, New York, July 8–September 14, 1969, *Selected Sculpture and Works on Paper*, p.124, ill.

References:
ARNASON, H. H., *History of Modern Art*, New York, 1968, pl.626

LORD, JAMES, "Alberto Giacometti, Sculptor and Painter" *The Selective Eye*, New York, 1955, pp.91–7.

55.1414

lowing his early studies with Bourdelle, Giacometti, the mid-1920's, turned briefly to Cubism and ceeded to evolve his own version of a Cubist lptural style. This work reflects his assimilation the formal innovations realized in the Cubist sculpture Lipchitz and Laurens; but it simultaneously marks icometti's early response to other tendencies of that iod, notably Surrealism and the influence of primitive The parallels with Cycladic sculpture are evident, as also the formal devices of African sculpture, which were already previously absorbed into Cubist sculpture itself – i.e. the equivalence of convexity and concavity and arbitrary canons of figure proportion. The witty and disturbing enlargement of a female torso into an over-sized, spoon-like hollow however, with its inverted reference to female pregnancy and fertility, is already beyond the realms of Cubist aesthetics and heralds Giacometti's brilliant explorations during the later 1920's and 1930's of a Surrealist world arising from subconscious dreams and emotions.

After the series of Surrealist sculptures he created between 1927 and 1934, Giacometti returned to a group of figurative works, including nudes and skull-heads, done from memory. Among these was a series of standing nude figures, including the present sculpture, which possess an elongated, hieratic flatness reminiscent of Egyptian art and which also foreshadow Giacometti's later, post-1940 style of extreme linear attenuation.

ALBERTO GIACOMETTI

Statue of a Headless Woman. 1932–36

Bronze, 58½" (148.6 cm.) high

Inscribed on base "Alberto Giacometti//1932–36"

First of seven casts made in June 1960, from the original plaster in the collection of the Peggy Guggenheim Foundation, Venice

Provenance:

Peggy Guggenheim, Venice, 1967

Exhibitions:

ARTS COUNCIL OF GREAT BRITAIN, London, December 31, 1964–March 7, 1965, *The Peggy Guggenheim Collection*, no.11, ill.

THE SOLOMON R. GUGGENHEIM MUSEUM, New York, July 8–September 14, 1969, *Selected Sculpture and Works on Paper*, p.125, ill.

References:

GUGGENHEIM, PEGGY, *Confessions of an Art Addict*, London, 1960, pp.131–132

DUPIN, JACQUES, *Alberto Giacometti*, Paris, 1963, p.217, ill. (Listed as "Nu. 1932–34//Bronze. h. 150 cm."; photograph of the plaster)

CALAS, NICOLAS and CALAS, ELENA, *The Peggy Guggenheim Collection of Modern Art*, New York, 1966, p.185, no.120; p.119, ill.

The Peggy Guggenheim Collection, Venice, Turin, 1966, no.133

67.1845

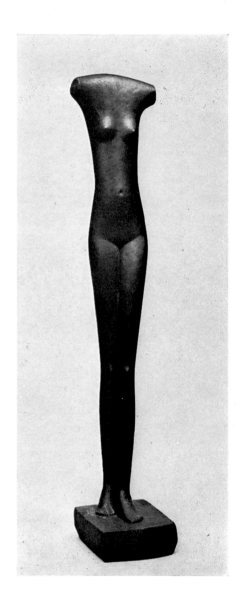

ALBERTO GIACOMETTI

The Nose (Le Nez). 1947

Bronze, 15³/₈″ (39.1 cm.) high

Inscribed on bottom "Alberto Giacometti//5/6" and "Susse Fondeur//Paris"

Fifth of six casts made from original plaster by Susse Fondeur, Paris. Steel cage, 31³/₄ x 18¹/₈ x 15¹/₈″ (87.7 x 46 x 38.4 cm.)

Provenance:
the artist
Pierre Matisse Gallery, New York, 1966

Exhibitions:
THE SOLOMON R. GUGGENHEIM MUSEUM, New York, July 8–September 14, 1969, *Selected Sculpture and Works on Paper*, p.126, ill.

66.1807

During the early 1940's, at the time of the German occupation of Paris, Giacometti turned to making very small sculptures, done from memory, as a means of reconstituting his art as a whole and of bringing it closer to his own sense of reality. At the same time he relied increasingly on drawings as a means of resolving the problems arising in his activity as a sculptor (cf. his letter of 1947 to Pierre Matisse, published in *Alberto Giacometti*, The Museum of Modern Art, New York, 1965, p.29). With *The Nose*, Giacometti illustrates his personal transformation as an artist during the early 1940's and the disquieting, expressive power thus attained. At the same time, *The Nose* temporarily resolves two often opposed tendencies found both in Giacometti and modern sculpture as a whole in the 1930's and 1940's. The rational, geometrical tradition, represented in this work by a space cage, here is joined to its antithesis, the aesthetics of expressionism and the Surrealist unconscious, as exemplified by the head, suspended perversely in space within the cage. It is the second tradition which will prevail during the remainder of Giacometti's career.

ALBERTO GIACOMETTI

Vase and Cup (Vase et Tasse). 1952

Pencil, 19³/₄ x 13⁷/₈″ (50.2 x 35.3 cm.)

Signed and dated l.r. "Alberto Giacometti 1954"

Provenance:
from the artist through Galerie Maeght, Paris, 1955

Exhibitions:
THE SOLOMON R. GUGGENHEIM MUSEUM, New York,
June 7–July 17, 1955, *Alberto Giacometti* (Checklist)

THE SOLOMON R. GUGGENHEIM MUSEUM, New York,
January 24–May 1, 1956, *Selection VI* (Checklist)

THE SOLOMON R. GUGGENHEIM MUSEUM, New York,
February 24–April 17, 1966, *European Drawings*, no.50;
traveled to UNIVERSITY ART GALLERY, Minneapolis,
May 10–31; DE CORDOVA MUSEUM, Lincoln, Massachusetts,
June 26–September 4; MUSEUM OF ART, RHODE ISLAND
SCHOOL OF DESIGN, Providence, September 14–October 8;
NATIONAL GALLERY OF CANADA, Ottawa, November 28–
December 25, 1966; MILWAUKEE ART CENTER, Wisconsin,
January 5–February 5, 1967; HIGH MUSEUM OF FINE ARTS,
Atlanta, March 1–31; DALLAS MUSEUM OF FINE ARTS,
April 15–May 15; KRANNERT ART MUSEUM, University of
Illinois, Champaign, May 28–June 25; NORTH CAROLINA
MUSEUM OF ART, Raleigh, July 15–August 15, 1967

THE SOLOMON R. GUGGENHEIM MUSEUM, New York,
July 8–September 14, 1969, *Selected Sculpture and Works
on Paper*, p.21, ill.

55.1430

ALBERTO GIACOMETTI

Teapot I (La Théière). 1954

Pencil, 19³/₄ x 12⁷/₈" (50.2 x 32.7 cm.)

Signed and dated l.r. "Alberto Giacometti 1954"

Provenance:
from the artist through Galerie Maeght, Paris, 1955

Exhibitions:
THE SOLOMON R. GUGGENHEIM MUSEUM, New York,
June 7–July 17, 1955, *Alberto Giacometti* (Checklist)

THE SOLOMON R. GUGGENHEIM MUSEUM, New York,
January 24–May 1, 1956, *Selection VI* (Checklist)

NATIONAL GALLERY OF ART, Washington, D.C., July 10–
August 19, 1965, *19th and 20th Century Drawings*, no.22, ill.;
organized by THE AMERICAN FEDERATION OF ARTS, traveled
to MUSEUM OF ART, Indiana University, Bloomington,
September 13–October 3; BALTIMORE MUSEUM OF ART,
October 18–December 12; AMERICAN FEDERATION OF ARTS
GALLERY, New York, December 22, 1965–January 16,
1966; ALLENTOWN ART MUSEUM, Pennsylvania, January 31–
February 20; MUSEUM OF ART, University of Michigan,
Ann Arbor, March 7–27; ALLEN MEMORIAL ART MUSEUM,
Oberlin College, Ohio, April 11–May 1; KRANNERT ART
MUSEUM, University of Illinois, Champaign, May 22–
June 19, 1966

THE SOLOMON R. GUGGENHEIM MUSEUM, New York,
July 8–September 14, 1969, *Selected Sculpture and Works
on Paper*, p.22, ill.

55.1432

ALBERTO GIACOMETTI

Portrait (Portrait of the British art Critic, Douglas Cooper).
1957

Pencil, 25³/₄ x 19³/₄″ (65.4 x 50.2 cm.)

Signed and dated l.r. "Alberto Giacometti 1957"

Provenance:
from the artist through Pierre Matisse Gallery, New
York, 1957

Exhibitions:
CONTEMPORARY ART MUSEUM, Houston, November 20,
1958–January 4, 1959, *Personal Contacts: A Decade of
Contemporary Drawings, 1948–1958*, ill.

ARTS CLUB OF CHICAGO, April 19–May 19, 1960, *Sculpture
and Drawings by Sculptors from The Solomon R. Guggenheim
Museum*, no.27, ill.

PHILADELPHIA MUSEUM OF ART, November 2, 1961–
January 7, 1962, *Guggenheim Museum Exhibition, A
Loan Collection of Paintings, Drawings, and Prints from The
Solomon R. Guggenheim Museum, New York*, no.36, ill.

AMERICAN FEDERATION OF ARTS, New York, December 12,
1963–January 2, 1964, *Images of Praise*

WASHINGTON UNIVERSITY GALLERY OF ART, St. Louis,
Missouri, March 13–May 8, 1966, *Master Drawings*

THE SOLOMON R. GUGGENHEIM MUSEUM, New York,
July 8–October 14, 1969, *Selected Sculpture and Works
on Paper*, p.23, ill.

57.1478

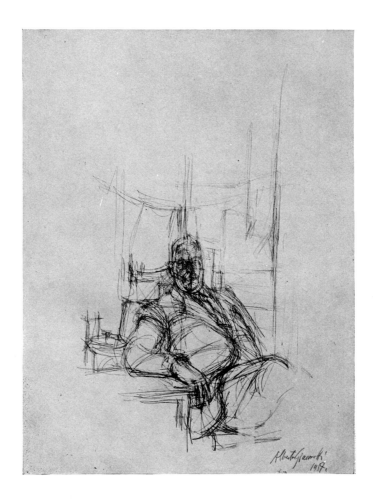

ALBERTO GIACOMETTI

Mountain. 1957

Pencil, 19³/₄ x 25³/₄″ (50.2 x 65.4 cm.)

Signed and dated l.r. "Alberto Giacometti//1957"

Provenance:

from the artist through Pierre Matisse Gallery, New York, 1957

Exhibitions:

THE SOLOMON R. GUGGENHEIM MUSEUM, New York, October 3–November 12, 1961, *Elements of Modern Painting*; circulated by THE AMERICAN FEDERATION OF ARTS, July 1962–September 1963, as *Elements of Modern Art*

THE MUSEUM OF MODERN ART, New York, June 9–October 10, 1965, *Alberto Giacometti*, no.131, ill.; traveled to ART INSTITUTE OF CHICAGO, November 5–December 12, 1965; LOS ANGELES COUNTY MUSEUM OF ART, January 11–February 20, 1966; SAN FRANCISCO MUSEUM OF ART, March 10–April 24, 1966

THE SOLOMON R. GUGGENHEIM MUSEUM, New York, July 8–September 14, 1969, *Selected Sculpture and Works on Paper*, p.25, ill.

MUSÉE DE L'ORANGERIE DES TUILERIES, Paris, October 7, 1969–January 12, 1970, *Giacometti*

57.1481

ALBERTO GIACOMETTI

Interior. 1957

Pencil, 25³/₄ x 19³/₄" (65.4 x 50.2 cm.)

Signed and dated l.r. "Alberto Giacometti//1957"

Provenance:

from the artist through Pierre Matisse Gallery, New York, 1957

Exhibitions:

THE SOLOMON R. GUGGENHEIM MUSEUM, New York, October 3–November 12, 1961, *Elements of Modern Painting*; circulated by THE AMERICAN FEDERATION OF ARTS, July 1962–September 1963, as *Elements of Modern Art*

THE SOLOMON R. GUGGENHEIM MUSEUM, New York, February 24–April 17, 1966, *European Drawings*, no.51; traveled to UNIVERSITY ART GALLERY, Minneapolis, May 10–31; DE CORDOVA MUSEUM, Lincoln, Massachusetts, June 26–September 4; MUSEUM OF ART, RHODE ISLAND SCHOOL OF DESIGN, Providence, September 14–October 8; NATIONAL GALLERY OF CANADA, Ottawa, November 28–December 25, 1966; MILWAUKEE ART CENTER, Wisconsin, January 5–February 5, 1967; HIGH MUSEUM OF FINE ARTS, Atlanta, March 1–31; DALLAS MUSEUM OF FINE ARTS, April 15–May 15; KRANNERT ART MUSEUM, University of Illinois, Champaign, May 28–June 25; NORTH CAROLINA MUSEUM OF ART, Raleigh, July 15–August 15, 1967

THE SOLOMON R. GUGGENHEIM MUSEUM, New York, July 8–October 14, 1969, *Selected Sculpture and Works on Paper*, p.24, ill.

57.1479

Giacometti was a prolific draftsman throughout his lifetime but more particularly after 1945 when drawing helped him to resolve problems of form pertinent to his sculpture. The multiple outlines as well as the erased portions of contours reflect the interaction of mass and void as seized by human perception. The subsequent disintegration of forms and volumes, reminiscent of Cézanne's experiments, express the elusive quality of objects to our sight. In these sketches, one can speak of neither traditional perspective nor flatness, as the image tends to dissolve the picture plane.

Albert Gleizes 1881–1953

Albert Gleizes was born December 8, 1881, in Paris. His father was a textile designer and Gleizes served as an apprentice in his studio. He began painting seriously, in a pointilliste technique, in around 1902, exhibiting at the *Société Nationale des Beaux-Arts* that same year.

By 1906–8, the artist had become involved with utopian socialism and had co-founded a free university (l'Association Ernest Renan) and a community of artists and writers (l'Abbaye de Créteil). His painting became stricter and more schematic until, in 1911, he arrived at his own personal Cubist idiom. In keeping with his philosophical views, Gleizes sought plastic equivalents for broad social and cultural issues. In his use of color and his attachment to universal themes, his Cubism was closer to Delaunay (whom he admired) than to Braque and Picasso. In 1912, Gleizes collaborated with Metzinger on the important treatise *Du Cubisme*, the first of many theoretical writings.

Gleizes visited New York for the first time in 1915. He returned for a longer visit in 1917–18. The visit coincided with a return to religious faith which was to influence his subsequent creative activity. In his painting of the 1920's, his search for the metaphysical principles of life and nature was expressed by attempted syntheses of light, space and time (translated by circular rhythms). In the mid-thirties, the lyrical abstraction of his late style began to appear.

Outside the mainstream of Cubism as practiced by Picasso and Braque, the art of Gleizes was based on a synthetic, dynamic and metaphysical vision of reality. Gleizes died June 23, 1953 in Avignon, France.

Portrait of an Army Doctor (Portrait d'un Médecin Militaire). 1914–15

Oil on canvas, 47¼ x 37½" (120 x 95 cm.)

Signed and dated l.r. "Alb Gleizes//Toul 1914"

Provenance:
Solomon R. Guggenheim, New York
Gift, Solomon R. Guggenheim, 1937

Exhibitions:
RENÉ GIMPEL GALERIE, New York, December 15, 1936–January 15, 1937, *Albert Gleizes, A Retrospective Exhibition*, no.8

PHILADELPHIA ART ALLIANCE, February 8–28, 1937, *Solomon R. Guggenheim Collection of Non-Objective Paintings*, no.166

GIBBES MEMORIAL ART GALLERY, Charleston, South Carolina, March 7–April 7, 1938, *Solomon R. Guggenheim Collection of Non-Objective Paintings*, no.238

SOLOMON R. GUGGENHEIM FOUNDATION, New York, June 1, 1939, *Art of Tomorrow* (Fifth catalogue of the Solomon R. Guggenheim Collection of Non-Objective Paintings), no.473

MUSEUM OF NON-OBJECTIVE PAINTING, New York, opening April 29, 1952, *Evolution to Non-Objectivity*, no.51

THE SOLOMON R. GUGGENHEIM MUSEUM, New York, February 3–May 3, 1953, *A Selection* (Checklist)

ART GALLERY OF TORONTO, April 2–May 9, 1954, *A Loan Exhibition of Paintings from The Solomon R. Guggenheim Museum*, no.15

THE SOLOMON R. GUGGENHEIM MUSEUM, New York, October 6, 1954–February 27, 1955, *Selection IV* (Checklist)

MONTREAL MUSEUM OF FINE ARTS, June 4–July 3, 1955, *A Selection from The Solomon R. Guggenheim Museum, New York*, no.12

THE SOLOMON R. GUGGENHEIM MUSEUM, New York, January 24–May 1, 1956, *Selection VI* (Checklist)

TATE GALLERY, London, April 16–May 26, 1957, *Paintings from The Solomon R. Guggenheim Museum*, no.23; organized by THE SOLOMON R. GUGGENHEIM MUSEUM, traveled to GEMEENTEMUSEUM, The Hague, June 25–September 1, no.23, ill.; ATENEIUMIN TAIDEKOKOELMAT, Helsinki, September 27–October 20, no.23, ill.; GALLERIA NAZIONALE D'ARTE MODERNA, Rome, December 5, 1957–January 8, 1958, no.29, ill.; WALLRAF-RICHARTZ-MUSEUM, Cologne, January 26–March 30, no.24, ill.; MUSÉE DES ARTS DÉCORATIFS, Paris, April 23–June 1, 1958, no.21, ill.

THE SOLOMON R. GUGGENHEIM MUSEUM, New York, October 21, 1959–June 19, 1960, *Inaugural Selection* (Checklist)

THE SOLOMON R. GUGGENHEIM MUSEUM, New York, August 30–October 8, 1961, *Modern Masters from the Collection of The Solomon R. Guggenheim Museum*

THE SOLOMON R. GUGGENHEIM MUSEUM, New York,
June 5–October 13, 1963, *Cézanne and Structure in Modern Painting*

THE SOLOMON R. GUGGENHEIM MUSEUM, New York,
September 15–November 1, 1964, *Albert Gleizes 1881–1953, A Retrospective Exhibition*, no.67, p.63, ill.; traveled to MUSÉE NATIONAL D'ART MODERNE, Paris, December 5, 1964–January 1965; MUSEUM AM OSTWALL, Dortmund, March 13–April 25, 1965

THE SOLOMON R. GUGGENHEIM MUSEUM, New York,
June 28–October 1, 1967, *Museum Collection, Seven Decades, A Selection* (Checklist)

THE SOLOMON R. GUGGENHEIM MUSEUM, New York,
April 11–May 26, 1968, *Acquisitions of the 1930's and 1940's*, p.24, ill.

References:

OZENFANT and JEANNERET, *La Peinture Moderne*, Paris, 1924, p.118, ill.

"Présence d'Albert Gleizes," *Zodiaque*, nos.6–7, January 1952, pp.32–33

COSTE, GENEVIÈVE, "New York et Paris d'accord pour réhabiliter Albert Gleizes", *Connaissance des Arts*, no.154, December 1964, p.125, ill.

37·473

This canvas was painted in late 1914-early 1915 at Toul, where Gleizes was stationed after the outbreak of World War I. The army doctor was his friend, Professor Courbet of Nancy. Basically composed of intersecting diagonals, the surface is inflected by a circular rhythm which will be characteristic of the artist's later work.

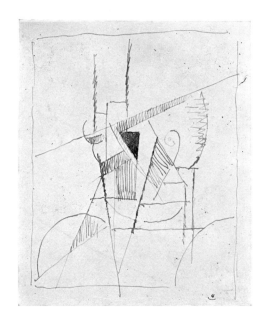

ALBERT GLEIZES

Study No.3 for "Portrait of an Army Doctor" (Étude 3 pour "Médecin Militaire"). 1915

Pencil, 8³/₈ x 6¹/₂″ (21.3 x 16.5 cm.)

Inscribed l.r. "Alb Gleizes//Toul 15//3" and on reverse "No.3/Étude pour "Médecin militaire" Toul//1915"

Provenance:
from the artist, 1938

Exhibitions:
THE SOLOMON R. GUGGENHEIM MUSEUM, New York, April 11–May 26, 1968, *Acquisitions of the 1930's and 1940's,* p.50, ill.

38.762

ALBERT GLEIZES

Study No.4 for "Portrait of an Army Doctor" (Étude 4 pour "Médecin Militaire"). 1915

Ink, 8³/₄ x 7¹/₈″ (22.2 x 18.1 cm.)

Inscribed l.r. "Alb Gleizes//Toul 15//4" and on reverse mount "4/Etude pr "Médecin militaire"//Toul Janvier. 1915"

Provenance:
from the artist, 1938

Exhibitions:
THE SOLOMON R. GUGGENHEIM MUSEUM, New York, August 30–October 8, 1961, *Modern Masters from the Collection of The Solomon R. Guggenheim Museum*

THE SOLOMON R. GUGGENHEIM MUSEUM, New York, April 11–May 26, 1968, *Acquisitions of the 1930's and 1940's,* p.50, ill.

38.763

At least eight studies survive for the portrait of Professor Lourbet, seven of which are in the Guggenheim Museum Collection, acquired from the artist in 1938. Five of the latter are sketches of heads, the other two representing the total figure such as it appears in the portrait. Studies for the most part of contrasting textures, tones and planes, they present an interesting set of variations on a single theme.

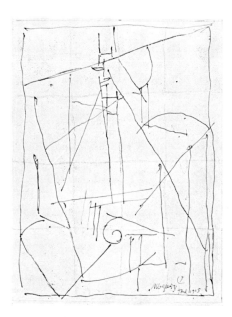

ALBERT GLEIZES

Study No.5 for "Portrait of an Army Doctor" (Étude 5 pour Médecin Militaire"). 1915

Pencil, 9⁵/₈ x 7³/₈″ (24.5 x 18.7 cm.)

Inscribed l.r. "Alb Gleizes//Toul 1915" and on reverse mount "5/Étude pr. "Médecin militaire"/Toul 1915"

Provenance:
from the artist, 1938

Exhibitions:

THE SOLOMON R. GUGGENHEIM MUSEUM, New York, May 13–October 11, 1953, *Selection II* (Checklist)

VANCOUVER ART GALLERY, November 16–December 12, 1954, *The Solomon R. Guggenheim Museum, A Selection from the Museum Collection,* no.11

MONTREAL MUSEUM OF FINE ARTS, June 4–July 3, 1955, *A Selection from The Solomon R. Guggenheim Museum, New York,* no.13

THE SOLOMON R. GUGGENHEIM MUSEUM, New York, August 30–October 8, 1961, *Modern Masters from the Collection of The Solomon R. Guggenheim Museum*

THE SOLOMON R. GUGGENHEIM MUSEUM, New York, April 11–May 26, 1968, *Acquisitions of the 1930's and 1940's,* p.51

THE SOLOMON R. GUGGENHEIM MUSEUM, New York, July 8–September 14, 1969, *Selected Sculpture and Works on Paper,* p.26, ill.

38.764

ALBERT GLEIZES

Study No.7 for "Portrait of an Army Doctor" (Étude 7 pour " Médecin Militaire"). 1915

Ink and crayon, 9³/₄ x 7⁷/₈″ (25 x 20 cm.)

Inscribed l.r. "Alb Gleizes Toul 1915" and on reverse "7/Etude pour "Médecin militaire"//Toul 1915"

Provenance:
from the artist, 1938

Exhibitions:

THE SOLOMON R. GUGGENHEIM MUSEUM, New York, August 30–October 8, 1961, *Modern Masters from the Collection of The Solomon R. Guggenheim Museum*

THE SOLOMON R. GUGGENHEIM MUSEUM, New York, September 15–November 1, 1964, *Albert Gleizes 1881–1953, A Retrospective Exhibition,* no.65; traveled to MUSÉE NATIONAL D'ART MODERNE, Paris, December 5, 1964–January 1965; MUSEUM AM OSTWALL, Dortmund, March 13–April 25, 1965

THE SOLOMON R. GUGGENHEIM MUSEUM, New York, April 11–May 26, 1968, *Acquisitions of the 1930's and 1940's,* p.52, ill.

38.766

ALBERT GLEIZES

Brooklyn Bridge. 1915

Oil and mixed media on canvas, 40¹/₈ x 40¹/₈″ (102 x 102 cm.)

Inscribed l.r. "Brooklyn Bridge//Alb Gleizes 1915"

Provenance:
John Quinn (Sale, 1927)
J. B. Neumann, 1944

Exhibitions:
MONTROSS GALLERY, New York, April 4–22, 1916, *Pictures by Crotti, Duchamp, Gleizes, Metzinger*, no.40

THE MUSEUM OF MODERN ART, New York, March 2–April 19, 1936, *Cubism and Abstract Art*, no.88

TOLEDO MUSEUM OF ART, Ohio, November 6–December 11, 1938, *Contemporary Movements in European Painting*, no.40

MUSEUM OF NON-OBJECTIVE PAINTING, New York, opening April 29, 1952, *Evolution to Non-Objectivity*, no.50

THE SOLOMON R. GUGGENHEIM MUSEUM, New York, May 13–October 11, 1953, *Selection II* (Checklist)

THE SOLOMON R. GUGGENHEIM MUSEUM, New York, October 6, 1954–February 27, 1955, *Selection IV* (Checklist)

BROOKLYN MUSEUM, New York, April 28–July 27, 1958, *The Brooklyn Bridge*, ill.

WORCESTER ART MUSEUM, Massachusetts, February 6–April 7, 1963, *Aspects of Twentieth Century Painting Lent by the The Solomon R. Guggenheim Museum*, no.13, p.24, ill.

THE SOLOMON R. GUGGENHEIM MUSEUM, New York, June 5–October 13, 1963, *Cézanne and Structure in Modern Painting*

THE SOLOMON R. GUGGENHEIM MUSEUM, New York, September 15–November 1, 1964, *Albert Gleizes 1881–1953, A Retrospective Exhibition*, p.72, no.84, ill.; traveled

to MUSÉE NATIONAL D'ART MODERNE, Paris, December 5, 1964–January 1965; MUSEUM AM OSTWALL, Dortmund, March 13–April 25, 1965

GALLERY OF MODERN ART, New York, October 18–November 14, 1965, *New York: Night and Day*

MUSÉE DES BEAUX-ARTS, Bordeaux, May 14–September 15, 1966, *La Peinture Française dans les Collections Américaines*, no.96

THE SOLOMON R. GUGGENHEIM MUSEUM, New York, April 11–May 26, 1968, *Acquisitions of the 1930's and 1940's* p.82, ill.

COLUMBUS GALLERY OF FINE ARTS, Ohio, October 5, 1968–September 7, 1969, *Paintings from The Solomon R. Guggenheim Museum*, p.17, ill.

References:
Literary Digest, November 27, 1915, p.1225 (visible in photograph of Gleizes)

SEUPHOR, MICHEL, *L'Art abstrait, ses origines, ses premiers maîtres*, Paris, 1950, p.146, ill.

ROSENBLUM, ROBERT, *Cubism and Twentieth-Century Art*, New York, 1960, p.121, ill.

44.942

Gleizes painted three oils on this subject, of which another version, dated 1917, is also in the Guggenheim Museum Collection. "The Bridge...is here synthesized into a dizzying structure in which a cityscape is seen through the great swing and intersecting patterns of the cables which dominate the canvas surface. In the first interview given after his arrival in America, Gleizes stated his admiration for the Brooklyn Bridge, comparing it to the noblest achievements of European architecture." (Daniel Robbins, *Albert Gleizes*, New York, 1964, p.56, cat. no.84.)

Adolph Gottlieb 1903–

Adolph Gottlieb was born in New York City in 1903. In 1920 he enrolled at the Art Students League where he studied under John Sloan and Robert Henri. In 1921 he worked passage to Europe where he attended the Académie de la Grande Chaumière, Paris, and other studio schools, returning to New York City in 1923. Gottlieb worked on the WPA Federal Arts Project in 1936, moving to Arizona the following year, and returning to New York in 1939.

There are three important phases in Gottlieb's development: the pictographs, 1941–51; imaginary landscapes, 1951–57; and "Burst" paintings, 1957 to the present. In the pictograph series, he arbitrarily divided the canvas into rectangular compartments and filled them with a variety of archetypal images. Around 1949 he began to strip the rectangular compartments of their images and the linear structure or grid became the subject of the paintings. During this period he also produced totemic works whose subjects derived from the same images which were now used as large, ominous central figures.

In 1951 he began to divide his canvases into two horizontal areas. In the upper part he applied areas of flat color while the bottom section was densely rendered. These paintings are the so-called "imaginary landscapes" in which the artist's concern was focused on problems of format, especially the relationship of floating forms above to static below. The third major phase of Gottlieb's work appeared in 1957 with the "Burst" paintings, which deal with the opposing forces of colored disks and exploding masses. These paintings are a direct outcome of the "imaginary landscapes".

W. 1954

Oil with sand on canvas, 72 x 36″ (182.9 x 91.5 cm.)

Signed l.r. "Adolph Gottlieb"

Provenance:

from the artist through Samuel M. Kootz Gallery, New York, 1954

Exhibititions:

THE SOLOMON R. GUGGENHEIM MUSEUM, New York, May 12–September 25, 1954, *Younger American Painters*, no. 20, ill.; traveled to PORTLAND ART MUSEUM, Oregon, September 2–October 9, 1955; HENRY GALLERY, University of Washington, Seattle, October 16–November 13; SAN FRANCISCO MUSEUM OF ART, November 15, 1955–January 22, 1956; LOS ANGELES COUNTY MUSEUM OF ART, February 1–29; UNIVERSITY OF ARKANSAS, Fayetteville, March 9–April 10; ISAAC DELGADO MUSEUM OF ART, New Orleans, April 15–May 20, 1956 (*W* included previous to circulation in INDIANA UNIVERSITY, Bloomington, October 20–November 20, 1954, *Midwestern College Art Conference* exhibition)

PICTURE GALLERY OF SAINT-GAUDENS MEMORIAL, Cornish, New Hampshire, August 3–September 4, 1956, *Painters of Today*, no. 7 (Organized by THE SOLOMON R. GUGGENHEIM MUSEUM)

ARTISTS GALLERY, New York, September 10–November 15, 1956, *Reunion on Lexington Avenue*

THE SOLOMON R. GUGGENHEIM MUSEUM, New York, October 21, 1959–June 19, 1960, *Inaugural Selection* (Checklist)

TATE GALLERY, London, April 16–May 26, 1957, *Paintings from The Solomon R. Guggenheim Museum,* no.24; organized by THE SOLOMON R. GUGGENHEIM MUSEUM, traveled to GEMEENTEMUSEUM, The Hague, June 25–September 1; ATENEIUMIN TAIDEKOKOELMAT, Helsinki, September 27–October 20; GALLERIA NAZIONALE D'ARTE MODERNA, Rome, December 5, 1957–January 8, 1958; WALLRAF-RICHARTZ-MUSEUM, Cologne, January 26–

March 30; MUSÉE DES ARTS DÉCORATIFS, Paris, April 23–
June 1, 1958

PHILADELPHIA MUSEUM OF ART, November 2, 1961–
January 7, 1962, *Guggenheim Museum Exhibition, A Loan
Collection of Paintings, Drawings, and Prints from The
Solomon R. Guggenheim Museum, New York*, no. 37

WALKER ART CENTER, Minneapolis, April 27–June 9, 1963,
Adolph Gottlieb, no.9, ill.; traveled to VII BIENAL DE SÃO
PAULO, September–December 1963, no.9, p.220

XXII BIENNALE INTERNAZIONALE D'ARTE VENEZIA,
June 20–October 18, 1964, *Today's Art in Museums: The
Solomon R. Guggenheim Museum*, no.8, p.33, pl.XXI

THE SOLOMON R. GUGGENHEIM MUSEUM, New York,
April 30–September 1, 1965, *Paintings from the Collection
of The Solomon R. Guggenheim Museum*, no.71, ill.

THE SOLOMON R. GUGGENHEIM MUSEUM, New York,
June 28–October 1, 1967, *Museum Collection, Seven
Decades, A Selection* (Checklist)

CINCINNATI ART MUSEUM, Ohio, October 3, 1969–
March 29, 1970, *Paintings from the Guggenheim Museum,
A Loan Exhibition of Modern Paintings Covering the Period
1949–1965, from The Solomon R. Guggenheim Museum*, no.10

4.1404

The curious splayed form in *W* relates to a group of
Gottlieb's paintings and gouaches of the first half of the
fifties, which have in common a central form, a kind of
plateau, from which secondary forms, like tentacles,
radiate to the edges of the painting. The best known of
the series is *Unstill Life*, 1952 (Collection Whitney
Museum of American Art). The W-form, from which
the painting's title was derived, relates to other small
tesserae-like forms found in the central area of comparable
paintings. In addition to its relationship to this strain of
images, *W* belongs to a transitional period. It falls
between the "imaginary landscapes" (1952) and the
"Burst" series. It is notable by a complex space, rare in
Gottlieb's art except at this period. Gottlieb did not
pursue this illusionist layered space, but simplified and
concentrated his subsequent work.

Juan Gris 1887–1927

Juan Gris (José Victoriano Gonzalez) was born in Madrid on March 3, 1887. He began his studies in 1902 at the School of Arts and Industry in Madrid and in 1904, left the school to study painting under the academic artist, José Maria Moreno Carbonero. While still in Madrid, he did Art Nouveau illustrations for books such as José Santos Chocano's *Alma America*. Gris arrived in Paris in 1906 and took up residence in the "Bateau Lavoir" where Picasso also had a studio. Through Picasso and Braque he met Guillaume Apollinaire, Max Jacob, André Salmon and, although he continued to produce illustrations, he began to paint seriously under the influence of this circle of creative leaders. By 1911 he was painting in oil in the Analytical Cubist style. In January 1912 he exhibited some works in Clovis Sagot's gallery and in March he exhibited with the Cubists at the *Section d'or*. At this time Kahnweiler made a contract to buy all his painting. This contract was suspended in 1915 and Gris made another with Léonce Rosenberg. These contracts alleviated somewhat Gris's almost perpetual financial difficulties. Diaghilev commissioned him to do sets and costumes for his ballet *Les Tentations de la Bergère* in 1922 and in 1923, he did *Fête Merveilleuse* and *La Colombe*. He had his first one-man exhibition at the Galerie Simon in Paris in March of 1923. In May 1924 Gris delivered his definitive lecture on Cubism at the Sorbonne entitled "On the Possibilities of Painting". His health began to deteriorate and in 1927 at the age of 40, Gris died in Paris.

Rooftops. 1911

Oil on canvas, $20^5/_8$ x $13^1/_2$" (52.4 x 34.3 cm.)

Signed l.l. "Juan Gris"

Provenance:
Karl Nierendorf, New York
Estate of Karl Nierendorf, 1948

Exhibitions:

THE SOLOMON R. GUGGENHEIM MUSEUM, New York, February 3–May 3, 1953, *A Selection* (Checklist)

THE SOLOMON R. GUGGENHEIM MUSEUM, New York, May 13–October 11, 1953, *Selection II* (Checklist)

THE SOLOMON R. GUGGENHEIM MUSEUM, New York, March 30–May 5, 1954, *Selection III* (Checklist)

THE SOLOMON R. GUGGENHEIM MUSEUM, New York, October 6, 1954–February 27, 1955, *Selection IV* (Checklist)

MONTREAL MUSEUM OF FINE ARTS, June 4–July 3, 1955, *A Selection from The Solomon R. Guggenheim Museum, New York*, no.14

TATE GALLERY, London, April 16–May 26, 1957, *Paintings from The Solomon R. Guggenheim Museum*, no.25; organized by THE SOLOMON R. GUGGENHEIM MUSEUM, traveled to GEMEENTEMUSEUM, The Hague, June 25–September 1; ATENEIUMIN TAIDEKOKOELMAT, Helsinki, September 27–October 20; GALLERIA NAZIONALE D'ARTE MODERNA, Rome December 5, 1957–January 8, 1958, no.14, ill.; WALLRAF-RICHARTZ-MUSEUM, Cologne, January 26–March 30; MUSÉE DES ARTS DÉCORATIFS, Paris, April 23–June 1, 1958

THE SOLOMON R. GUGGENHEIM MUSEUM, New York, October 21, 1959–June 19, 1960, *Inaugural Selection* (Checklist)

THE SOLOMON R. GUGGENHEIM MUSEUM, New York, August 30–October 8, 1961, *Modern Masters from the Collection of The Solomon R. Guggenheim Museum*

PHILADELPHIA MUSEUM OF ART, November 2, 1961–January 7, 1962, *Guggenheim Museum Exhibition, A Loan Exhibition of Paintings, Drawings, and Prints from The Solomon R. Guggenheim Museum, New York*, no.39

LEONARD HUTTON GALLERIES, New York, October 28–December 5, 1964, *Albert Gleizes and the Section d'Or*, no.27, p.23, ill.

THE SOLOMON R. GUGGENHEIM MUSEUM, New York, April 30–September 1, 1965, *Paintings from the Collection of The Solomon R. Guggenheim Museum*, no.17, p.25, ill.

MUSEUM AM OSTWALL, Dortmund, October 23–December 4, 1965, *Juan Gris*, no.6, traveled to WALLRAF-RICHARTZ-MUSEUM, Cologne, November 28, 1965–February 3, 1966

THE SOLOMON R. GUGGENHEIM MUSEUM, New York, June 28–October 1, 1967, *Museum Collection, Seven Decades, A Selection* (Checklist)

In 1908–9, Picasso and Braque painted landscapes containing houses and rooftops. Although inspired by Cézanne, these works had a cubic structure and were colored in the muted greens and browns typical of the early Cubist style. Their influence is clear in this 1911 view of Barcelona roofs, done the same year that Gris began to paint in oils. The flat planes here are broken up; the formal distribution of light and dark forms throughout the canvas show interest in the Cubist mode. However, the delicate tones of pink, blue and gray are a radical departure from the colors of Picasso and Braque in their Cubist years and indicate the unique color sense which characterizes the artist's later works.

JUAN GRIS

Still Life. March 1916

Oil on canvas, 18¹/₈ x 15″ (46 x 38.1 cm.)

Signed and dated on reverse "Juan Gris//3-16//1"

Provenance:
Katherine S. Dreier, West Redding, Connecticut
Estate of Katherine S. Dreier, 1941
Gift, Katherine S. Dreier Estate, 1953

Exhibitions:
YALE UNIVERSITY ART GALLERY, New Haven, December 15, 1952–February 1, 1953, *In Memory of Katherine S. Dreier 1877–1952: Her Own Collection of Modern Art*, no.31 (as *Abstraction in Blue and Yellow, no.1*)

THE SOLOMON R. GUGGENHEIM MUSEUM, New York, May 13–October 11, 1953, *Selection II* (Checklist)

ART GALLERY OF TORONTO, April 2–May 9, 1954, *A Loan Exhibition of Paintings From The Solomon R. Guggenheim Museum*, no.17

VANCOUVER ART GALLERY, November 16–December 12, 1954, *The Solomon R. Guggenheim Museum, A Selection from the Museum Collection*, no.13, ill.

MONTREAL MUSEUM OF FINE ARTS, June 4–July 3, 1955, *A Selection from The Solomon R. Guggenheim Museum, New York*, no.15

THE SOLOMON R. GUGGENHEIM MUSEUM, New York, July 26–October 9, 1955, *Selection V* (Checklist)

TATE GALLERY, London, April 16–May 26, 1957, *Paintings from The Solomon R. Guggenheim Museum*, no.26; organized by THE SOLOMON R. GUGGENHEIM MUSEUM, traveled to GEMEENTEMUSEUM, The Hague, June 25–September 1, no.26; ATENEIUMIN TAIDEKOKOELMAT, Helsinki, September 27–October 20, no.26; GALLERIA NAZIONALE D'ARTE MODERNA, Rome, December 5, 1957–January 8, 1958; no.15, ill.; WALLRAF-RICHARTZ-MUSEUM, Cologne, January 26–March 30, no.27, ill.; MUSÉE DES ARTS DÉCORATIFS, Paris, April 23–June 1, 1958, no.51, ill.

THE SOLOMON R. GUGGENHEIM MUSEUM, New York, August 30–October 8, 1961, *Modern Masters from the Collection of The Solomon R. Guggenheim Museum*

THE SOLOMON R. GUGGENHEIM MUSEUM, New York, June 28–October 1, 1967, *Museum Collection, Seven Decades, A Selection* (Checklist)

THE SOLOMON R. GUGGENHEIM MUSEUM, New York, February 9–April 7, 1968, *Neo-Impressionism*, no.171, ill.

COLUMBUS GALLERY OF FINE ARTS, Ohio, October 5, 1968–September 7, 1969, *Paintings from The Solomon R. Guggenheim Museum*, p.21, ill.

53.1341

"Gris, Picasso and Braque all introduced prominent areas of dabbed brushstrokes into their paintings in 1914, when the individual planes of Synthetic Cubism were commonly given a uniform texture, rather than the chiaroscuro of 1911–12. They may have been inspired by Metzinger, Marcoussis and members of the 'Puteaux group' who had continued to use mosaic and checkerboard brushwork through 1912 and 1913. Gris and Picasso did not concern themselves with color theory at all, and the dabs are instead a decorative homage to Neo-Impressionism. D. H. Kahnweiler (*Critique*, January–February 1947) believes that the Neo-Impressionist facture also appealed to the Cubists because it eliminated bravura and personal brushwork – as Fénéon had noted – and therefore suited the impersonal feeling of collage and flat plane. Gris was conscious of being a spiritual heir of Seurat…" (Robert Herbert, *Neo-Impressionism*, New York, 1968, no.171, p.232).

JUAN GRIS

Fruit Bowl (Compotier). February 1917

Oil on wood, 21⁵/₈ x 12⁷/₈″ (55 x 32.3 cm.)

Signed and dated l.l. "Juan Gris 2 1917"

Provenance:
Rose Valland, Paris, 1938

Exhibitions:
SOLOMON R. GUGGENHEIM FOUNDATION, New York,
June 1, 1939, *Art of Tomorrow*, (Fifth catalogue of the
Solomon R. Guggenheim Collection of
Non-Objective Paintings), no. 237, ill.

THE SOLOMON R. GUGGENHEIM MUSEUM, New York,
February 3-May 3, 1953, *A Selection* (Checklist)

THE SOLOMON R. GUGGENHEIM MUSEUM, New York,
October 6, 1954–February 27, 1955, *Selection IV*
(Checklist)

THE SOLOMON R. GUGGENHEIM MUSEUM, New York,
July 26–October 9, 1955, *Selection V* (Checklist)

THE SOLOMON R. GUGGENHEIM MUSEUM, New York,
January 24–May 1, 1956, *Selection VI* (Checklist)

THE SOLOMON R. GUGGENHEIM MUSEUM, New York,
June 5–October 13, 1963, *Cézanne and Structure in Modern
Painting*

THE SOLOMON R. GUGGENHEIM MUSEUM, New York,
April 30–September 1, 1965, *Paintings from the Collection of
The Solomon R. Guggenheim Museum*, no.42, ill.

THE SOLOMON R. GUGGENHEIM MUSEUM, New York,
April 11–May 26, 1968, *Acquisitions of the 1930's and 1940's*,
p.36, ill.

References:
ALVARD, JULIEN, "L'Espace Cubiste", *Art d'aujourd'hui*,
series 4, nos.3–4, May–June 1953, p.50, ill.

38.237

JUAN GRIS

Fruit Bowl on Checkered Cloth. November 1917

Oil on wood, 31 ³/₄ x 21 ³/₈″ (80.5 x 54.3 cm.)

Signed l.l. "Juan Gris//Paris 11–17"

Provenance:
Rose Valland, Paris, 1938

Exhibitions:
SOLOMON R. GUGGENHEIM FOUNDATION, New York,
June 1, 1939, *Art of Tomorrow*, (Fifth catalogue of the
Solomon R. Guggenheim Collection of Non-
Objective Paintings) no.238, ill.

THE SOLOMON R. GUGGENHEIM MUSEUM, New York,
February 3–May 3, 1953, *A Selection* (Checklist)

THE SOLOMON R. GUGGENHEIM MUSEUM, New York,
October 6, 1954–February 27, 1955, *Selection IV*
(Checklist)

THE SOLOMON R. GUGGENHEIM MUSEUM, New York,
July 26–October 9, 1955, *Selection V* (Checklist)

THE SOLOMON R. GUGGENHEIM MUSEUM, New York,
January 24–May 1, 1956, *Selection VI* (Checklist)

THE MUSEUM OF MODERN ART, New York, April 9–June 1,
1958. *Juan Gris*, p.83, ill.

THE SOLOMON R. GUGGENHEIM MUSEUM, New York,
October 21, 1959–June 19, 1960, *Inaugural Selection*
(Checklist)

THE SOLOMON R. GUGGENHEIM MUSEUM, New York,
August 30–October 8, 1961, *Modern Masters from the
Collection of The Solomon R. Guggenheim Museum*

WORCESTER ART MUSEUM, Massachusetts, February 6–
April 7, 1963, *Aspects of Twentieth Century Painting Lent by
The Solomon R. Guggenheim Museum*, no.14, p.27, ill.

THE SOLOMON R. GUGGENHEIM MUSEUM, New York,
June 5–October 13, 1963, *Cézanne and Structure in Modern
Painting*

THE SOLOMON R. GUGGENHEIM MUSEUM, New York,
April 30–September 1, 1965, *Paintings from the Collection of
The Solomon R. Guggenheim Museum*, no.43

THE SOLOMON R. GUGGENHEIM MUSEUM, New York,
June 28–October 1, 1967, *Museum Collection, Seven
Decades, A Selection* (Checklist)

THE SOLOMON R. GUGGENHEIM MUSEUM, New York,
April 11 –May 26, 1968, *Acquisitions of the 1930's and 1940's*,
p.37, ill.

References:

KAHNWEILER, DANIEL-HENRY, *Juan Gris: His Life and
Work*, New York, 1947, pl.42

SOBY, JAMES THRALL, *Juan Gris*, New York, 1958, p.78, ill.

32.238

The strong and sharply delineated black, white and tan of
Fruit Bowl affirm Gris's Spanish heritage. In a *Still Life* of
the same month (The Minneapolis Institute of Arts), Gris
has used the same compositional elements and similar
stylizations to describe the curves of the fruit bowl and
bottle. The typically tight structuring of his forms
and his interest in the play between an object and its
shadow is evident in both of these works, although *Fruit
Bowl* is a more abstract composition.

In the spring of 1917 there was a notable change in Gris's
painting style as his work became more complex.
The colors and varied textures which he produced so
skillfully in his collages of 1914 begin to reappear in *Fruit
Bowl on Checkered Cloth* of November 1917.

JUAN GRIS

Still Life with Guitar. 1921

Oil on canvas, 24 x 19³/₄″ (61 x 50.2 cm.)

Signed and dated l.r. "Juan Gris 9–21"

Provenance:
Mrs. Leo Simon, New York
Gift, Mrs. Leo Simon, 1969

69.1908

In the very productive last period of his life, 1920–27,
Gris's work was often distinguished by a greater illusionism and more emphasis on irregularity of contour.
However the strong geometrization of his earlier work
remained. In this still life of 1921 the curvilinear outlines
of the tablecloth spread across the flattened angularity
of the table illustrates this combination of two disparate
styles. A greater sense of illusionism is apparent in the
bowl of grapes, guitar and bottle of this work than in
the 1917 paintings. In the latter, the predominance of
geometric planes makes it difficult to distinguish
the true identities of the objects.

Philip Guston 1913–

Philip Guston was born in 1913 in Montreal, Canada. He grew up in Los Angeles and is self-trained as an artist except for three months at the Otis Art Institute, Los Angeles, in 1930. Interest in Renaissance frescoes and contemporary Mexican murals drew him to Mexico in 1934. Guston moved to New York in 1935 and worked for the WPA Federal Arts Project through 1940. Exposure to Cubist and abstract art in New York resulted in an increased interest in bringing the objects in his paintings up to the surface plane. In 1941, Guston turned from mural to easel painting. From that year to 1945, he taught at the State University of Iowa, and Washington University, St. Louis, Missouri. By 1947, he was established as a leading American figure painter.

In 1948, Guston began to move toward an abstract painting style abandoning spatial depth in favor of overlapping flat shapes. In 1950, he completely eliminated figural and landscape references from his painting. His work of the 1950's is impressionist in feeling – characterized by passages of related colors that produce a shimmering quality. In the early sixties, he expanded his color areas which became somber and more expressive. The solemnity of mood has increased during the last decade.

Guston has participated in numerous important group exhibitions and has been given many one-man shows. The artist resides in New York.

PHILIP GUSTON

Drawing No. 4. 1950

Ink on rice paper, 24$^1/_2$ x 38$^7/_8$″ (62.2 x 98.8 cm.)

Signed l.r. "Philip Guston"

Provenance:
from the artist, 1962

Exhibitions:
THE SOLOMON R. GUGGENHEIM MUSEUM, New York, May 3–July 1, 1962, *Philip Guston*; traveled to STEDELIJK MUSEUM, Amsterdam, September 21–October 15; WHITECHAPEL ART GALLERY, London, January 1–February 15, 1963; SOCIÉTÉ DES EXPOSITIONS, PALAIS DES BEAUX-ARTS, Brussels, March 1–31; LOS ANGELES COUNTY MUSEUM OF ART, May 14–June 30, 1963

THE SOLOMON R. GUGGENHEIM MUSEUM, New York, September 17–October 25, 1964, *American Drawings*, no.34

THE SOLOMON R. GUGGENHEIM MUSEUM, New York, July 8–September 14, 1969, *Selected Sculpture and Works on Paper*, p.28, ill.

62.1702

This drawing was done at a pivotal moment in Guston's career. Whereas drawings of the late forties were conceived in representational terms and elaborated to the point of abstraction, in this piece Guston is experimenting with the possibility of beginning a sketch without specific figures or a predetermined composition. Illusionist space has disappeared; all elements are brought toward the surface plane, leaving merely a suggestion of depth through the overlapping lines.

DUO. 1961

Oil on canvas, 72 1/8 x 68″ (183.2 x 172.7 cm.)

Signed l.l. "Philip Guston"

Provenance:
from the artist through Sidney Janis Gallery, New York,
1964

Exhibitions:

THE SOLOMON R. GUGGENHEIM MUSEUM, New York,
October 31, 1961–January 1, 1962, *American Abstract
Expressionists and Imagists*, no.23, ill.

THE SOLOMON R. GUGGENHEIM MUSEUM, New York,
May 3–July 1, 1962, *Philip Guston,* no.91, ill.; traveled to
STEDELIJK MUSEUM, Amsterdam, September 21–October 15,
as *Philip Guston Retrospective Exhibition;* WHITECHAPEL
ART GALLERY, London, January 1–February 15, 1963;
SOCIÉTÉ DES EXPOSITIONS, PALAIS DES BEAUX-ARTS, Brussels,
March 1–31; LOS ANGELES COUNTY MUSEUM OF ART,
May 14–June 30, 1963

XXXII BIENNALE INTERNAZIONALE D'ARTE VENEZIA, June 20–
October 18, 1964, *Today's Art in Museums: The Solomon
R. Guggenheim Museum*, no.9, p.33

POSES INSTITUTE OF FINE ARTS, Rose Art Museum, Brandeis
University, Waltham, Massachusetts, February 27–
March 27, 1966, *Philip Guston,* no.22

THE SOLOMON R. GUGGENHEIM MUSEUM, New York,
April 30–September 1, 1965, *Paintings from the Collection
of The Solomon R. Guggenheim Museum,* no.83, ill.

CINCINNATI ART MUSEUM, Ohio, October 3, 1969–
March 29, 1970, *Paintings from the Guggenheim Museum,
A Loan Exhibition of Modern Paintings Covering the Period
1949–1965, from The Solomon R. Guggenheim Museum,*
no.24, ill.

References:

PELLEGRINI, ALDO, *New Tendencies in Art,* New York,
1966, p.125, ill.

ARNASON, H. H., *History of Modern Art,* New York, 1968,
pl.209

64.1683

This painting is typical of Guston's work of the early
sixties. It "is dominated by two great black personages in
conclave in a miasmic gray setting. The figures open and
close, that to the right over grayed but luminous reds;
that to the left interpenetrated by the gray of the setting
and peering forth from a brilliant green eye. The black
personages stand forth from a limited but very tangible
depth composed of the grays that go under and through
the blacks; blues, oranges and pinks that go under the
floating grays. Each brush stroke vibrates with life as the
total mass of the strokes bind together every part of the
picture into an entity." (H. H. Arnason, *Philip Guston*,
New York, 1962, p.37)

Günter Haese 1924–

Günter Haese was born on February 18, 1924 in Kiel, Germany. After military service, he studied at the *Kunstschule auf dem Steinberg*, Plön, Holstein, from 1948–49, and at the Düsseldorf Academy with Bruno Goller and Ewald Mataré from 1950–57. Haese was a traditional painter and sculptor until 1960 when he dismantled a clock. Fascinated by the delicately poised and trembling mechanism, he began to work with the tiny components. He traced and made plaster casts of the parts and produced a series of monotypes from them. Then he reconstructed the elements within delicate wire frameworks, creating fantastic and fragile assemblages. Haese's earliest pieces were static. As his work evolved, the clock parts which were Haese's original inspiration retreated into the background. Wire and wire mesh, formerly accessories, became the basic elements of the compositions, and the works began to vibrate, set in motion by the slightest impulses. Kinetic and playful, Haese's work has affinities with Calder and Rickey. Haese lives in Düsseldorf.

Olymp. 1967

Brass, copper, 36⁵/₈ x 29³/₄ x 23¹/₈″ (93.1 x 75.6 x 58.8 cm.)

Not inscribed

Provenance:
from the artist, Purchase Award, Guggenheim International Exhibition, 1967

Exhibitions:
THE SOLOMON R. GUGGENHEIM MUSEUM, New York, October 20, 1967–February 4, 1968, *Guggenheim International Exhibition 1967: Sculpture from Twenty Nations*, p.93, ill.
THE SOLOMON R. GUGGENHEIM MUSEUM, New York, July 8–September 14, 1969, *Selected Sculpture and Works on Paper*, p.127, ill.

References:
FRY, EDWARD F., "Sculpture in the Sixties", *Art in America*, vol.55, no.5, September–October 1967, p.38, ill.
ARNASON, H. H., *History of Modern Art*, New York, 1968, pl.1089

67.1863

Since the early 1960's Haese has steadily developed a unique style and working method, based on the poetics of motion within the structural context of an eccentric but often highly elegant linear framework. His sculptures are never representational but usually function as evocative metaphors, with particular reference to nature and natural forces. *Olymp* numbers among the artist's largest and most complex works. It is also one of his most logical and symmetrical compositions, thus reinforcing the implicit reference of its title to the heavens and the cosmos.

Despite the superficial formal similarities to Paul Klee often cited by critics, Haese in this and other works is involved in a complex of artistic issues far removed from Klee. As a kinetic artist, Haese has become a master of micro-movement: at the slightest touch or with a breath of air, his sculptures come to life with precisely ordained degrees and varieties of motion; the organic metaphors created by these motions ally him to the European tradition of vitalism in twentieth-century sculpture. Conversely, the formidable intricacies of structure and the arduousness of execution place Haese within an old German cultural tradition that has always honored craftsmanship, perfection, and purity.

Jean Hélion 1904–

Jean Hélion was born April 21, 1904, in Couterne (Orne), France. In 1921 he moved to Paris to study architecture and worked as an architect's apprentice. In 1922 he began to paint on his own, but he did not devote all his activity to painting until 1925. He exhibited at the *Salon des Indépendants* in 1928.

From an initially figurative art, Hélion's art grew increasingly abstract until, under the influence particularly of van Doesburg and Neo-Plasticism, by 1929, it was totally abstract. Co-founder of two Parisian abstract artists' movements – *Art Concret*, 1930, and *Abstraction-Création*, 1931 – Hélion was one of the major French proponents of a geometric art with spiritual content, active between the two wars.

Between 1936 and 1946, Hélion lived and worked in the United States, except for the period 1940–42, when he was in the army and imprisoned in France. His painting and ideas had a great influence on younger American painters. After 1943, however, Hélion returned to a figurative style, which he has pursued until the present. The artist returned to Paris in 1946, where he resides today.

Composition. Paris, 1934

Oil on canvas, 56⅝ x 78¾″ (143.8 x 199.4 cm.)

Inscribed on reverse "Hélion//Paris 34"

Provenance:
Paul Nelson, Cambridge, Massachusetts, 1960
Joseph Cantor, Carmel, Indiana, 1961

Exhibitions:
GALLERY OF MODERN ART, New York, November 3–December 27, 1964, *Paintings by Jean Hélion, 1928–1964*, no.6

THE SOLOMON R. GUGGENHEIM MUSEUM, New York, April 30–September 1, 1965, *Paintings from the Collection of The Solomon R. Guggenheim Museum*, no.62, ill.

THE SOLOMON R. GUGGENHEIM MUSEUM, New York, June 28–October 1, 1967, *Museum Collection, Seven Decades, A Selection* (Checklist)

COLUMBUS GALLERY OF FINE ARTS, Ohio, October 5, 1968–September 7, 1969, *Paintings from The Solomon R. Guggenheim Museum*, p.34, ill.

References:
MESSER, THOMAS M., *Elements of Modern Painting*, New York, 1961, ill. (Revised edition, New York, 1962, as *Modern Art: An Introductory Commentary*

61.1586

During the brief period of 1932–34, Hélion executed a series of abstract canvases similar to this. The earlier paintings were composed of squares, rectangles and lines on a white ground and organized in a continuous chain. Gradually the shapes and their spatial articulation became looser and more fluid. By 1934 there is a closer integration of figures and field; the grounds have turned to gray and the forms are rhythmically disposed in a sequence of irregular horizontal alignments.

Influenced by van Doesburg and Neo-Plasticism, Hélion also admired Mondrian, Arp and Léger. Analogously, he sought a humanistic abstract art, the balance and transparency of his paintings depicting spiritual harmony and clarity.

Auguste Herbin 1882–1960

Auguste Herbin was born April 29, 1882, in Quiévy in northern France. After attending the École des Beaux-Arts in Lille, in 1901, he moved to Paris. His early paintings were in an Impressionist style. Upon moving into a studio in the "Bateau Lavoir" in 1909 – near Braque, Picasso and Gris – he fell under the influence of Cubism until, by 1913, he was painting in an Analytical Cubist vein.

By 1918, Herbin had broken with "the object" as the inspiration for his paintings, turning his attention to the autonomous quantities and qualities of color and form as the basis of pictorial language. His ideas developed slowly but consistently in this direction until, in the 1940's, he elaborated the "plastic alphabet" which was to govern his creative activity for the next twenty years. His theory of abstraction – developed through a methodical study of forms and color relationships and their infinite potential of spiritual expression – was formulated in his book of 1949: *L'art non-figuratif non-objectif.*

Herbin was a co-founder with Vantongerloo of the *Abstraction-Création* group in 1931 as well as of the annual *Salon des Réalités Nouvelles* in 1949, where he exhibited until his death. The artist died in Paris on January 31, 1960.

Composition on the Name "Rose". 1947

Oil on canvas, 32 x 25⁵/₈" (81.3 x 65.1 cm.)

Inscribed l.r. "herbin 1947" and l.c. "rose"

Provenance:
from the artist, 1949

Exhibitions:
MUSEUM OF NON-OBJECTIVE PAINTING, New York, May 31–October 9, 1949, *Tenth Anniversary Exhibition*

GEORGE THOMAS HUNTER GALLERY OF ART, Chattanooga, Tennessee, February–December 1954, *A Loan Exhibition from The Solomon R. Guggenheim Museum Collection;* organized by THE SOLOMON R. GUGGENHEIM MUSEUM, traveled to WOMEN'S COLLEGE, UNIVERSITY OF NORTH CAROLINA, Greensboro, December 1954–June 1955; UNIVERSITY OF MISSISSIPPI, Oxford, August 1955– May 1956; SIENNA HEIGHTS COLLEGE, Adrian, Michigan, September 1956–March 1957

THE SOLOMON R. GUGGENHEIM MUSEUM, New York, October 21, 1959–June 19, 1960, *Inaugural Selection* (Checklist)

AMERICAN FEDERATION OF THE ARTS, New York, July 1962–September 1963, *Elements of Modern Art* (organized by THE SOLOMON R. GUGGENHEIM MUSEUM, circulated by AMERICAN FEDERATION OF THE ARTS)

THE SOLOMON R. GUGGENHEIM MUSEUM, New York, June 28–October 1, 1967, *Museum Collection, Seven Decades, A Selection* (Checklist)

COLUMBUS GALLERY OF FINE ARTS, Ohio, October 5, 1968– September 7, 1969, *Paintings from The Solomon R. Guggenheim Museum,* p.35, ill.

49.1183

From the 1940's until his death in 1960, Herbin elaborated several series of paintings on the theme of words or proper nouns, such as: Evil, Wine, Wheat, Christmas, Bird, Christ, Midnight, Rose. Composed of extremely simple forms (so as not to distract from the direct impact of color), these paintings illustrate the artist's theory of a "plastic alphabet". Herbin's objective was to express the "plastic" and spiritual resonance of a word through corresponding quantities and qualities of color, thereby obtaining universally meaningful images.

Hans Hofmann 1880–1966

Hans Hofmann was born March 21, 1880, in Weissenburg, Bavaria, and educated in Munich. In 1898 he began to study painting with Willi Schwarz, who introduced him to Impressionism. The patronage of Philip Freudenberg, a Berlin art collector, enabled him to live in Paris from 1904 to 1914, the decade which saw the development of Fauvism and Cubism. Hofmann took an active role in avant-garde circles; his friendship with Delaunay influenced his development as a colorist. At the onset of the war, Hofmann returned to Munich and opened an art school. In the summer of 1930 Hofmann was invited to teach at Berkeley, California. The next year he settled permanently in America. He opened the Hofmann School of Art in New York in 1934 and in 1935 began conducting summer sessions in Provincetown, Massachusetts, becoming one of the most influential art teachers in America. His first one-man exhibition was held at Peggy Guggenheim's Art of This Century Gallery early in 1944.

After a period devoted exclusively to drawing, Hofmann set out in 1935 on his mature course as a painter. His still-lifes and landscapes combined Matisse's Fauvism with Braque's and Picasso's Cubism. The artist's effective transition to abstraction took place in the forties. During that decade his discoveries anticipated Still's anti-Cubist drawing and Pollock's "drip" paintings. It was in the late fifties that Hofmann began his characteristic paintings in which the rectangle was employed as an anchoring device.

In 1964 Hofmann gave forty-five paintings to The University Art Gallery, Berkeley, in memory of his wife Maria, and in gratitude for help in "rescuing" him from Hitler. The artist died on February 17, 1966.

HANS HOFMANN

The Gate. 1960

Oil on canvas, 74⅝ x 48¼″ (189.6 x 122.6 cm.)

Signed and dated l.r. "hans hofmann 60"

Provenance:
from the artist through Samuel M. Kootz Gallery, New York, 1962

Exhibitions:
XXX BIENNALE INTERNAZIONALE D'ARTE VENEZIA, June–October 1960, *United States,* no.26, p.314

WORCESTER ART MUSEUM, Massachusetts, February 6–April 7, 1963, *Aspects of Twentieth Century Painting Lent by The Solomon R. Guggenheim Museum,* no.16, ill.

THE MUSEUM OF MODERN ART, New York, September 11–November 28, 1963, *Hans Hofmann,* no.18, p.33, ill.

THE SOLOMON R. GUGGENHEIM MUSEUM, New York, April 30–September 1, 1965, *Paintings from the Collection of The Solomon R. Guggenheim Museum,* no.82, ill.

MARLBOROUGH-GERSON GALLERY, New York, September 27–October 14, 1967, *The New York Painter, A Century of Teaching: Morse to Hofmann, Benefit Exhibition for the New York University Art Collection,* p.72, ill.

References:
GREENBERG, CLEMENT, *Hofmann,* Paris, 1961, p.31, ill.

ASHTON, DORE, "'Summer Night Bliss', A New Painting by Hans Hofmann", *The Baltimore Museum of Art News,* vol.XXV, no.3, Spring 1962, p.6, ill.

HUNTER, SAM, *Hans Hofmann,* New York, 1963, pl.110

ARNASON, H. H., *History of Modern Art,* New York, 1968, colorpl.202

62.1620

The series of paintings which Hofmann painted in the last ten years of his career represents the culmination of his search for a format in which color could be made synonymous with his personal pictorial organization. The solution was in the superimposed "floating" rectangles, which anchored the painting by lining up edge for edge with the support as the major design element of the picture surface.

In *The Gate* Hofmann painted a dense background of broad horizontal and vertical strokes – visible as strokes – that are themselves rectangles. These however are dappled and of variable depth, as opposed to the flat "floating" rectangles in front of them. The color is fully saturated in both the background and foreground planes. The two dominant rectangles repeat the proportions of the support although the central (red) one does so in opposite proportion. The color relationships of rectangles to background in *The Gate*, as in the entire group of paintings of Hofmann's late period to which it is related, is exceedingly complex. It shows the extreme to which Hofmann pushed his experiments with repetition and contrast in both the organization of the image and the manipulation of hues.

Jean Ipoustéguy 1920–

Jean Ipoustéguy was born in Dun-sur-Meuse, France, on January 6, 1920. In 1938 he became a pupil of Robert Lesbounit. He executed and exhibited paintings, stained-glass windows, tapestries and lithographs before devoting himself exclusively to sculpture in 1949. He exhibited his sculpture first at the *Salon de Mai* in 1956 in Paris, and has subsequently shown in numerous group and one-man exhibitions in Europe and the United States. His first one-man exhibition in the United States was at the Albert Loeb Gallery, New York in 1964.

The formal and expressive range in Ipoustéguy's sculpture is broad. Distinctions between abstraction and figuration, between objects and human forms are often blurred. In some figurative work, grand scale, muscular anatomy, and gesture provide links with heroic, classical sculpture. Other sculptures contain stylistic references to prehistoric or archaic figures. Such characteristics coexist with a specifically contemporary brutalism. Smooth surfaces are shattered and fissured by shrapnel-like scars. Polarities are encompassed in a single work: chaos and order, serenity and decay exist simultaneously.

Lenin. 1967

Marble and metal, 23″ (58.4 cm.) high

Signed and dated on base of left shoulder "IPOUSTEGUY 67"

Provenance:
from the artist through Galerie Claude Bernard, Paris, 1968

Exhibitions:
GALERIE CLAUDE BERNARD, Paris, November-December, 1968, *Ipoustéguy: Marbres*, ill.
THE SOLOMON R. GUGGENHEIM MUSEUM, New York, July 8–September 14, 1969, *Selected Sculpture and Works on Paper*, p.130, ill.

References:
La Chronique des Arts (Supplément à *La Gazette des Beaux Arts*), no.1201, February 1969, no.370, p.91, ill.

68.1872

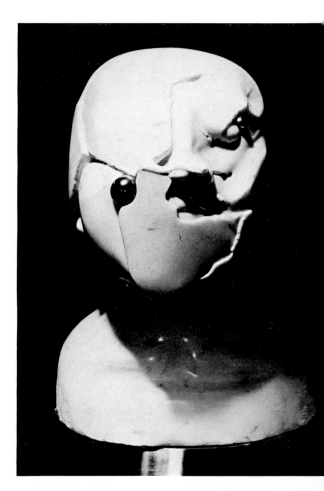

EAN IPOUSTÉGUY

The Great Rule (La Grande Règle). 1968

Marble, two sections: upper section 20″ (50.8 cm.) high;
lower section 39½″ (100.3 cm.) high

Signed at right on waist "IPOUSTEGUY 68"

Provenance:
From the artist through Galerie Claude Bernard, Paris,
1968

Exhibitions:
GALERIE CLAUDE BERNARD, Paris, November–Decem-
ber, 1968, *Ipoustéguy: Marbres*, ill.
THE SOLOMON R. GUGGENHEIM MUSEUM, New York,
July 8–September 14, 1969, *Selected Sculpture and Works
on Paper*, p.131, ill.

68.1873

Typically, Ipoustéguy refers to the art of the past in
Lenin and *The Great Rule*. In *Lenin*, the face emerging
from the stone recalls Michelangelo's figures emerging
from blocks of marble. Ipoustéguy, too, is concerned
with the dichotomy of spirit and flesh. He has said "We
have two faces, the one which is in the air and the one
which is in the blood, the latter traced inside the other,
under the skin. It is this face, made visible, that Veronica
received on her veil." The head, with its displaced,
unmatched metal eyes and odd smile, is overlaid with a
strange, surreal feeling. In *The Great Rule*, the stiff-legged,
strictly frontal pose and tubular forms refer to archaic
sculpture, in particular to the pre-classical Greek Heras.
But the cruel fragmentation of the body (the missing
head at once recalls the ruined statues of history and
imparts a note of violence), the mysterious forms, and the
brutal and aggressive emphasis on sexual organs originate
in Ipoustéguy's unique vision.

Helene with Red Turban. 1910

Oil on board, 37^1/$_2$ x 32″ (95.2 x 81.3 cm.)

Signed and dated u.l. "A. Jawlensky // 1910"; on reverse another portrait, inscribed "A. Jawlensky//N… 1910// Helene mit//…

Provenance:

the artist
Private collection, Locarno (Estate of the artist)
Galerie Wilhelm Grosshennig, Düsseldorf, 1962
Lock Galleries, New York and Stephen Silagy, Beverly Hills
Leonard Hutton Galleries, New York, 1965

Exhibitions:

GALERIE WILHELM GROSSHENNIG, Düsseldorf, October 3–31, 1961, *Sonderausstellung Alexej v. Jawlensky*, cover ill.
PASADENA ART MUSEUM, California, April 14–May 19, 1964, *Alexei Jawlensky, A Centennial Exhibition*, no.18
LEONARD HUTTON GALLERIES, New York, February 17–March 1965, *A Centennial Exhibition of Paintings by Alexej Jawlensky, 1864-1941*, no.14, ill; traveled to
BALTIMORE MUSEUM OF ART, April 2–May 23, 1965, as *A Centennial Exhibition of Paintings by Alexej Jawlensky, 1864–1941, A Selection from Each Year 1901–1917*, cat. no.10
THE SOLOMON R. GUGGENHEIM MUSEUM, New York, June 23–October 23, 1966, *Gauguin and the Decorative Style*, ill.
THE SOLOMON R. GUGGENHEIM MUSEUM, New York, June 28–October 1, 1967, *Museum Collection, Seven Decades, A Selection* (Checklist)

References:

WEILER, CLEMENS, *Alexej Jawlensky*, Cologne, 1959, no.55, p.78, ill.
Die Weltkunst, Munich, XXXVI Jahrgang, no.1, January 1, 1966, p.14, cover ill.
ARNASON, H. H., *History of Modern Art*, New York, 1968, p.184, pl.66

65.1773

Alexej Jawlensky 1864–1941

The son of a colonel in the Russian Imperial Army, Jawlensky entered military school at the age of 18 in 1882. By 1890 he was taking evening classes at the Imperial Art Academy in St. Petersburg, where he met Marianne von Werefkin. He withdrew from the Academy to paint in her studio where he met Helene Nesnakomoff, a young girl raised in Werefkin's family.

In 1896, Jawlensky went to Munich with Marianne von Werefkin where he met Kandinsky and in 1902, his son Andreas was born to Helene Nesnakomoff. After working for a brief period in 1907 in Matisse's studio, his paintings began to reflect Matisse's decorative arrangement of color and form. In 1909, he was one of the co-founders of the *Neue Künstlervereinigung*.

Shortly after the outbreak of the war in 1914, he fled with Werefkin to Switzerland but by 1922 had broken with her and married Helene, settling permanently in Wiesbaden. In 1914 he abruptly stopped painting expressive portraits and executed several series of abstract landscapes. In 1922 he returned to the heads which were now transformed from the sensual portraits of the early years to schematic abstractions of the human face.

In 1924, he joined the Blue Four group with Klee, Kandinsky and Feininger. By 1938 he had ceased to paint because of crippling arthritis. Jawlensky died March 15, 1941 in Wiesbaden.

Jawlensky's painting from 1907 to 1910 combined bold Fauvist color and simplified linear structure with an intense personal feeling for the subject. The monumental *Helene with Red Turban* is a portrait of Helene Nesnakomoff, who had borne the artist a son in 1902 and whom he was to marry in 1922. It is very likely that this painting is based on Matisse's *Red Madras Headdress* of 1907-8 (Barnes Foundation, Merion, Pa.) which is a portrait of the artist's wife in a red turban. Jawlensky has taken Matisse's brilliant color and painterly surface treatment but adds an emotional interest in the personality of the sitter which is not found in Matisse's style.

Asger Jorn 1914–

Asger Jorn was born in Vejrum, Denmark, in 1914. He studied in Copenhagen with Askel Jorgensen and in Paris with Léger under whose direction he executed works for the Paris 1937 International Exhibition in collaboration with Le Corbusier. In 1938 he was given his first one-man exhibition in Copenhagen. He spent the war years in Denmark where he became acquainted with the work of Ensor and Klee. Klee's "psychic improvisation " – the rendering of the spontaneous images of the subconscious mind – encouraged Jorn to portray the archetypal images of Nordic legends, images and myths that inspired him. Jorn's paintings of the somber, often violent Scandinavian imagination are handled in an explosive, dynamic manner.

In 1946, Jorn helped to found the group COBRA in reaction against the principles of order and harmony of concrete art, then dominant in Europe. The unifying doctrine of COBRA was complete freedom of expression with accent on color and brushstroke. Jorn exhibited with COBRA at the Stedelijk Museum, Amsterdam in 1949, and in 1951 in Liège.

Jorn has produced important ceramic murals and graphic work as well as paintings, and has exhibited extensively, including the World's Fair, Brussels, 1958, the Carnegie International Exhibition, 1958, the Fourth Guggenheim International Exhibition, New York, 1964, and Documenta III, Kassel, 1964. In 1962 he was given his first one-man exhibition in the United States and in 1964, a major international retrospective was held of his work.

ASGER JORN

Green Ballet. 1960

Oil on canvas, 57 x 78³/₄″ (144.8 x 199.7 cm.)

Inscribed l.r. "Jorn" and on reverse "Balleto verde// Jorn//60//The Green ballet"

Provenance:
Jon N. Streep, New York, 1962

Exhibitions:
WORCESTER ART MUSEUM, Massachusetts, February 6– April 7, 1963, *Aspects of Twentieth Century Painting Lent by The Solomon R. Guggenheim Museum,* no.17, p.33, ill.

THE SOLOMON R. GUGGENHEIM MUSEUM, New York, July 1–September 13, 1964, *Van Gogh and Expressionism*

SAN FRANCISCO MUSEUM OF ART, October 15– November 28, 1965, *Colorists 1950–65,* ill.

CINCINNATI ART MUSEUM, Ohio, October 3, 1969– March 29, 1970, *Paintings from the Guggenheim Museum, A Loan Exhibition of Modern Paintings Covering the Period 1949–1965, from The Solomon R. Guggenheim Museum,* no.22, ill.

References:
ARNASON, H. H., *History of Modern Art,* New York, 1968, p.535, no.945, ill.

62.1608

Jorn's painting is generally less figurative in inspiration than that of his COBRA colleagues. In this canvas, where bright and primary colors are applied in a seeming frenzy, control is established by the large sweeping movements and asymmetrically balanced color shapes. A sense of genesis, produced by the balance between creative and destructive forces, emerges as the subject of the work.

and Arp and contact with the Surrealists is reflected in hi[s]
late paintings where biomorphic forms and softer colo[r]
replace the more rigorous compositions of the Bauhau[s]
period. He died in Paris on December 13, 1944.

The Solomon R. Guggenheim Museum has one of the mos[t]
comprehensive collections of the artist's work in existence
numbering 79 oils and 62 watercolors, exclusive of graphi[c]
works. The extensiveness of the selection here allows us t[o]
trace Kandinsky's total development through examples o[f]
some of the finest works of each period.

Vasily Kandinsky 1866–1944

Vasily Kandinsky, born in Moscow in 1866, received a law
degree from the University of Moscow in 1892. By 1896,
he had given up a career in law and economics to go to
Munich and become a painter. He soon was playing an
active part in the Munich art world. He founded the art
association "The Phalanx" in 1901. In 1909 he organized
the *Neue Künstlervereiningung* and in 1911, with Franz Marc,
the famous *Blaue Reiter* group. Between 1903 and 1908 he
traveled between Germany and Russia, to Holland, Venice,
Tunisia, Rapallo, spending a year near Paris in 1906. In 1909
Kandinsky settled in Murnau near Munich, where he remained until World War I broke out.

During this period he was formulating ideas that would
lead eventually to abstraction. In his paintings color became intensified and progressively independent of any
representational function. In his writings, *On the Spiritual
in Art* (finished in 1910; published 1912) and *Reminiscences*
(1913), he explains his concept of color and form as "content", or the autonomous subject of his paintings. For
Kandinsky, art was a portrayal of spiritual values. "The
harmony of color and form must be based solely on the
principle of the proper contact with the human soul."

Kandinsky returned to Russia in 1917 after marrying his
second wife, Nina. Here he was active as a teacher, lecturer
and administrator of the arts until 1921, when, at the revolutionary government's growing hostility to abstract art,
he decided to leave.

In 1922 he returned to Germany and accepted a post at the
Bauhaus in Weimar. He moved with the school to Dessau
in 1926. There he taught until it was closed by the Nazis in
1933. During this time his painting, influenced by his contact with the Suprematists and Constructivists in Russia,
changed from free expressionist abstraction to geometric
abstraction. His theories on abstract composition, *Point and
Line to Plane*, were published by the Bauhaus in 1926.

Kandinsky settled in Paris late in 1933 and became a French
citizen in 1939. He was associated with the *Abstraction-
Création* group of abstract artists. His friendship with Miró

VASILY KANDINSKY

Amsterdam, No.52. 1904

Oil on board, $9^3/_8$ x $13^1/_8$" (23.3 x 33.2 cm.)

Signed l.r. "Kandinsky"

Provenance:

B.C. Citroën, Amsterdam
Mrs. Hilda Bachrach, Forest Hills, New York, 1946

Exhibitions:

MUSEUM OF NON-OBJECTIVE PAINTING, New York,
opening April 29, 1952, *Evolution to Non-Objectivity*,
no.67

PALAIS DES BEAUX-ARTS, Brussels, May 17–June 30, 1957,
*45 Works by Kandinsky from The Solomon R. Guggenheim
Museum, New York*, p.1, ill.; organized by THE SOLOMON
R. GUGGENHEIM MUSEUM; traveled to MUSÉE NATIONAL
D'ART MODERNE, Paris, November 15, 1957–January 5,
1958; TATE GALLERY, London, January 14–February 28;
MUSÉE DES BEAUX-ARTS DE LYON, March 8–April 6;
KUNSTNERNES HUS, Oslo, April 18–May 4, 1958; GALLERIA
NAZIONALE D'ARTE MODERNA, Rome, May 15–June 30, 195[8]
(hereinafter cited as PALAIS DES BEAUX-ARTS, Brussels,
1957, *Kandinsky*)

ART GALLERY OF TORONTO, April 24–May 24, 1959,
45 Kandinskys from The Solomon R. Guggenheim Museum

THE SOLOMON R. GUGGENHEIM MUSEUM, New York,
March 30–June 19, 1960, *Inaugural Selection (Kandinsky
Galleries)* (exhibition opened October 21, 1959)

PHILADELPHIA MUSEUM OF ART, November 2, 1961–
January 7, 1962, *Guggenheim Museum Exhibition, A Loan
Collection of Paintings, Drawings, and Prints from
The Solomon R. Guggenheim Museum, New York*, no.52

THE SOLOMON R. GUGGENHEIM MUSEUM, New York,
January 25–April 7, 1963, *Vasily Kandinsky 1866–1944: A
Retrospective Exhibition*, no.3, ill.; traveled to MUSÉE
NATIONAL D'ART MODERNE, Paris, April 29–June 24, 1963;
GEMEENTEMUSEUM, The Hague, July 1–August 30, 1963;
KUNSTHALLE, Basel, September 7–November 7, 1963

(hereinafter cited as THE SOLOMON R. GUGGENHEIM MUSEUM, New York, 1963, *Kandinsky*)

THE SOLOMON R. GUGGENHEIM MUSEUM, New York, April 30–September 1, 1965, *Paintings from the Collection of The Solomon R. Guggenheim Museum*, no.7, ill.

THE SOLOMON R. GUGGENHEIM MUSEUM, New York, *Kandinsky, Selections from the Collection*, April 19– September 1966; November 4, 1966–February 27, 1967

BALTIMORE MUSEUM OF ART, October 22–December 18, 1968, *From El Greco to Pollock: Early and Late Works by European and American Artists*, no.113, p.136, ill.

THE SOLOMON R. GUGGENHEIM MUSEUM, New York, *Kandinsky, Selections from the Collection*, February 14–

March 9, 1969; July 8–September 14, 1969; October 12– December 1969

References:

GROHMANN, WILL, *Wassily Kandinsky, Life and Work*, New York, 1958, p.342, CC 535, ill.

HARMS, ERNST, "My Association with Kandinsky", *American Artist*, vol.27, no.6, June 1963, p.37, ill.

DOLEMAN, CORNELIUS, *Wassily Kandinsky*, New York, 1964, p.21, ill.

46.1055

Munich, No.71 (Upperpalatinate). 1904

Oil on canvasboard, $9^3/_8$ x $12^5/_8''$ (23.7 x 32 cm.)

Not inscribed

Provenance:
Otto Stangl, Munich, 1950

Exhibitions:
THE SOLOMON R. GUGGENHEIM MUSEUM, New York,
Kandinsky, Selections from the Collection, April 19–
September 1966; November 4, 1966–February 27, 1967;
October 8, 1968–January 12, 1969; February 14–March 9,
1969; July 8–September 14, 1969; October 12–
November 1969

References:
GROHMANN, WILL, *Wassily Kandinsky, Life and Work,*
New York, 1958, p.342, CC 539, ill.

50.1292

VASILY KANDINSKY

Untitled (Fishing Boats, Rapallo). 1906

Oil on canvasboard, 9³/₈ x 12⁷/₈" (23.7 x 32.8 cm.)

Not inscribed

Provenance:
Otto Stangl, Munich, 1950

Exhibitions:
ART GALLERY OF TORONTO, April 24–May 24, 1959,
5 Kandinskys from The Solomon R. Guggenheim Museum
THE SOLOMON R. GUGGENHEIM MUSEUM, New York,
Kandinsky, Selections from the Collection, April 19–September 1966; November 4, 1966–February 27, 1967;
October 8, 1968–January 12, 1969; February 14–March 9,
1969; July 8–September 14, 1969; October 12–December
1969

References:
GROHMANN, WILL, *Wassily Kandinsky, Life and Work,*
New York, 1958, p.344, CC 555, ill.

50.1293

Kandinsky, in his *Reminiscences,* recalled that Monet's canvas *Haystacks,* which he saw at a French Impressionist exhibition in 1895, was an experience which "stamped my entire way of life and which shook me to the marrow". When Kandinsky founded "The Phalanx" in Munich (1901–4), he exhibited Monet and the Neo-Impressionists, Signac, Luce and Angrand.

The influence of Impressionism and Neo-Impressionism on Kandinsky and his natural love for vibrant and expressive color can be seen in these three early studies of Amsterdam, Munich and Rapallo. Kandinsky traveled extensively during these early years, recording impressions in his sketch books. These small oil sketches are typical in size and format of his *plein-air* color notations.

VASILY KANDINSKY

Blue Mountain, No.84 (Der Blaue Berg). 1908

Oil on canvas, 42 x 38¹/₂″ (106.7 x 97.8 cm.)

Inscribed l.r. "Kandinsky//1908" and on reverse
"Kandinsky no. 84"

Provenance:
Staatliche Gemäldegalerie, Dresden
Gutekunst und Klipstein, Bern, 1939
Solomon R. Guggenheim, New York
Gift, Solomon R. Guggenheim, 1941

Exhibitions:
MUSEUM OF NON-OBJECTIVE PAINTING, New York,
March 15–May 15, 1945, *In Memory of Wassily Kandinsky*,
no.1

CARNEGIE INSTITUTE (Department of Fine Arts), Pittsburgh,
April 11–May 12, 1946, *Memorial Exhibition of Paintings by
Wassily Kandinsky 1866–1944*, no.1

MUSEUM OF NON-OBJECTIVE PAINTING, New York,
opening April 29, 1952, *Evolution to Non-Objectivity*,
no.69

PALAIS DES BEAUX-ARTS, Brussels, 1957, *Kandinsky*
(joined the exhibition in Lyon) no.5

BALTIMORE MUSEUM OF ART, September 30–November 2, 1958, *16 Kandinskys from The Solomon R.
Guggenheim Museum*

ART GALLERY OF TORONTO, April 24–May 24, 1959,
45 Kandinskys from The Solomon R. Guggenheim Museum

THE SOLOMON R. GUGGENHEIM MUSEUM, New York,
October 21, 1959–June 19, 1960, *Inaugural Selection
(Kandinsky Galleries)* (Checklist)

PHILADELPHIA MUSEUM OF ART, November 2, 1961–
January 7, 1962, *Guggenheim Museum Exhibition, A Loan
Collection of Paintings, Drawings, and Prints from The
Solomon R. Guggenheim Museum, New York*, no.46

THE SOLOMON R. GUGGENHEIM MUSEUM, New York,
1963, *Kandinsky*, no.9, p.37, ill.

THE SOLOMON R. GUGGENHEIM MUSEUM, New York,
July 1–September 13, 1964, *Van Gogh and Expressionism*

THE SOLOMON R. GUGGENHEIM MUSEUM, New York,
April 30–September 1, 1965, *Paintings from the Collection of
The Solomon R. Guggenheim Museum*, no.10, p.20, ill.

THE SOLOMON R. GUGGENHEIM MUSEUM, New York,
April 19–June 20, 1966, *Kandinsky, Selection from the
Collection*

THE SOLOMON R. GUGGENHEIM MUSEUM, New York,
June 23–October 23, 1966, *Gauguin and the Decorative
Style*, ill.

EXPO 67, Montreal, April 28–October 27, 1967, *Man and
His World*, no.92, p.192, ill.

THE SOLOMON R. GUGGENHEIM MUSEUM, New York,
April 11–May 26, 1968, *Acquisitions of the 1930's and 1940's*,
p.67, ill.

COLUMBUS GALLERY OF FINE ARTS, Ohio, October 5, 1968–
September 7, 1969, *Paintings from The Solomon R.
Guggenheim Museum*, pp.10–11, ill.

THE SOLOMON R. GUGGENHEIM MUSEUM, New York,
Kandinsky, Selections from the Collection, October 12–
December 1969; January 19–February 8, 1970

References:
KANDINSKY, VASILY, *Kandinsky Album, Rückblicke 1901–
1913*, Berlin, 1913, pl.37

KANDINSKY, VASILY, *On the Spiritual in Art*, New York,
1946, p.107, ill.

ESTIENNE, CHARLES, *Kandinsky*, Paris, 1950, p.6, ill.

EICHNER, JOHANNES, *Kandinsky und Gabrielle Munter*,
Munich, 1956, no.53, ill.

GROHMANN, WILL, *Wassily Kandinsky, Life and Work*,
New York, 1958, p.263, no.84, ill.

KROLL, JACK, "Kandinsky: Last of the Heresiarchs", *Art
News*, February 1963, p.39, ill.

HARMS, ERNST, "My Association with Kandinsky",
American Artist, vol.27, no.6, June 1963, p.38, no.84, ill.

ROBBINS, DANIEL, "Vasily Kandinsky: Abstraction and
Image", *College Art Journal*, vol.XXII, no.3, Spring 1963,
cover ill.

LASSAIGNE, JACQUES, *Kandinsky*, Geneva, 1964, p.32, ill.

DOLEMAN, CORNELIUS, *Wassily Kandinsky*, New York,
1964, p.25, ill.

GROHMANN, WILL, "La grande unité d'une grande
œuvre", *XXe Siècle*, no.XXVII, December 1966, p.10, ill.

ARNASON, H. H., *History of Modern Art*, New York, 1968,
p.172, no.314, ill.

AWAZU, NORIO, *Klee/Kandinsky (Art du Monde*, 20),
Tokyo, 1968, p.92, ill.

41.505

His strong belief in emotional and spiritual content led
Kandinsky to a new form of pictorial expression. In an
effort to portray an "inner necessity", he began gradually
to suppress all recognizable subject matter in his paintings.

By 1908, as one can see in *Blue Mountain*, the referential
themes in Kandinsky's paintings – while still discernable
– were losing their impact as representational images.
Color, increasingly intense and arbitrary, tended to deny
the three-dimensionality of the canvas. In *Blue Mountain*,
Kandinsky has adopted the Neo-Impressionist technique
of applied color dots organized in large, flat areas, across
which the riders move in an even rhythm.

VASILY KANDINSKY

Crinolines, No.89 (Reifrockgesellschaft). 1909

Oil on canvas, 37¹/₂ x 59¹/₄″ (100.3 x 150.5 cm.)

Inscribed l.l. "Kandinsky 1909" and on reverse
"Kandin… eifrock… (1909)"

Provenance:
Hans Goltz, Munich
W. Beffie, Amsterdam
Nierendorf Gallery, New York, 1945

Exhibitions:

GALERIE HANS GOLTZ, Munich, 1913, *Kandinsky Kollektiv-
ausstellung 1902–12* (as *Reifrockdamen* 1909), no.6

NEW BURLINGTON GALLERIES, London, 1938, *Twentieth-
Century German Art*

NIERENDORF GALLERY, New York, December 1942–
February 1943, *Kandinsky Retrospective*

MUSEUM OF NON-OBJECTIVE PAINTING, New York,
March 15–May 15, 1945, *In Memory of Wassily Kandinsky*,
no.4

ART GALLERY OF TORONTO, April 2–May 9, 1954, *A Loan
Exhibition of Paintings from The Solomon R. Guggenheim
Museum*, no.18

THE SOLOMON R. GUGGENHEIM MUSEUM, New York,
October 6, 1954–February 27, 1955, *Selection IV*
(Checklist)

INSTITUTE OF CONTEMPORARY ART, Boston, March 9–
April 17, 1955, *Selection from The Solomon R. Guggenheim
Museum Collection*

MONTREAL MUSEUM OF FINE ARTS, June 4–July 3, 1955, *A
Selection from The Solomon R. Guggenheim Museum*, no.16

PALAIS DES BEAUX-ARTS, Brussels, 1957, *Kandinsky*, no.4, ill

ART GALLERY OF TORONTO, April 24–May 24, 1959,
45 Kandinskys from The Solomon R. Guggenheim Museum

THE SOLOMON R. GUGGENHEIM MUSEUM, New York,
October 21, 1959–September 29, 1961, *Inaugural Selection
(Kandinsky Galleries)* (Checklist)

PHILADELPHIA MUSEUM OF ART, November 2, 1961–
January 7, 1962, *Guggenheim Museum Exhibition, A Loan
Collection of Paintings, Drawings, and Prints from The
Solomon R. Guggenheim Museum, New York*, no.47, ill.

THE SOLOMON R. GUGGENHEIM MUSEUM, New York,
1963, *Kandinsky*, no.12, ill.

THE SOLOMON R. GUGGENHEIM MUSEUM, New York,
Kandinsky, Selections from the Collection, April 19, 1966–
September 1966; November 1966–February 27, 1967

THE SOLOMON R. GUGGENHEIM MUSEUM, New York,
April 11–May 26, 1968, *Acquisitions of the 1930's and 1940's*
p.88, ill.

THE SOLOMON R. GUGGENHEIM MUSEUM, New York,
Kandinsky, Selections from the Collection, October 8, 1968–
January 12, 1969; February 14–March 9, 1969; March 28–
May 11, 1969; July 8–September 14, 1969; October 13–
December 1969; January 19–February 8, 1970

References:

KANDINSKY, VASILY, *Kandinsky Album Rückblicke, 1901–
1913*, Berlin, 1913, p.46, ill. (as 1910)

GROHMANN, WILL, *Wassily Kandinsky, Life and Work*, New
York, 1958, no.89, CC 30

HARMS, ERNST, "My Association with Kandinsky",
American Artist, vol. 27, no.6, June 1963, p.39, ill.

DOLEMAN, CORNELIUS, *Wassily Kandinsky*, New York,
1964, p.26, ill.

45.966

Natural landscape studies were only one aspect of
Kandinsky's early work. The romantic and imaginative
side of his personality is revealed in many paintings
executed "from memory".

As early as 1902, *Bright Air* (Collection Nina Kandinsky)
showed ladies dressed in white crinolines of the Biedermeier period (mid 19th century). Several paintings of
Biedermeier scenes, as well as a series of paintings with
medieval subject matter, were completed during this
period. They may be related to the Russian Art Nouveau
group, 'World of Art', and its interest in theater design.
Crinolines, as well as a similar painting of the same title
and date (Collection Tretyakov Gallery, Moscow) have
the shallow depth, linear figure arrangement and
decorative quality of a stage set.

VASILY KANDINSKY

Study for "Composition no.2". (Composition, no.35 or Composition, no.2). 1910

Oil on canvas, 38³/₈ x 51³/₄″ (97.5 x 130.5 cm.)

Signed and dated l.r. "Kandinsky//1910"

Provenance:

Baron von Gamp, Berlin
Nierendorf Gallery, New York, 1945

Exhibitions:

KUNSTHALLE, Bern, February 21–March 29, 1937, *Wassily Kandinsky*, no.5

NEW BURLINGTON GALLERIES, London, 1938, *Twentieth-Century German Art*

MUSEUM OF NON-OBJECTIVE PAINTING, New York, March 15–May 15, 1945, *In Memory of Wassily Kandinsky*, no.7

NIERENDORF GALLERY, New York, February 8, 1945, on temporary exhibition

CARNEGIE INSTITUTE (Department of Fine Arts), Pittsburgh, April 11–May 12, 1946, *Memorial Exhibition of Paintings by Wassily Kandinsky 1866–1944*, no.5

MUSEUM OF NON-OBJECTIVE PAINTING, New York, opening April 29, 1952, *Evolution to Non-Objectivity*, no.70 (as *Composition Two*, 1910)

THE SOLOMON R. GUGGENHEIM MUSEUM, New York, May 13–October 11, 1953, *Selection II* (as *Composition, No.35*) (Checklist)

BUSCH-REISINGER MUSEUM OF GERMANIC ART, Cambridge, Massachusetts, January 21–February 24, 1955, *Blaue Reiter*, no.17, ill.

PALAIS DES BEAUX-ARTS, Brussels, 1957, *Kandinsky*, no.6 (left exhibition after Tate Gallery showing)

PALAIS DES BEAUX-ARTS, Brussels, April 17–July 21, 1958, *50 Ans d'Art Moderne*, no.142, pl.59

THE SOLOMON R. GUGGENHEIM MUSEUM, New York, October 21, 1959–September 29, 1961, *Inaugural Selection (Kandinsky Galleries)* (Checklist)

PHILADELPHIA MUSEUM OF ART, November 2, 1961–January 7, 1962, *Guggenheim Museum Exhibition, A Loan Collection of Paintings, Drawings, and Prints from The Solomon R. Guggenheim Museum, New York*, no.48

THE SOLOMON R. GUGGENHEIM MUSEUM, New York, 1963, *Kandinsky*, no.13, p.4, ill.

THE SOLOMON R. GUGGENHEIM MUSEUM, New York, July 1–September 13, 1964, *Van Gogh and Expressionism*

UCLA ART GALLERIES, Los Angeles, January 24–March 7, 1965, *Years of Ferment: The Birth of Twentieth Century Art*, cat. no.89, frontispiece; traveled to SAN FRANCISCO MUSEUM OF ART, March 28–May 16, 1965; CLEVELAND MUSEUM OF ART, July 13–August 22, 1965

THE SOLOMON R. GUGGENHEIM MUSEUM, New York, *Kandinsky, Selections from the Collection*, April 19–September 1966; November 1966–February 27, 1967

THE METROPOLITAN MUSEUM OF ART, New York, November 15, 1967–April 1, 1968, *Selections from the Collection of The Solomon R. Guggenheim Museum*

THE SOLOMON R. GUGGENHEIM MUSEUM, New York, *Kandinsky, Selections from the Collection*, October 8, 1968–January 4, 1969; February 14–March 9, 1969; March 28–May 11, 1969; July 8–September 14, 1969; October 12–December 1969; January 19–February 8, 1970

References:

GROHMANN, WILL, *Wassily Kandinsky*, Leipzig, 1924, (Junge Kunst, Band 42) ill. (as *Composition II*)

GROHMANN, WILL, *Kandinsky*, Paris, 1930, p.3, no.4, ill. (as *Composition II*)

BILL, MAX, *Wassily Kandinsky*, Paris, 1951, p.125, ill. (as *Composition II*)

GROHMANN, WILL, *Wassily Kandinsky, Farben und Klänge*, vol.II, Baden-Baden, 1956, pl.1 (detail)

KANDINSKY, VASILY, *On the Spiritual in Art*, New York, 1958, pp.118–120; p.109, ill.

READ, HERBERT, *A Concise History of Modern Painting*, New York, 1959, p.165, ill.

BRION, MARCEL, *Kandinsky*, London, 1961, p.21, ill.

MESSER, THOMAS M., *Modern Art*, New York, 1962, ill.

ROBBINS DANIEL, "Vasily Kandinsky: Abstraction and Image", *College Art Journal*, vol. XXII, no.3, Spring 1963, fig.3

GROHMANN, WILL, "La grande unité d'une grande œuvre", *XXe Siècle*, no.XXVII, December 1966, p.14, ill.

FELDMAN, EDMUND BURKE, *Art as Image and Idea*, Englewood Cliffs, New Jersey, 1967, p.252, ill.

ARNASON, H. H., *History of Modern Art*, New York, 1968, p.182, no.58, ill.

AWAZU, NORIO, *Klee/Kandinsky (Art du Monde, 20)*, Tokyo, 1968, p.93, ill.

45.961

In Kandinsky's works of 1909–13, motifs which were visible in *Blue Mountain* – horses and riders, women in folk dress, the mountain, rounded trees or stem-like trunks – reappear but in a modified order and subordinated to expressive color and form. In this sense, *Blue Mountain* provides a key to many of Kandinsky's semi-abstract and abstract works.

Study for "Composition no.2", which is a study for a larger oil (78³/₄ x 108 ¹/₄″ or 200 x 275 cm.) formerly in the collection of Baron von Gamp, Berlin and now destroyed repeats these themes and other recurrent Kandinsky symbols (reclining couple, domed city, lightning) in a slightly more abstract fashion than that of the earlier canvases.

VASILY KANDINSKY

Pastorale, No.132. 1911

Oil on canvas, 41⁷/₈ x 61³/₄″ (106.3 x 156.8 cm.)

Signed and dated l.r. "Kandinsky 1911"

Provenance:
Galerie Arnold, Dresden (?)
Fritz Schön, Berlin
R. C. Schön, Quebec
Dominion Gallery, Montreal, 1943
Nierendorf Gallery, New York, 1945

Exhibitions:

MUSEUM OF NON-OBJECTIVE PAINTING, New York,
March 15–May 15, 1945, *In Memory of Wassily Kandinsky*,
no.12

THE SOLOMON R. GUGGENHEIM MUSEUM, New York,
October 6, 1954–February 27, 1955, *Selection IV*
(Checklist)

PALAIS DES BEAUX-ARTS, Brussels, 1957, *Kandinsky*, p.9, ill.

ART GALLERY OF TORONTO, April 24–May 24, 1959,
45 Kandinskys from The Solomon R. Guggenheim Museum

THE SOLOMON R. GUGGENHEIM MUSEUM, New York,
October 21, 1959–March 28, 1960, *Inaugural Selection
(Kandinsky Galleries)* (Checklist)

UNIVERSITY OF KENTUCKY, Lexington, May 8–June 18, 1960,
*European Paintings from The Solomon R. Guggenheim
Museum*, no.9

THE SOLOMON R. GUGGENHEIM MUSEUM, New York,
1963, *Kandinsky*, no.24, p.51, ill.

THE SOLOMON R. GUGGENHEIM MUSEUM, New York,
April 30–September 1, 1965, *Paintings from The Solomon
R. Guggenheim Museum*, no.18, p.26, ill.

THE SOLOMON R. GUGGENHEIM MUSEUM, New York,
Kandinsky, Selections from the Collection, April 19–
September 1966; November 1966–February 27, 1967

THE SOLOMON R. GUGGENHEIM MUSEUM, New York,
April 11–May 26, 1968, *Acquisitions of the 1930's and 1940's*
p.68, p.87, ill.

THE SOLOMON R. GUGGENHEIM MUSEUM, New York,
Kandinsky, Selections from the Collection, October 8, 1968–
January 12, 1969; October 12–December 1969;
January 19–February 8, 1970

References:

GROHMANN, WILL, "Kandinsky", *Cahiers d'art*, 1930, p.8,
no.10, ill.

GROHMANN, WILL, *Wassily Kandinsky, Life and Work*,
New York, 1958, p.127, CC 132, ill.

45.965

In *Pastorale* (1911) the Biedermeier ladies of *Crinolines*
(1909) reappear, filling the right-hand side of the canvas;
but the stage set quality of the 1909 work has been
transformed into an attenuated semi-abstraction with
idyllic landscape associations.

Pastorale is another illustration of Kandinsky's progression
toward abstraction, as noted in *Study for Composition no.2*
(1910). The implicitly romantic figurative associations
are of secondary impact, as compared to the rhythmic
forms, rapid brush strokes and primary colors which flow
through and are modulated by an abundant use of white.

VASILY KANDINSKY

Study for "Improvisation 25" (Garden of Love). 1912.

Watercolor and ink, 12¼ x 18¾″ (31.2 x 47.6 cm.)

Signed with monogram l.r. "VK".

Provenance:
Piet Regnault, Holland
Hildegarde Prytek, Rego Park, New York, 1948

Exhibitions:
THE SOLOMON R. GUGGENHEIM MUSEUM, New York, January 24–May 1, 1956, *Selection VI* (Checklist)
PALAIS DES BEAUX-ARTS, Brussels, 1957, *Kandinsky*, no.7, ill.
PASADENA ART MUSEUM, January 15–February 15, 1963, *Vasily Kandinsky 1866–1944, A Retrospective Exhibition*; organized in collaboration with THE SOLOMON R. GUGGENHEIM MUSEUM, traveled to SAN FRANCISCO MUSEUM OF ART, March 1–April 4; PORTLAND ART MUSEUM, Oregon, April 15–May 15; MARION KOOGLER MCNAY ART INSTITUTE, San Antonio, June 1–July 1; COLORADO SPRINGS FINE ART CENTER, July 15–August 25; BALTIMORE MUSEUM OF ART, September 9–October 20; COLUMBUS GALLERY OF FINE ARTS, Ohio, November 11–December 5; WASHINGTON UNIVERSITY ART GALLERY, St. Louis, December 22, 1963–January 6, 1964; MONTREAL MUSEUM OF FINE ARTS, February 5–March 5; WORCESTER ART MUSEUM, Massachusetts, March 20–April 20, 1964 (hereinafter cited as PASADENA ART MUSEUM, 1963, *Kandinsky*)
THE SOLOMON R. GUGGENHEIM MUSEUM, New York, *Kandinsky, Selections from the Collection*, April 19–September 1966; November 1966–February 27, 1967
THE SOLOMON R. GUGGENHEIM MUSEUM, New York, April 11–May 26, 1968, *Acquisitions of the 1930's and 1940's*, p.101, ill.
THE SOLOMON R. GUGGENHEIM MUSEUM, New York, October 8, 1968–January 12, 1969, *Kandinsky, Selection from the Collection*

THE SOLOMON R. GUGGENHEIM MUSEUM, New York, July 8–September 14, 1969, *Selected Sculpture and Works on Paper*, p.31, ill.
THE SOLOMON R. GUGGENHEIM MUSEUM, New York, October 12–November 1969, *Kandinsky, Selection from the Collection*

References:
GROHMANN, WILL, *Wassily Kandinsky, Life and Work*, New York, 1958, p.75, ill.
DEUTSCH, MAX, "La rencontre avec Schoenberg", *XXe Siècle*, no.XXVII, December 1966, p.29.

48.1162

"In *On the Spiritual in Art* Kandinsky defined 'Impressions' as those paintings in which the direct impression of outer nature remains recognizable; 'Improvisations' as those produced out of an inner impulse, sudden and unconscious; and 'Compositions', those works which had crystallized slowly on the basis of preliminary studies and sketches, and in whose structure the conscious mind played a considerable part". (Grohmann, *Kandinsky*, New York, 1958, p.103).

The series of "Improvisations" was begun in 1909 and Kandinsky did many imaginative watercolors as studies for these works. Often the intended "Improvisations" were never executed, but Grohmann has identified this work as a study for *Improvisation 25 (Garden of Love)* formerly in the Museum of Smolensk, Russia. It is also related to *Improvisation 27 (Garden of Love)*. Both paintings were completed in 1912.

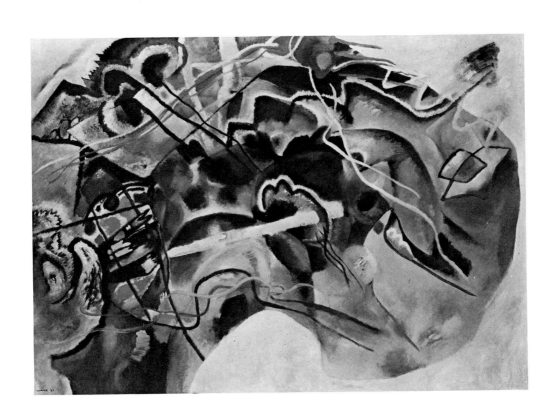

ASILY KANDINSKY

cture with White Edge, No.173. 1913

il on canvas, 55³/₈ x 79″ (140.7 x 200.7 cm.)

gned and dated l.l. "Kandinsky 1913"

ovenance:
llection Kluxen (see *Rückblicke*, 1913)
lomon R. Guggenheim, New York
ft, Solomon R. Guggenheim, 1937

khibitions:
R STURM, Berlin, September–November 1913,
ster Deutscher Herbstsalon, no.182

ILADELPHIA ART ALLIANCE, February 8–28, 1937,
*lomon R. Guggenheim Collection of Non-Objective
intings*, no.76, p.75, ill.

BBES MEMORIAL ART GALLERY, Charleston, South
arolina, March 7–April 7, 1938, *Solomon R. Guggenheim
llection of Non-Objective Paintings*, no.76, p.75, ill.

USEUM OF NON-OBJECTIVE PAINTING, New York,
arch 15–May 15, 1945, *In Memory of Wassily Kandinsky*,
.24

ARNEGIE INSTITUTE (Department of Fine Arts),
tsburgh, April 11–May 12, 1946, *Memorial Exhibition
Paintings by Wassily Kandinsky 1866–1944*, no.3, ill.

IE SOLOMON R. GUGGENHEIM MUSEUM, New York,
bruary 3–May 3, 1953, *A Selection* (Checklist)

IE SOLOMON R. GUGGENHEIM MUSEUM, New York,
ay 13–October 11, 1953, *Selection II* (Checklist)

T GALLERY OF TORONTO, April 2–May 9, 1954, *A Loan
hibition of Paintings from The Solomon R. Guggenheim
useum*, no.21

NCOUVER ART GALLERY, November 16–December 12,
54, *The Solomon R. Guggenheim Museum, A Selection
m the Museum Collection*, no.19, ill.

N FRANCISCO MUSEUM OF ART, June 17–July 10, 1955,
t in the Twentieth Century, p.14

IE SOLOMON R. GUGGENHEIM MUSEUM, New York,
ly 26–October 9, 1955, *Selection V* (Checklist)

DENVER ART MUSEUM, October 1–November 18, 1956,
Turn of the Century, no.16

TATE GALLERY, London, April 16–May 26, 1957, *Paint-
ings from The Solomon R. Guggenheim Museum*, no.30;
organized by THE SOLOMON R. GUGGENHEIM MUSEUM,
traveled to GEMEENTEMUSEUM, The Hague, June 25–
September 1; ATENEIUMIN TAIDEKOKOELMAT, Helsinki,
September 27–October 20; GALLERIA NAZIONALE D'ARTE
MODERNA, Rome, December 5, 1957–January 8, 1958;
WALLRAF-RICHARTZ-MUSEUM, Cologne, January 26–
March 30; MUSÉE DES ARTS DÉCORATIFS, Paris,
April 23–June 1, 1958

THE SOLOMON R. GUGGENHEIM MUSEUM, New York,
October 21, 1959–June 19, 1960, *Inaugural Selection
(Kandinsky Galleries)* (Checklist)

PHILADELPHIA MUSEUM OF ART, November 2, 1961–
January 7, 1962, *Guggenheim Museum Exhibition, A Loan
Collection of Paintings, Drawings, and Prints from The
Solomon R. Guggenheim Museum, New York*, no.52

SEATTLE WORLD'S FAIR, April 21–September 4, 1962,
Masterpieces of Modern Art, no.59, ill.

THE SOLOMON R. GUGGENHEIM MUSEUM, New York, 1963,
Kandinsky, p.32, ill.

THE SOLOMON R. GUGGENHEIM MUSEUM, New York,
Kandinsky, Selections from the Collection, April 19–
September 1966; November 1966–February 27, 1967;
October 8, 1968–January 12, 1969; February 14–March 9,
1969; July 8–September 14, 1969; October 12–
December, 1969; January 19– February 8, 1970

References:
KANDINSKY, VASILY, *Kandinsky Album, Rückblicke 1901–1913*,
Berlin, 1913, p.13, ill., pp.XXXIX–XXXXI, commentary

KANDINSKY, VASILY, *On the Spiritual in Art*, New York,
1946, p.116, ill.

GROHMANN, WILL, *Wassily Kandinsky, Life and Work*,
New York, 1958, p.332, CC 90, ill.

LANKHEIT, KLAUS, "Kandinsky et Franz Marc", *XXe
Siècle*, no.XXVII, December 1966, p.32, ill.

37.245

VASILY KANDINSKY

Painting with White Form, No.166 (Bild mit Weisser Form, No.166). 1913

Oil on canvas, 47³/₈ x 55¹/₈″ (120.3 x 140 cm.)

Inscribed l.l. "KANDINSKY 1913" and on reverse "Bild mit Weisser Form 1913 Bild No.166"

Provenance:

the artist, 1913
Herwarth Walden, Berlin
Otto Rolfs, Braunschweig
Rudolf Bauer, Berlin, 1937

Exhibitions:

DER STURM, Berlin, September –November 1913, *Erster Deutscher Herbstsalon*, no.185

GIBBES MEMORIAL ART GALLERY, Charleston, South Carolina, March 7–April 7, 1938, *Solomon R. Guggenheim Collection of Non-Objective Paintings* (as *Light Form*), no.104, p.91, ill.

BALTIMORE MUSEUM OF ART, January 6–29, 1939, *Solomon R. Guggenheim Collection of Non-Objective Paintings,* ill.

MUSEUM OF NON-OBJECTIVE PAINTING, New York, March 15–May 15, 1945, *In Memory of Wassily Kandinsky*, no.19 (as *Light Form 1912*)

INSTITUTE OF CONTEMPORARY ART, Boston, March 27–April 27, 1952, *Vasily Kandinsky*; traveled to M. KNOEDLER & CO., INC., New York, May 10–June 6; SAN FRANCISCO MUSEUM OF ART, July 20–August 26; WALKER ART CENTER, Minneapolis, September 14–October 26; CLEVELAND MUSEUM OF ART, Ohio, November 6–December 7, 1952 (hereinafter cited as INSTITUTE OF CONTEMPORARY ART, Boston, 1952, *Kandinsky*)

THE SOLOMON R. GUGGENHEIM MUSEUM, New York, May 13–October 11, 1953, *Selection II* (as *Light Form, No.166*, 1913) (Checklist)

ADDISON GALLERY OF AMERICAN ART, Andover, Massachusetts, January 8–February 15, 1954, *Variations* (as *Light Form,* 1913)

TWEED GALLERY, UNIVERSITY OF MINNESOTA, Duluth, December 1–31, 1954, *Object of the Month Exhibition*

PALAIS DES BEAUX-ARTS, Brussels, 1957, *Kandinsky*, no.14, ill.

ART GALLERY OF TORONTO, April 24–May 24, 1959, *45 Kandinskys from The Solomon R. Guggenheim Museum*

MUSEUM OF FINE ARTS, Boston, October 30–December 13, 1959, *A Salute to the Guggenheim, 75 Selected Works*

CLEVELAND MUSEUM OF ART, Ohio, October 4–November 13, 1960, *Paths of Abstract Art*, no.31, ill.

PHILADELPHIA MUSEUM OF ART, November 2, 1961–January 7, 1962, *Guggenheim Museum Exhibition, A Loan Collection of Paintings, Drawings, and Prints from The Solomon R. Guggenheim Museum, New York*, no.51

GALERIE MAEGHT, Paris, October 26–November 1962, *Der Blaue Reiter* (Catalogue published as *Derrière Le Miroir*, nos.133–134, October-November 1962) p.16, ill.

THE SOLOMON R. GUGGENHEIM MUSEUM, New York, 1963, *Kandinsky*, no.31, p.57, ill.

THE SOLOMON R. GUGGENHEIM MUSEUM, New York, July 1–September 13, 1964, *Van Gogh and Expressionism*

SIDNEY JANIS GALLERY, New York, November 24–December 26, 1964, *3 Generations*, no.11, ill.

MUSEUM OF FINE ARTS, St. Petersburg, Florida, February 6–March 6, 1965, *Inaugural Exhibition*

THE SOLOMON R. GUGGENHEIM MUSEUM, New York, *Kandinsky, Selections from the Collection*, April 19–September 1966; November 1966–February 27, 1967

MUSEO NACIONAL DE BELLAS ARTES, Buenos Aires, May 15–June 5, 1968, *De Cézanne à Miró*, p.46, ill.; organized by the International Council of THE MUSEUM OF MODERN ART, New York; traveled to MUSEO DE ARTE CONTEMPORANEO DE LA UNIVERSIDAD DE CHILE, Santiago, June 26–July 17, 1968; MUSEO DE BELLAS ARTES, Caracas, August 4–25, 1968

THE SOLOMON R. GUGGENHEIM MUSEUM, New York, *Kandinsky, Selections from the Collection,* October 8, 1968–January 12, 1969; February 14–March 19; October 12–November 1969

References:

KANDINSKY, VASILY, *Kandinsky Album, Rückblicke 1901–1913*, Berlin, 1913, pl.7

BAHR, HERMANN, *Expressionismus*, Munich, 1920, pl. opp. p.120 (as *Bild mit Weisser Form*, Sammlung Herwarth Walden, Berlin)

BURGER, FRITZ, *Cézanne und Hodler*, Munich, 1923, no.17, ill.

GROHMANN, WILL, "Wassily Kandinsky", *Cahiers d'art*, 4th year, no.7, 1929, p.25

GROHMANN, WILL, *Wassily Kandinsky, Life and Work*, New York, 1958, p.138, CC 166, ill.

READ, HERBERT, *The Origins of Form in Art*, New York, 1965, no.53, p.184, ill.

OVERY, PAUL, *Kandinsky, The Language of the Eye*, New York, 1969, no.25, ill.

37.240

Painting with White Form and *Picture with White Edge,* both painted in 1913, are similar in many respects. By studying the oil sketch (Grohmann, CC 84) for *Painting with White Form* and a preliminary watercolor (Grohmann, p.94), it is possible to trace the landscape origins in this now abstract tumult of lines and colored forms. Kandinsky's description of *Picture with White Edge* in his *Reminiscences* clarifies its landscape origins: "…at the lower left an abyss, a white wave rising from it, which falls suddenly, and then encloses the right side of the

painting in a lazily winding form, traces a lake at the
upper right, and disappears at the upper left corner in
order to emerge one last time and definitively as a white
zig zag. Since this border was the solution of the
problem, I named the whole painting after it". (*Kandinsky
Album, Rückblicke*, Berlin, 1913, p.xxxxi, translated by
Grohmann).

The "white edge" in the canvas described, and the
"white form" in its companion piece serve comparable
purposes. The white in each of these works comes toward

the viewer, in contrast to the gradually darkening forms
which recede, spiraling into space. The bar – black in
one, white in the other – slashing across the surface in
both works leads the eye back to the front plane.

Kandinsky warns against over-interpretation, but the
sense of turmoil and restlessness implicit in both works
recall the themes of destruction which began to appear in
his paintings of 1912 and 1913.

187

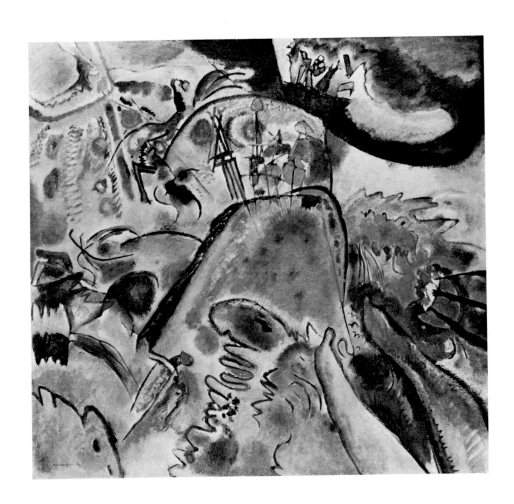

Little Pleasures, No.174 (Kleine Freuden, No.174;
Petites Joies, No.174). 1913

Oil on canvas, 43½ x 47½" (110.5 x 120.6 cm.)

Inscribed l.r. "Kandinsky 1913" and on reverse
"Kandinsky Kleine Freuden (1913) No.174"

Provenance:
The artist, 1913
W. Beffie, Amsterdam
Nierendorf Gallery, New York, 1943

Exhibitions:
DER STURM, Berlin, 1913
NEW BURLINGTON GALLERIES, London, 1938,
Twentieth-Century German Art
NIERENDORF GALLERY, New York, December 1942–
February 1943, *Kandinsky Retrospective*
MUSEUM OF NON-OBJECTIVE PAINTING, New York,
March 15–May 15, 1945, *In Memory of Wassily Kandinsky,*
no.21
CARNEGIE INSTITUTE (Department of Fine Arts),
Pittsburgh, April 11–May 12, 1946, *Memorial Exhibition of*
Paintings by Wassily Kandinsky 1866–1944, no.17
HAUS DER KUNST, Munich, September–October 1949, *Der*
Blaue Reiter, no.67, p.26, ill.
MUSEUM OF NON-OBJECTIVE PAINTING, New York,
opening April 29, 1952, *Evolution to Non-Objectivity,*
no.71 (as *Small Pleasures*)
THE SOLOMON R. GUGGENHEIM MUSEUM, New York,
October 6, 1954–February 27, 1955, *Selection IV* (as *Small*
Pleasures, No.179) (Checklist)
PALAIS DES BEAUX-ARTS, Brussels, 1957, *Kandinsky,* no.12,
ill. (*Petits Plaisirs, No.179*)
ART GALLERY OF TORONTO, April 24–May 24, 1959,
45 Kandinskys from The Solomon R. Guggenheim Museum
MUSEUM OF FINE ARTS, Boston, October 30–December 13,
1959, *A Salute to The Guggenheim, 75 Selected Works*
THE SOLOMON R. GUGGENHEIM MUSEUM, New York,
March 30, 1960–September 29, 1961, *Inaugural Selection*
(Kandinsky Galleries) (Checklist)
THE SOLOMON R. GUGGENHEIM MUSEUM, New York, 1963,
Kandinsky, no.33, p.59, ill.
THE SOLOMON R. GUGGENHEIM MUSEUM, New York,
Kandinsky, Selections from the Collection, April 19–
September 1966; November 1966–February 27, 1967
THE SOLOMON R. GUGGENHEIM MUSEUM, New York,
April 11–May 26, 1968, *Acquisitions of the 1930's and 1940's,*
pp.80–81, ill.
THE SOLOMON R. GUGGENHEIM MUSEUM, New York,
Kandinsky, Selections from the Collection, October 8, 1968–
January 12, 1969; February 14–March 9; July 8–Sep-
tember 14; October 12–December 15, 1969; January 19–
February 8, 1970

References:
KANDINSKY, VASILY, *Kandinsky Album, Rückblicke 1901–*
1913, Berlin, 1913, pl.6
GROHMANN, WILL, "Kandinsky", *Cahiers d'art,* 1930,
p.10, no.12, ill.
KANDINSKY, VASILY, *On the Spiritual in Art,* New York,
1946, p.155, ill.
GROHMANN, WILL, *Wassily Kandinsky, Life and Work,*
New York, 1958, no.174, p.137, ill.
ROBBINS, DANIEL, "Vasily Kandinsky: Abstraction and
Image", *College Art Journal,* vol.XXII, no.3, Spring 1963,
fig.4
DOLEMAN, CORNELIUS, *Wassily Kandinsky,* New York,
1964, no.37, p.37, ill.

43.921

Improvisation 21a, 1911 and the glass painting *Small*
Pleasures, c.1912 (Collection Städtische Galerie im
Lenbachhaus, Munich) contain the same motifs as *Little*
Pleasures of 1913. From the earlier works one can
decipher mountains, a domed city, three galloping
horsemen, a couple at the lower left and three rowers
in a boat to the lower right. According to Dr. Hans
Konrad Röthel (*Kandinsky Glass Painting,* The Solomon
R. Guggenheim Museum, December 1966–February
1967, no.19), rowing, loving and riding were the
"pleasures" depicted in Kandinsky's work.

Black Lines, No.189. 1913

Oil on canvas, 51¼ x 51³⁄₈″ (130.2 x 130.5 cm.)

Inscribed l.l. "Kandinsky 1913" and on reverse
"Kandinsky Schwarze Linien (1913) no.189"

Provenance:
Solomon R. Guggenheim, New York
Gift, Solomon R. Guggenheim, 1937

Exhibitions:

GALERIE THANNHAUSER, Munich, 1914, *Kandinsky Exhibition*

GIBBES MEMORIAL ART GALLERY, Charleston, South
Carolina, March 1–April 12, 1936, *Solomon R. Guggenheim Collection of Non-Objective Paintings*, no.69, p.47, ill.

PHILADELPHIA ART ALLIANCE, February 8–28, 1937, *Solomon R. Guggenheim Collection of Non-Objective Paintings*, no.79, p.71, ill.

GIBBES MEMORIAL ART GALLERY, Charleston, South
Carolina, March 7–April 7, 1938, *Solomon R. Guggenheim Collection of Non-Objective Paintings*, no.190, p.93, ill.

BALTIMORE MUSEUM OF ART, January 6–29, 1939, *Solomon R. Guggenheim Collection of Non-Objective Paintings*

SOLOMON R. GUGGENHEIM FOUNDATION, New York, June 1, 1939, *Art of Tomorrow*, (Fifth Catalogue of the Solomon R. Guggenheim Collection of Non-Objective Paintings), p.127, no.154

MUSEUM OF NON-OBJECTIVE PAINTING, New York,
March 15–May 15, 1945, *In Memory of Wassily Kandinsky*, no.27 and frontispiece

MUSÉE NATIONAL D'ART MODERNE, Paris, May–June 1952, *L'œuvre du XXe siècle*; traveled to TATE GALLERY, London, July 15–August 17, 1952, as *XXth Century Masterpieces*, no.37, pl.v

THE SOLOMON R. GUGGENHEIM MUSEUM, New York,
February 3–May 3, 1953, *A Selection* (Checklist)

THE SOLOMON R. GUGGENHEIM MUSEUM, New York,
October 6, 1954–March 13, 1955, *Selection IV* (Checklist)

THE SOLOMON R. GUGGENHEIM MUSEUM, New York,
September 12–October 9, 1955, *Selection V* (Checklist)

THE SOLOMON R. GUGGENHEIM MUSEUM, New York,
January 24–May 1, 1956, *Selection VI* (Checklist)

TATE GALLERY, London, April 16–May 26, 1957, *Paintings from The Solomon R. Guggenheim Museum*, no.30; organized by THE SOLOMON R. GUGGENHEIM MUSEUM, traveled to GEMEENTEMUSEUM, The Hague, June 25–September 1; ATENEIUMIN TAIDEKOKOELMAT, Helsinki, September 27–October 20; GALLERIA NAZIONALE D'ARTE MODERNA, Rome, December 5, 1957–January 8, 1958, no.45, ill.; WALLRAF-RICHARTZ-MUSEUM, Cologne, January 26–March 30; MUSÉE DES ARTS DÉCORATIFS, Paris, April 23–June 1, 1958

THE SOLOMON R. GUGGENHEIM MUSEUM, New York,
October 21, 1959–June 19, 1960, *Inaugural Selection (Kandinsky Galleries)* (Checklist)

PHILADELPHIA MUSEUM OF ART, November 2, 1961–January 7, 1962, *Guggenheim Museum Exhibition, A Loan Collection of Paintings, Drawings, and Prints from The Solomon R. Guggenheim Museum, New York*, no.53

THE SOLOMON R. GUGGENHEIM MUSEUM, New York, 1963, *Kandinsky*, no.35, p.65, ill.

MARLBOROUGH-GERSON GALLERY, New York, November 12–December 27, 1963, *Artists and Maecenas; A Tribute to Curt Valentin*, not in catalogue (Substituted for a work illustrated in catalogue)

THE SOLOMON R. GUGGENHEIM MUSEUM, New York,
July 1–September 13, 1964, *Van Gogh and Expressionism*

THE SOLOMON R. GUGGENHEIM MUSEUM, New York,
Kandinsky, Selection from the Collection, April 19–June 1966

THE SOLOMON R. GUGGENHEIM MUSEUM, New York,
June 23–October 23, 1966, *Gauguin and the Decorative Style*

THE SOLOMON R. GUGGENHEIM MUSEUM, New York,
June 28–October 1, 1967, *Museum Collection, Seven Decades, A Selection* (Checklist)

THE METROPOLITAN MUSEUM OF ART, New York,
November 15, 1967–April 1, 1968, *Selections from the Collection of The Solomon R. Guggenheim Museum*

THE SOLOMON R. GUGGENHEIM MUSEUM, New York,
April 11–May 26, 1968, *Acquisitions of the 1930's and 1940's*, p.14, ill.

THE SOLOMON R. GUGGENHEIM MUSEUM, New York,
Kandinsky, Selections from the Collection, October 8, 1968–January 1969; February 14–March 9; March 28–May 11; July 8–September 14; October 13–December 1969; January 19–February 8, 1970

References:

REBAY, HILLA, *Innovation*, Paris, 1937, p.55, ill.

KANDINSKY, VASILY, *On the Spiritual in Art*, New York, 1946, cover ill.

GROHMANN, WILL, *Wassily Kandinsky, Life and Work*, New York, 1958, no.189, p.141, ill.

BRION, MARCEL, *Kandinsky*, London, 1961, p.37, ill.

DOLEMAN, CORNELIUS, *Wassily Kandinsky*, New York, 1964, p.36, ill.

LASSAIGNE, JACQUES, *Kandinsky*, Geneva, 1964, p.72, ill.

KUH, KATHERINE, *Break-up: The Core of Modern Art*, Greenwich, Connecticut, 1965, p.97, no.66

HAMILTON, GEORGE HEARD, *Painting and Sculpture in Europe 1880–1940*, Harmondsworth, 1967, pl.72B

ROSENBERG, HAROLD, *Artworks and Packages*, New York, 1969, p.91, ill.

OVERY, PAUL, *Kandinsky, The Language of the Eye*, New York, 1969, no.24, ill.

37.241

VASILY KANDINSKY

Light Picture, No.188 (Heller Bild). 1913

Oil on canvas, 30³/₄ x 39¹/₂″ (76.2 x 100.4 cm.)

Signed and dated l.l. "Kandinsky 1913"

Provenance:
Collection Kluxen
Solomon R. Guggenheim, New York
Gift, Solomon R. Guggenheim, 1937

Exhibitions:
GALERIE THANNHAUSER, Munich, 1914, *Kandinsky Exhibition*

GIBBES MEMORIAL ART GALLERY, Charleston, South Carolina, March 1–April 12, 1936, *Solomon R. Guggenheim Collection of Non-Objective Paintings*, no.68

THE MUSEUM OF MODERN ART, New York, December 7, 1936–January 17, 1937, *Fantastic Art, Dada, and Surrealism*, no.55

PHILADELPHIA ART ALLIANCE, February 8–28, 1937, *Solomon R. Guggenheim Collection of Non-Objective Paintings*, no.77, ill.

GIBBES MEMORIAL ART GALLERY, Charleston, South Carolina, March 7–April 7, 1938, *Solomon R. Guggenheim Collection of Non-Objective Paintings*, no.107, p.107, ill.

MUSEUM OF NON-OBJECTIVE PAINTING, New York, March 15–May 15, 1945, *In Memory of Wassily Kandinsky*, no.28, p.12, ill.

THE SOLOMON R. GUGGENHEIM MUSEUM, New York, February 3–May 3, 1953, *A Selection* (Checklist)

THE SOLOMON R. GUGGENHEIM MUSEUM, New York, May 13–October 11, 1953, *Selection II* (Checklist)

VANCOUVER ART GALLERY, November 16–December 12, 1954, *The Solomon R. Guggenheim Museum, A Selection from the Museum Collection*, no.20

INSTITUTE OF CONTEMPORARY ART, Boston, March 9–April 17, 1955, *Selection from The Solomon R. Guggenheim Museum Collection*

PALAIS DES BEAUX-ARTS, Brussels, 1957, *Kandinsky*, no.13, ill.

UNIVERSITY OF INDIANA, Bloomington, October 1–22, 1958, *German Expressionist Art*

ART GALLERY OF TORONTO, April 24–May 24, 1959, *45 Kandinskys from The Solomon R. Guggenheim Museum*

THE SOLOMON R. GUGGENHEIM MUSEUM, New York, October 21, 1959–March 8, 1960, *Inaugural Selection (Kandinsky Galleries)* (Checklist)

UNIVERSITY OF KENTUCKY, Lexington, May 8–June 18, 1960, *European Paintings from The Solomon R. Guggenheim Museum*, no.11

COUNCIL OF EUROPE, MUSÉE NATIONAL D'ART MODERNE, Paris, November 9, 1960–January 23, 1961, *Les Sources du XXe Siècle, Les Arts en Europe de 1884 à 1914*, no.294

THE SOLOMON R. GUGGENHEIM MUSEUM, New York, April 30–September 1, 1965, *Paintings from the Collection of The Solomon R. Guggenheim Museum*, no.29, ill.

PASADENA ART MUSEUM, 1963, *Kandinsky*, no.23, ill.

THE SOLOMON R. GUGGENHEIM MUSEUM, New York, *Kandinsky, Selection from the Collection*, April 19–September 1966

THE SOLOMON R. GUGGENHEIM MUSEUM, New York, April 11–May 26, 1968, *Acquisitions of the 1930's and 1940's*, p.16, ill.

THE SOLOMON R. GUGGENHEIM MUSEUM, New York, *Kandinsky, Selections from the Collection*, October 8–January 12, 1969; February 14–March 9; July 8–September 14; October 12–December 1969; January 19–February 8, 1970

References:
GROHMANN, WILL, *Wassily Kandinsky*, Leipzig, 1924, (Junge Kunst, Band 42) ill.

GROHMANN, WILL, "Kandinsky", *Cahiers d'art*, 1930, p.14, no.16, ill.

GROHMANN, WILL, *Wassily Kandinsky, Life and Work*, New York, 1958, no.188, CC 100

READ, HERBERT, *Kandinsky*, London, 1959, p.10, pl.2

37.244

Dissimilar to the forebodings of war felt in *Picture with White Edge* and *Painting with White Form* are the bright and airy atmospheres of *Black Lines* and *Light Picture* of the same year. Grohmann compares them to celestial landscapes filled with astral forms. He also notes that they are reminiscent of Oriental paintings in India ink, suggesting, in the case of *Black Lines*, "exotic flowers" floating on water. (Grohmann, *Kandinsky*, New York, 1958, p.138)

VASILY KANDINSKY

Untitled, No.24. c.1914

Watercolor, $15^3/_4$ x $14^1/_4''$ (40 x 36.2 cm.)

Signed with monogram l.r. "vк"

Provenance:

Hildegarde Prytek, Rego Park, New York, 1947

Exhibitions:

THE SOLOMON R. GUGGENHEIM MUSEUM, New York,
January 24–May 1, 1956, *Selection VI* (Checklist)

PALAIS DES BEAUX-ARTS, Brussels, 1957, *Kandinsky,* no.17,
ill.

ART GALLERY OF TORONTO, April 24–May 24, 1959,
45 Kandinskys from The Solomon R. Guggenheim Museum

THE SOLOMON R. GUGGENHEIM MUSEUM, New York,
March 30–June 19, 1960, *Inaugural Selection, (Kandinsky
Galleries)* (Checklist)

PHILADELPHIA MUSEUM OF ART, November 2, 1961–
January 7, 1962, *Guggenheim Museum Exhibition, A Loan
Collection of Paintings, Drawings, and Prints from The
Solomon R. Guggenheim Museum, New York,* no.56

THE SOLOMON R. GUGGENHEIM MUSEUM, New York,
1963, *Kandinsky,* watercolor no.3

THE SOLOMON R. GUGGENHEIM MUSEUM, New York,
Kandinsky, Selections from the Collection, April 19–
September 1966; November 1966–February 27, 1967

THE SOLOMON R. GUGGENHEIM MUSEUM, New York,
April 11–May 26, 1968, *Acquisitions of the 1930's and 1940's,*
p.96, ill.

THE SOLOMON R. GUGGENHEIM MUSEUM, New York,
October 8, 1968–January 12, 1969, *Kandinsky, Selection
from the Collection*

THE SOLOMON R. GUGGENHEIM MUSEUM, New York,
July 8–September 14, 1969, *Selected Sculpture and Works
on Paper,* p.32, ill.

THE SOLOMON R. GUGGENHEIM MUSEUM, New York,
October 12–December 22, 1969, *Kandinsky, Selection
from the Collection*

41.1057

Although more clearly readable as a landscape, this
watercolor is comparable in color and tone to *Light
Picture* and *Black Lines.* The heavy blue of the sky sets off
the softer hues of the scene below. Compositionally,
Untitled, No.24 is related to *Painting with White Edge.*

VASILY KANDINSKY

Painting No.198 (Autumn; Intense Souvenir; Painting; Tableau; Composition). 1914

Oil on canvas, 64 x 48¼" (162.5 x 122.5 cm.)

Signed with monogram and dated l.l. "VK//1914"

Provenance:
the artist, 1914
Edwin R. Campbell, New York
Murray Hoffman, Palm Beach, Florida
James St. L. O'Toole, New York, 1941

Exhibitions:
GUMMESSON GALLERY, Stockholm, February 1916,
Kandinsky Exhibition

MUSEUM OF NON-OBJECTIVE PAINTING, New York,
March 15–May 15, 1945, *In Memory of Wassily Kandinsky*,
no.31, p.15, ill. (as *Souvenir* 1914)

THE SOLOMON R. GUGGENHEIM MUSEUM, New York,
March 30–May 5, 1954, *Selection III* (Checklist)

VANCOUVER ART GALLERY, November 16–December 12,
1954, *The Solomon R. Guggenheim Museum, A Selection
from the Museum Collection*, no.21

THE MUSEUM OF MODERN ART, New York, May 23–
August 3, 1956, *Kandinsky Murals Re-United After 25 Years*

PALAIS DES BEAUX-ARTS, Brussels, 1957, *Kandinsky*, no.15
(as *Composition* 1914)

ART GALLERY OF TORONTO, April 24–May 24, 1959,
45 Kandinskys from The Solomon R. Guggenheim Museum

THE SOLOMON R. GUGGENHEIM MUSEUM, New York,
October 21, 1959–September 29, 1961, *Inaugural
Selection, (Kandinsky Galleries)* (Checklist)

PHILADELPHIA MUSEUM OF ART, November 2, 1961–
January 7, 1962, *Guggenheim Museum Exhibition, A Loan
Collection of Paintings, Drawings, and Prints from The Solo-
mon R. Guggenheim Museum, New York*, no.54

THE SOLOMON R. GUGGENHEIM MUSEUM, New York, 1963,
Kandinsky, no.41, p.62, ill.

THE SOLOMON R. GUGGENHEIM MUSEUM, New York,
April 30–September 1, 1965, *Paintings from the Collection
of The Solomon R. Guggenheim Museum*, no.36, ill.

THE SOLOMON R. GUGGENHEIM MUSEUM, New York,
Kandinsky, Selections from the Collection, April 19–
September 1966; November 1966–January 1967

KUNSTHALLE, Hamburg, January 4–September 6, 1967
(Exchange for Klee loan)

THE SOLOMON R. GUGGENHEIM MUSEUM, New York,
April 11–May 26, 1968, *Acquisitions of the 1930's and 1940's*
p.77, ill.

THE SOLOMON R. GUGGENHEIM MUSEUM, New York,
Kandinsky, Selections from the Collection, October 8, 1968–
January 12, 1969; February 14–March 9; March 28–
May 11; July 8–September 14; October 12–December 22
1969; January 19–February 8, 1970

References:
ESTIENNE, CHARLES, *Kandinsky*, Paris, 1950, p.7

LINDSAY, KENNETH, "Kandinsky in 1914 New York:
Solving a Riddle," *Art News*, vol.55, no.3, May 1956,
pp.32, 58–60, p.33, ill.

GROHMANN, WILL, *Wassily Kandinsky, Life and Work*,
New York, 1958, CC 198, p.281, p.142, ill.

BUCHHEIM, LOTHAR-GÜNTHER. *Der Blaue Reiter*, Germany,
1959, p.125, ill.

KROLL, JACK, "Kandinsky: Last of the Heresiarchs", *Art
News*, February 1963, p.40, ill.

KRAMER, HILTON, "The Guggenheim Retrospective Raises
Questions Concerning Kandinsky's Contribution as
Artist and Theoretician", *Artforum*, vol.1, no.11, May
1963, pp.21–27, ill.

DOLEMAN, CORNELIUS, *Kandinsky*, New York, 1964, p.75,
p.39, ill.

ARNASON, H. H., *History of Modern Art*, New York, 1968,
p.192, no.60, ill.

41.869

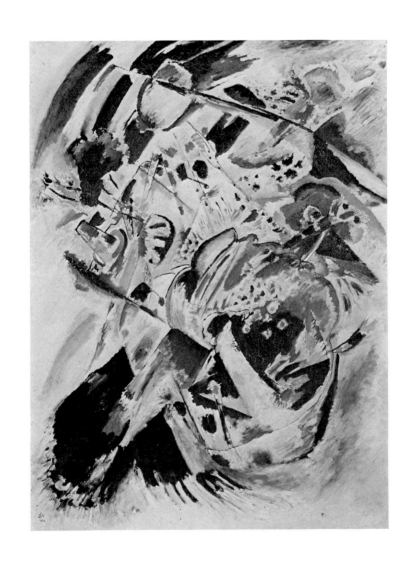

VASILY KANDINSKY

Painting No.199 (Winter; Enchantment; Carnival; Composition). 1914

Oil on canvas, $64^1/_4$ x $48^3/_8''$ (163.2 x 122.8 cm.)

Signed with monogram and dated l.l. "VK//1914"

Provenance:
the artist, 1914
Edwin R. Campbell, New York
Murray Hoffman, Palm Beach, Florida
James St. L. O'Toole, New York, 1941

Exhibitions:
GUMMESSON GALLERY, Stockholm, February 1916, *Kandinsky Exhibition*

MUSEUM OF NON-OBJECTIVE PAINTING, New York, March 15–May 15, 1945, *In Memory of Wassily Kandinsky*, no.30, p.14, ill. (as *Carnival*)

ART GALLERY OF TORONTO, April 2–May 9, 1954, *A Loan Exhibition of Paintings from The Solomon R. Guggenheim Museum*, no.22 (as *Composition 1914*)

THE MUSEUM OF MODERN ART, New York, May 23–August 3, 1956, *Kandinsky Murals Re-United after 25 years*

WORLD HOUSE GALLERIES, New York, January 22–February 23, 1957, *The Struggle for New Form* (Loan Exhibition for the benefit of Just One Break, Inc.), no.55 (as *Composition 1914*)

PALAIS DES BEAUX-ARTS, Brussels, 1957, *Kandinsky*, no.16 (as *Composition 1914*)

ART GALLERY OF TORONTO, April 24–May 24, 1959, *45 Kandinskys from The Solomon R. Guggenheim Museum*

THE SOLOMON R. GUGGENHEIM MUSEUM, New York, October 21, 1959–September 29, 1961, *Inaugural Selection, (Kandinsky Galleries)* (Checklist)

PHILADELPHIA MUSEUM OF ART, November 2, 1961–January 7, 1962, *Guggenheim Museum Exhibition, A Loan Collection of Paintings, Drawings, and Prints from The Solomon R. Guggenheim Museum*, no.55

THE SOLOMON R. GUGGENHEIM MUSEUM, New York, 1963, *Kandinsky*, no.42, p.63, ill.

BALTIMORE MUSEUM OF ART, October 6–November 15, 1964, *1914*, no.100, p.79, ill.

THE SOLOMON R. GUGGENHEIM MUSEUM, New York, July 1–September 13, 1964, *Van Gogh and Expressionism*

THE SOLOMON R. GUGGENHEIM MUSEUM, New York, April 30–September 1, 1965, *Paintings from the Collection of The Solomon R. Guggenheim Museum*, no.37, p.39, ill.

THE SOLOMON R. GUGGENHEIM MUSEUM, New York, *Kandinsky, Selections from the Collection*, April 19–September 1966; November 1966–January 1967

KUNSTHALLE, Hamburg, January 4–September 6, 1967 (Exchange for Klee Loan)

THE SOLOMON R. GUGGENHEIM MUSEUM, New York, April 11–May 26, 1968, *Acquisitions of the 1930's and 1940's*, p.76, ill.

THE SOLOMON R. GUGGENHEIM MUSEUM, New York, *Kandinsky, Selections from the Collection*, February 14–March 9, 1969; July 8–September 14; October 12–December 22, 1969; January 19–February 8, 1970

References:
ESTIENNE, CHARLES, *Kandinsky*, Paris, 1950, p.7

LINDSAY, KENNETH, "Kandinsky in 1914 New York: Solving a Riddle", *Art News*, vol.55, no.3, May 1956, pp.32, 58–60

GROHMANN, WILL, *Wassily Kandinsky, Life and Work*, New York, 1958, CC 199, p.281, p.142, ill.

READ, HERBERT, *Kandinsky*, London, 1959, p.12, pl.3

KROLL, JACK, "Kandinsky: Last of the Heresiarchs", *Art News*, February 1963, p.40, ill.

SOUPAULT-NIEMEYER, RE., "Du Cheval au Cercle", *XXe Siècle*, no.XXVII, December 1966, p.37, ill.

ARNASON, H. H., *History of Modern Art*, New York, 1968, p.182, pl.61

41.868

In 1914 Edwin R. Campbell, at Arthur Jerome Eddy's suggestion, commissioned four panels for the foyer of his Park Avenue apartment. It seems probable that two of the panels were thought of as *Autumn* and *Winter* and the other slightly narrower pair, as *Spring* and *Summer*. (The second pair is now in the Collection of The Museum of Modern Art, New York). The size of these four canvases conforms exactly to the panels in Mr. Campbell's circular vestibule, leaving a seven inch margin between the paintings and the molding.

Grohmann feels that Kandinsky would have considered the paintings *Improvisations*. Kenneth Lindsay, in *Art News* of May 1956, concluded that these works are probably renditions of the four seasons, but the earlier titles of *Souvenir* and *Carnival* leave other interpretations open.

VASILY KANDINSKY

Untitled. 1916

Watercolor and ink, 18⁷/₈ x 19¹/₈″ (47.8 x 48.5 cm.)

Signed with monogram and dated c.l. "vκ//16"

Provenance:
Hildegarde Prytek, Rego Park, New York, 1947

Exhibitions:
THE SOLOMON R. GUGGENHEIM MUSEUM, New York, 1963,
Kandinsky, no.5

THE SOLOMON R. GUGGENHEIM MUSEUM, New York,
April 11–May 26, 1968, *Acquisitions of the 1930's and 1940's,*
p.97, ill.

THE SOLOMON R. GUGGENHEIM MUSEUM, New York,
Kandinsky, Selections from the Collection, February 14–
March 9, 1969; July 8–September 14; October 12–
December 1969; January 19–February 8, 1970

47.1058

This diamond-shaped watercolor containing both
Biedermeier motifs and oriental qualities is probably
related to the artist's "Trifles", a series of 14 Biedermeier
watercolors entitled *Birds, Horsemen, Lady in Crinoline,*
executed in Stockholm early in 1916. Kandinsky also
made 17 glass paintings in Moscow in 1917, which
convey a similar mood.

VASILY KANDINSKY

Untitled. 1918

Watercolor and ink, 11 3/8 x 9″ (28.7 x 22.9 cm.)

Signed with monogram and dated l.l. "VK//18"

Provenance:

Livraria Askanasy Ltda., Rio de Janeiro, 1949

Exhibitions:

THE SOLOMON R. GUGGENHEIM MUSEUM, New York,
October 3–November 12, 1961, *Elements of Modern
Painting*; circulated by THE AMERICAN FEDERATION OF ARTS,
July 1962–September 1963 as *Elements of Modern Art*

PASADENA ART MUSEUM, 1963, *Vasily Kandinsky*, watercolor no.4

THE SOLOMON R. GUGGENHEIM MUSEUM, New York,
July 8–September 14, 1969, *Selected Sculpture and Works
on Paper*, p.33, ill.

THE SOLOMON R. GUGGENHEIM MUSEUM, New York,
Kandinsky, Selections from the Collection, October 12–
December 1969; January 19–February 8, 1970

49.1236

"Between November 9, 1917, when the Bolsheviks
seized power, and July 1919, for more than a year and a
half, Kandinsky did not produce a single painting; but
between 1915 and 1919 he did produce a number of
drawings, watercolors, and paintings on glass... Most of
the watercolors executed in this period date from 1918...
They seem to be varied in style, having little in common
with each other unless it is a somewhat more marked
cheerfulness and animation both of line and color."
(Grohmann, *Kandinsky*, New York, 1958, p.164).

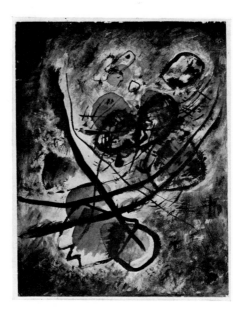

VASILY KANDINSKY

Blue Circle, No.242 (Cercle Bleu, No.242). 1922

Oil on canvas, 42⁷/₈ x 39″ (108.9 x 99 cm.)

Signed with monogram and dated l.l. "VK//22"

Provenance:
Katherine S. Dreier, West Redding, Connecticut, 1946

Exhibitions:
THE MUSEUM OF MODERN ART, New York, November 19, 1934–January 20, 1935, *Modern Works of Art, Fifth Anniversary Exhibition*, no.34, ill.

MUSEUM OF NON-OBJECTIVE PAINTING, New York, March 15–May 15, 1945, *In Memory of Wassily Kandinsky*, no.47

CARNEGIE INSTITUTE (Department of Fine Arts), Pittsburgh, April 11–May 12, 1946, *Memorial Exhibition of Paintings by Wassily Kandinsky*, no.19

THE SOLOMON R. GUGGENHEIM MUSEUM, New York, February 3–May 3, 1953, *A Selection* (Checklist)

VANCOUVER ART GALLERY, November 16–December 12, 1954, *The Solomon R. Guggenheim Museum, A Selection from the Museum Collection*, no.15

NEWARK MUSEUM, New Jersey, April 27–June 10, 1956, *Abstract Art, 1910 to Today*, no.32

PALAIS DES BEAUX-ARTS, Brussels, 1957, *Kandinsky*, p.23, ill.

BALTIMORE MUSEUM OF ART, September 30–November 2, 1958, *16 Kandinskys from The Solomon R. Guggenheim Museum*

THE SOLOMON R. GUGGENHEIM MUSEUM, New York, October 21, 1959–September 29, 1961, *Inaugural Selection (Kandinsky Galleries)* (Checklist)

THE SOLOMON R. GUGGENHEIM MUSEUM, New York, 1963, *Kandinsky*, no.49, p.74, ill.

M. KNOEDLER & CO., INC., New York, December 5–29, 1967, *Space and Dream*, p.52, ill.

THE SOLOMON R. GUGGENHEIM MUSEUM, New York, *Kandinsky, Selections from the Collection*, October 12–December 1969; January 19–February 8, 1970

THE SOLOMON R. GUGGENHEIM MUSEUM, New York, February 20–April 19, 1970, *Kandinsky, Klee, Feininger, 3 Bauhaus Painters*

References:
Staatliches Bauhaus in Weimar 1919–1923, Weimar-München, 1923 (?), p.186, no.122

REBAY, HILLA, "Pioneer in Non-Objective Painting", *Carnegie Magazine*, vol.XX, no.1, May 1946, p.8, ill.

GROHMANN, WILL, *Wassily Kandinsky, Life and Work*, New York, 1958, CC 133

WINGLER, HANS MARIA, *Das Bauhaus*, Bramsche, 1962, p.248, ill. (English edition, Cambridge, Massachusetts, 1969, p.271, ill.)

GOWANS, ALAN, *The Restless Art, A History of Painters and Painting 1760–1960*, Philadelphia, 1966, p.354, no.44B, ill.

46.1051

Kandinsky returned to Germany from Russia in 1921 and in 1922 he joined the faculty at the Bauhaus. During his stay in Russia, he turned from free to geometric abstraction under the influence of Suprematism and Constructivism. *Blue Circle* shows this transformation in the combination of circles, triangles and arcs with freely brushed forms.

VASILY KANDINSKY

In the Black Square, No.259. 1923

Oil on canvas, 38³/₈ x 36³/₄″ (98.5 x 93.3 cm.)

Signed with monogram and dated l.l. "vĸ//23" and on reverse "vĸ no.259 1923"

Provenance:

Solomon R. Guggenheim, New York
Gift, Solomon R. Guggenheim, 1937

Exhibitions:

PHILADELPHIA ART ALLIANCE, February 8–28, 1937, *Solomon R. Guggenheim Collection of Non-Objective Paintings*, no.84, ill.

GIBBES MEMORIAL ART GALLERY, Charleston, South Carolina, March 7–April 7, 1938, *Solomon R. Guggenheim Collection of Non-Objective Paintings*, no.114, ill.

SOLOMON R. GUGGENHEIM FOUNDATION, New York, June 1, 1939, *Art of Tomorrow*, (Fifth catalogue of the Solomon R. Guggenheim Collection of Non-Objective Paintings), p.127, no.254, ill.

HAUS DER KUNST, Munich, April 27, 1950–January 15, 1951, *Die Maler am Bauhaus*, no.75, p.51

THE SOLOMON R. GUGGENHEIM MUSEUM, New York, October 6, 1954–February 27, 1955, *Selection IV*

PALAIS DES BEAUX-ARTS, Brussels, 1957, *Kandinsky*, p.25, ill.

BALTIMORE MUSEUM OF ART, September 30–November 2, 1958, *16 Kandinskys from The Solomon R. Guggenheim Museum*

ART GALLERY OF TORONTO, April 24–May 24, 1959, *45 Kandinskys from The Solomon R. Guggenheim Museum*

THE SOLOMON R. GUGGENHEIM MUSEUM, New York, October 21, 1959–September 29, 1961, *Inaugural Selection*

PHILADELPHIA MUSEUM OF ART, November 2, 1961–January 7, 1962, *Guggenheim Museum Exhibition, A Loan Collection of Paintings, Drawings, and Prints from The Solomon R. Guggenheim Museum, New York*, no.61

THE SOLOMON R. GUGGENHEIM MUSEUM, New York, 1963, *Kandinsky*, no.52, ill.

SIDNEY JANIS GALLERY, New York, January 2–31, 1967, *Two Generations of 20th Century Art*, no.20

THE SOLOMON R. GUGGENHEIM MUSEUM, New York, June 28–October 1, 1967, *Museum Collection, Seven Decades, A Selection* (Checklist)

THE SOLOMON R. GUGGENHEIM MUSEUM, New York, April 11–May 26, 1968, *Acquisitions of the 1930's and 1940's* p.17, ill.

THE SOLOMON R. GUGGENHEIM MUSEUM, New York, *Kandinsky, Selections from the Collection*, February 14–March 9, 1969; March 28–May 11; July 8–September 14; October 12–December 1969; January 19–February 8, 1970

THE SOLOMON R. GUGGENHEIM MUSEUM, New York, February 20–April 19, 1970, *Kandinsky, Klee, Feininger, 3 Bauhaus Painters*

References:

NEUMANN, J. B. ed., *Artlover*, vol.3, no.4, 1936, p.60, ill.

GROHMANN, WILL, *Wassily Kandinsky, Life and Work*, New York, 1958, no.259, CC 147

READ, HERBERT, *Kandinsky*, London, 1959, p.14, pl.4

LASSAIGNE, JACQUES, *Kandinsky*, Geneva, 1964, p.89, ill.

BESSET, MAURICE, *Who Was Le Corbusier?*, Geneva, 1968, p.48, ill.

OVERY, PAUL, *Kandinsky, The Language of the Eye*, New York, 1969, p.133, no.42, ill.

37.254

Painted in the year following Kandinsky's appointment to the Bauhaus, *In the Black Square* is related to two types of compositions of the 1923–24 period: "accented corners" and "circle pictures". Here the circles play a subordinate role within the composition; the main tensions reside near the edges and corners through the opposition of the trapezoid to the black square.

VASILY KANDINSKY

Several Circles, No.323 (Some Circles). 1926

Oil on canvas, 55^1/$_8$ x 55^1/$_8$″ (140 x 140 cm.)

Inscribed with monogram l.l. "vk//26" and on reverse
with monogram "vk//No.323// 1926//Einige Kreise"

Provenance:
Staatliche Gemäldegalerie, Dresden
Gutekunst und Klipstein, Bern, 1939
Solomon R. Guggenheim, New York
Gift, Solomon R. Guggenheim, 1941

Exhibitions:
INTERNATIONAL KUNSTAUSSTELLUNG, Dresden, 1926

SOLOMON R. GUGGENHEIM FOUNDATION, New York,
June 1, 1939, *Art of Tomorrow*, (Fifth catalogue of the
Solomon R. Guggenheim Collection of Non-Objective
Paintings), no.283, ill.

MUSEUM OF NON-OBJECTIVE PAINTING, New York,
March 15–May 15, 1945, *In Memory of Wassily Kandinsky*,
no.97 *(as Some Circles)*

CARNEGIE INSTITUTE (Department of Fine Arts), Pittsburgh,
April 11–May 12, 1946, *Memorial Exhibition of Paintings
by Wassily Kandinsky*, no.45, ill.

MUSEUM OF NON-OBJECTIVE PAINTING, New York,
opening May 31, 1949, *Tenth Anniversary Exhibition*

THE SOLOMON R. GUGGENHEIM MUSEUM, New York, 1963,
Kandinsky, no.57, ill.

MARLBOROUGH-GERSON GALLERY, New York, November
12–December 27, 1963, *Artists and Maecenas; A Tribute to
Curt Valentin*, not in catalogue (Substituted for a work
illustrated in catalogue)

THE SOLOMON R. GUGGENHEIM MUSEUM, New York,
April 30–September 1, 1965, *Paintings from the Collection
of The Solomon R. Guggenheim Museum*, no.56, ill.

BUSCH-REISINGER MUSEUM OF GERMANIC ART, Cambridge,
Massachusetts, November 1–December 10, 1966,
Masters of the Bauhaus

THE SOLOMON R. GUGGENHEIM MUSEUM, New York,
June 28–October 1, 1967, *Museum Collection, Seven
Decades, A Selection* (Checklist)

ALBRIGHT-KNOX ART GALLERY, Buffalo, March 3–April 1.
1968, *Plus by Minus: Today's Half-Century*, no.65

THE SOLOMON R. GUGGENHEIM MUSEUM, New York,
Kandinsky, Selections from the Collection, October 12–
December 1969; January 19–February 8, 1970

References:

BILL, MAX, *Wassily Kandinsky*, Paris, 1951, p.53, ill.

GROHMANN, WILL, *Wassily Kandinsky, Life and Work*,
New York, 1958, pp.355 and 205, ill.

BRION, MARCEL, *Kandinsky*, London, 1961, p.62, ill.

VOLBOUDT, PIERRE, "Philosophie de Kandinsky", *XXe
Siècle*, no.XXVII, December 1966, p.59, ill.

WHITFORD, FRANK, *Kandinsky*, London, 1967, pl.29

ARNASON, H. H., *History of Modern Art*, New York, 1968.
p.261, pl.95

AWAZU, NORIO, *Klee/ Kandinsky*, (Art du Monde, 20),
Tokyo, 1968, p.111, ill.

41.283

"Even during [Kandinsky's] most rigidly geometric
period, his paintings were dynamic in structure, with
triangles, circles and lines flashing in and out of one
another in unstable diagonals. He continued to use varie
gated color areas as contrasts with the geometry of the
line. At times the mood becomes quiet: in *Several Circle
No.323*, 1926, the transparent color circles float serenely
across one another in a gray-black space". (H. H. Arnaso
History of Modern Art, New York, 1968, p.261)

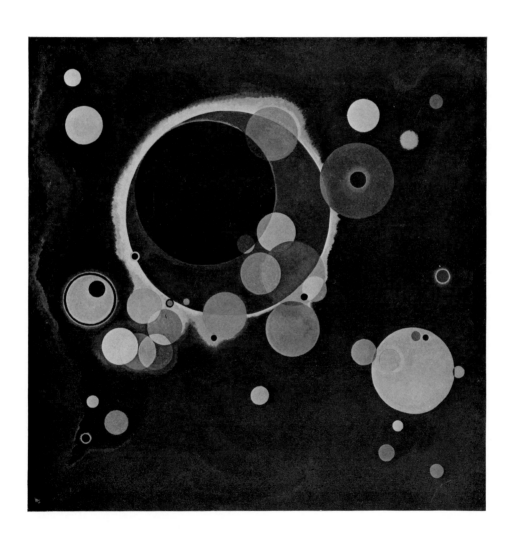

Two Sides Red, No.437 (Zwei Seiten rot). 1928

Oil on canvas, 22³/₄ x 17¹/₈″ (57.8 x 43.3 cm.)

Signed with monogram and dated l.l. "VK 28" and on reverse with monogram "VK Zwei Seiten rot//no.437// 1928//43 x 57"

Provenance:

Nierendorf Gallery, New York, 1945

Exhibitions:

NIERENDORF GALLERY, New York, March 1941, *Kandinsky*, no.55

MUSEUM OF NON-OBJECTIVE PAINTING, New York, March 15–May 15, 1945, *In Memory of Wassily Kandinsky*, no.138

VANCOUVER ART GALLERY, November 16–December 12, 1954, *The Solomon R. Guggenheim Museum, A Selection from the Museum Collection*, no.25

THE SOLOMON R. GUGGENHEIM MUSEUM, New York, July 26–October 9, 1955, *Selection V* (Checklist)

PALAIS DES BEAUX-ARTS, Brussels, 1957, *Kandinsky*, p.32, ill.

BALTIMORE MUSEUM OF ART, September 30–November 2, 1958, *16 Kandinskys from The Solomon R. Guggenheim Museum*

ART GALLERY OF TORONTO, April 24–May 24, 1959, *45 Kandinskys from The Solomon R. Guggenheim Museum*

THE SOLOMON R. GUGGENHEIM MUSEUM, New York, October 21, 1959–March 3, 1960, *Inaugural Selection (Kandinsky Galleries)* (Checklist)

THE SOLOMON R. GUGGENHEIM MUSEUM, New York, October 3, 1961–January 9, 1962, *Elements of Modern Painting*

PASADENA ART MUSEUM, 1963, *Kandinsky*, no.41

THE SOLOMON R. GUGGENHEIM MUSEUM, New York, June 28–October 1, 1967, *Museum Collection, Seven Decades, A Selection* (Checklist)

THE SOLOMON R. GUGGENHEIM MUSEUM, New York, *Kandinsky, Selections from the Collection*, October 12– December 1969; January 19–February 8, 1970

References:

GROHMANN, WILL, *Wassily Kandinsky, Life and Work*, New York, 1958, p.373, CC 294, no.437

AWAZU, NORIO, *Klee/Kandinsky, (Art du Monde, 20)*, Tokyo, 1968, p.61, ill.

45.981

SILY KANDINSKY

vels, No.452 (Etagen). 1929

l on board, 22¹/₄ x 16″ (56.5 x 40.7 cm.)

gned with monogram and dated l.l. "VK//29" and on
verse "VK//Etagen No.452// 1929// 41 x 56 [cm.]"

ovenance:

Tériade, Paris
e Shryer, New York, 1946

hibitions:

USEUM OF NON-OBJECTIVE PAINTING, New York,
ening May 31, 1949, *Tenth Anniversary Exhibition*

US DER KUNST, Munich, April 27, 1950–January 15,
51, *Die Maler am Bauhaus,* no.88

STITUTE OF CONTEMPORARY ART, Boston, 1952, *Kandinsky*

LAIS DES BEAUX-ARTS, Brussels, 1957, *Kandinsky,*
.35, ill.

T GALLERY OF TORONTO, April 24–May 24, 1959,
Kandinskys from The Solomon R. Guggenheim Museum

USEUM OF FINE ARTS, Boston, October 30–December 13,
59, *A Salute to the Guggenheim, 75 Selected Works*

STITUTE OF CONTEMPORARY ARTS, London, October 26–
cember 3, 1960, *The Mysterious Sign*

IE SOLOMON R. GUGGENHEIM MUSEUM, New York, 1963,
andinsky, p.87, no.64, ill.

IE SOLOMON R. GUGGENHEIM MUSEUM, New York,
ne 28–October 1, 1967, *Museum Collection, Seven*
cades, A Selection (Checklist)

IE SOLOMON R. GUGGENHEIM MUSEUM, New York,
andinsky, Selections from the Collection, February 14–
arch 9, 1969; July 8–September 14; October 12–
cember 1969; January 19–February 8, 1970

ferences:

OHMANN, WILL, *Wassily Kandinsky, Life and Work,*
ew York, 1958, no.452, p.337

SSAIGNE, JACQUES, *Kandinsky,* Geneva, 1964, p.95, ill.

VAZU, NORIO, *Klee/ Kandinsky, (Art du Monde,* 20),
okyo, 1968, p.113, ill.

.1049

...in these paintings, as in his Compositions, Kandinsky
s subordinated several centers or points of gravity to
e total conception, and the pictorial ideas in them are
ly loosely connected. These works, even more than
hers, must be seen in color to be understood: for
stance *Two Sides Red* (1928) will appear a cold canvas to
yone unaware that the whole work is painted in red
d dark brown tones of violet. Far from being crystal-
e, this painting is inherently dynamic, yet without the
d, even the division at the center must seem expression-
ss." (Grohmann, *Kandinsky,* New York, 1958, p.210).

VASILY KANDINSKY

Accompanied Contrast, No.613 (Contraste Accompagné, No.613). 1935

Oil with sand on canvas, 38¼ x 63½″ (97.2 x 161.3 cm.)

Signed with monogram and dated l.l. "VK//35" and on reverse "VK//No.613//1935"

Provenance:
the artist, 1935
Solomon R. Guggenheim, New York
Gift, Solomon R. Guggenheim, 1937

Exhibitions:
PHILADELPHIA ART ALLIANCE, February 8–28, 1937, *Solomon R. Guggenheim Collection of Non-Objective Paintings*, no.111, p. 39, ill.

GIBBES MEMORIAL ART GALLERY, Charleston, South Carolina, March 7–April 7, 1938, *Solomon R. Guggenheim Collection of Non-Objective Paintings*, no.144, ill.

SOLOMON R. GUGGENHEIM FOUNDATION, New York, June 1, 1939, *Art of Tomorrow*, (Fifth catalogue of the Solomon R. Guggenheim Collection of Non-Objective Paintings), no.338, ill.

MUSEUM OF NON-OBJECTIVE PAINTING, New York, March 15–May 15, 1945, *In Memory of Wassily Kandinsky*, no.210

CARNEGIE INSTITUTE (Department of Fine Arts), Pittsburgh, April 11–May 12, 1946, *Memorial Exhibition of Paintings by Wassily Kandinsky 1866–1944*, no.54

MUSEUM OF NON-OBJECTIVE PAINTING, New York, opening May 31, 1949, *Tenth Anniversary Exhibition*

THE SOLOMON R. GUGGENHEIM MUSEUM, New York, March 30–May 5, 1954, *Selection III* (Checklist)

FORT WORTH ART CENTER, Texas, 1954, *Inaugural Exhibition*

THE SOLOMON R. GUGGENHEIM MUSEUM, New York, July 26–October 9, 1955, *Selection V* (Checklist)

PALAIS DES BEAUX-ARTS, Brussels, 1957, *Kandinsky*, p.40, ill.

PALAIS DES BEAUX-ARTS, Brussels, April 17–July 21, 1958, *50 Ans d'Art Moderne*, no.145, p.144, ill.

ART GALLERY OF TORONTO, April 24–May 24, 1959, *45 Kandinskys from The Solomon R. Guggenheim Museum*

THE SOLOMON R. GUGGENHEIM MUSEUM, New York, October 21, 1959–September 29, 1961, *Inaugural Selection (Kandinsky Galleries)* (Checklist)

THE SOLOMON R. GUGGENHEIM MUSEUM, New York, 1963, *Kandinsky*, no.71

THE SOLOMON R. GUGGENHEIM MUSEUM, New York, June 28–October 1, 1967, *Museum Collection, Seven Decades, A Selection* (Checklist)

THE SOLOMON R. GUGGENHEIM MUSEUM, New York, *Kandinsky, Selections from the Collection*, October 8, 1968–January 12, 1969; February 14–March 9; March 28–May 11; July 8–September 14; October 12–December 1969; January 19–February 8, 1970

References:
GROHMANN, WILL, *Wassily Kandinsky, Life and Work*, New York, 1958, p.340, no.613, CC 443 (as *Contrast with Accompaniment*)

READ, HERBERT, *A Concise History of Modern Painting*, New York, 1959, pp.168–169, ill.

LASSAIGNE, JACQUES, *Kandinsky*, Geneva, 1964, p.105, ill.

OVERY, PAUL, *Kandinsky, The Language of the Eye*, New York, 1969, no.55, p.155, ill.

Kandinsky: Parisian Period 1933–1944, M. Knoedler & Co. Inc., New York, 1969, p.18, ill. (not in exhibition)

37.338

Beginning in 1934, Kandinsky added fine sand to his paint which enabled him to differentiate between color planes and forms. These paintings are distinctive by their delicate color tone in contrast to the heavier texture of the surface.

VASILY KANDINSKY

Dominant Curve, No.631. 1936

Oil on canvas, 50⁷/₈ x 76¹/₂″ (129.3 x 194.3 cm.)

Signed with monogram and dated l.l. "VK//36" and on reverse "VK//No.633//1936//Courbe Dominante"

Provenance:
the artist
Peggy Guggenheim, New York
Nierendorf Gallery, New York, 1945

Exhibitions:
KUNSTHALLE, Bern, February 21–March 29, 1937, *Wassily Kandinsky*, no.70

MUSEUM OF NON-OBJECTIVE PAINTING, New York, opening April 29, 1952, *Evolution to Non-Objectivity*, no.92

ART GALLERY OF TORONTO, April 2–May 9, 1954, *A Loan Exhibition of Paintings from The Solomon R. Guggenheim Museum*, no.30

THE SOLOMON R. GUGGENHEIM MUSEUM, New York, October 6, 1954–February 27, 1955, *Selection IV* (Checklist)

MONTREAL MUSEUM OF FINE ARTS, June 4–July 3, 1955, *A Selection From The Solomon R. Guggenheim Museum, New York*, no.21

THE SOLOMON R. GUGGENHEIM MUSEUM, New York, July 26–October 9, 1955, *Selection V* (Checklist)

PALAIS DES BEAUX-ARTS, Brussels, 1957, *Kandinsky*, no.41, ill.

ART GALLERY OF TORONTO, April 24–May 24, 1959, *45 Kandinskys from The Solomon R. Guggenheim Museum*

THE SOLOMON R. GUGGENHEIM MUSEUM, New York, October 21, 1959–June 12, 1960, *Inaugural Selection (Kandinsky Galleries)* (Checklist)

THE SOLOMON R. GUGGENHEIM MUSEUM, New York, 1963, *Kandinsky*, no.74, ill.

THE SOLOMON R. GUGGENHEIM MUSEUM, New York, *Kandinsky, Selections from the Collection*, October 8, 1968–

January 12, 1969; February 14–March 9; March 28–May 11; July 8–September 14; October 12–December 1969; January 19–February 8, 1970

References:
GUGGENHEIM, PEGGY, ed., *Art of This Century*, New York, 1942, p.42

GUGGENHEIM, PEGGY, *Out of This Century*, New York, 1946, ill. in photograph of "Abstract and Cubist gallery, designed by Berenice Abbott," opp. p.311

GROHMANN, WILL, *Wassily Kandinsky, Life and Work*, New York, 1958, no.631, p.340, pl.231

BILL, MAX, *Wassily Kandinsky*, Paris, 1951, p.66, ill.

GUGGENHEIM, PEGGY, *Confessions of an Art Addict*, New York, 1960, p.110

OVERY, PAUL, "Wassily Kandinsky", *Granta*, vol.LXV, no.1213, December 1961, fig.6, p.8

WHITFORD, FRANK, *Kandinsky*, London, 1967, pl.38
Kandinsky: Parisian Period 1933–1944,M. Knoedler & Co., Inc., New York, 1969, p.11, ill. (not in exhibition)

45.989

"…in *Dominant Curve*… the broadly designed curve dominates its surroundings like some exotic creature its native forests or temple stairs. The small hieroglyphic forms are like inscriptions on the larger figures. There is a tablet with signs at the upper left and three black circles at the upper right, which serve as a poetic and technological accent, conveying an impression of Baroque strangeness. After the romantic chords of Baroque richness." (Grohmann, *Kandinsky*, New York, 1958, p.228)

VASILY KANDINSKY

Fragment, No.718. 1943

Oil on board, $16\frac{1}{2}$ x $22\frac{3}{4}''$ (42 x 57.8 cm.)

Signed with monogram and dated l.l. "vk//42" and on reverse "vk//No.690// 1942"

Provenance:

the artist
Nina Kandinsky, Neuilly-sur-Seine, France, 1949

Exhibitions:

GALERIE RENÉ DROUIN, Paris, November 7–December 7, 1952, *Wassily Kandinsky*

INSTITUTE OF CONTEMPORARY ART, Boston, 1952, *Kandinsky*

PALAIS DES BEAUX-ARTS, Brussels, 1957, *Kandinsky,* no.44, ill.

THE SOLOMON R. GUGGENHEIM MUSEUM, New York, October 3, 1961–January 9, 1962, *Elements of Modern Painting*

PASADENA ART MUSEUM, 1963, *Kandinsky,* no.64, p.90, ill.

THE SOLOMON R. GUGGENHEIM MUSEUM, New York, *Kandinsky, Selections from the Collection,* October 8, 1968–January 12, 1969; February 14–March 9; March 28–May 11; July 8–September 14; October 12–December 1969

References:

BILL, MAX, *Wassily Kandinsky,* Paris, 1951, p.86, ill.

GROHMANN, WILL, *Wassily Kandinsky, Life and Work,* New York, 1958, no.718, p.325, ill.

49.1224

Twilight, No.720 (Crépuscule). 1943

Oil on board, 22³/₄ x 16¹/₂″ (57.3 x 42 cm.)

Signed with monogram and dated l.l. "VK//43" and on reverse "VK//No.718// 1943/58 x 42 [cm.]"

Provenance:

the artist
Nina Kandinsky, Neuilly-sur-Seine, France, 1946

Exhibitions:

PALAIS DES BEAUX-ARTS, Brussels, 1957, *Kandinsky*, no.39

ART GALLERY OF TORONTO, April 24–May 24, 1959,
45 Kandinskys from the Solomon R. Guggenheim Museum

THE SOLOMON R. GUGGENHEIM MUSEUM, New York,
October 21, 1959–September 29, 1961, *Inaugural Selection
(Kandinsky Galleries)* (Checklist)

PASADENA ART MUSEUM, 1963, *Vasily Kandinsky*, no.65,
p.91, ill.

THE SOLOMON R. GUGGENHEIM MUSEUM, June 28–
October 1, 1967, *Museum Collection, Seven Decades,
A Selection* (Checklist)

THE SOLOMON R. GUGGENHEIM MUSEUM, New York,
Kandinsky, Selections from the Collection, October 8, 1968–
January 12, 1969; February 14–March 9; March 28–
May 11; July 8–September 14; October 12–December
1969; January 19–February 8, 1970

References:

GROHMANN, WILL, *Wassily Kandinsky, Life and Work*,
New York, 1958, p.392, CC 520; p.342, no.720 (as *Dusk*)

SINICHI, SEGUI, "Kandinsky et l'Orient", *XXe Siècle*,
no.XXVII, December 1966, p.110, ill.

49.1223

After 1942, Kandinsky's works were small in scale, the most frequent format being 22¹/₂ x 16″ on wood or cardboard. Paints and supplies were difficult to obtain during the war. During these last years Kandinsky explored the potentials of an emblematic and symbolic vocabulary.

In *Fragment* (1943) a form "lies on a blue-black ground as in a grave, around which is set a mosiac of brightly colored stones. This mosaic has three small hollows in it with hieroglyph-like offerings to the dead and the whole is surrounded by a violent brown border. Forebodings?" (Grohmann, *Kandinsky*, New York, 1958, p.240.)

Blue, Green, Yellow, Orange, Red. 1966

Acrylic on canvas, 5 sections, each 60 x 48″ (152.4 x 122 cm.)

Signed on reverse of first canvas "E.K."

Provenance:

from the artist through Sidney Janis Gallery, New York, 1967

Exhibitions:

THE SOLOMON R. GUGGENHEIM MUSEUM, New York, September 21–November 27, 1966, *Systemic Painting*, p.30, ill.

THE SOLOMON R. GUGGENHEIM MUSEUM, New York, June 28–October 1, 1967, *Museum Collection, Seven Decades, a Selection* (Checklist)

References:

ARNASON, H. H., *History of Modern Art,* New York, 1968, p.594, pl.254

67.1833

Ellsworth Kelly 1923–

Ellsworth Kelly was born at Newburgh, New York on May 31, 1923. After serving in the Army (1943–45) and attending the Boston Museum School (1946–48) he went to France to study art on the G.I. Bill. He remained there until 1954, when he moved to New York.

Kelly's early work shows the combined influence of Cubism and Matisse's paper cut-outs in its clear, flat images and sharp color contrasts. As his forms have grown progressively less evocative, his color has become proportionately autonomous and eloquent.

The artist had his first one-man show at the Galerie Arnaud, Paris in 1951. He was first shown in New York by the Betty Parsons Gallery in 1956. Besides frequent participation in national and international exhibitions, he represented the United States at the Venice Biennale in 1966. He has executed several architectural commissions in New York and Philadelphia and in the past decade has turned his hand to sculpture in addition to painting.

Kelly's work of the early fifties and sixties emphasized irregular biomorphic shapes and asymmetrical compositions in which the spatial interplay of figure and ground could fluctuate according to the color arrangement. Although shape was important, it was not significant for its own sake but served instead as a vehicle for his color. In paintings such as this example, however, color has been freed from any equivocal association with form. To emphasize the autonomy of color, Kelly has frequently used individual panels, one for each color, so that color becomes synonymous with shape. Although Kelly had started experimenting with juxtaposing identical panels of color as early as 1952–1953, the recent work is most notable in allowing, through the use of greatly increased scale and hue saturation, the maximum expression of color. Intuitive in his arrangements of color, in contrast to Albers's systematic organization of color principles, Kelly is nevertheless consistent in his selection of colors. The fundamental organization of this painting is the establishment of the positions of the primary colors, blue, yellow, and red, with the intermediary positions occupied by the complementary colors, green and orange. Given this forthright structure, however, it is significant that Kelly creates an optical balance from five unequal colors. It is in the masterful arrangements of color and the subordination of shape and line that Kelly has produced a radically new imagery.

Nudes. 1908

Charcoal, 13 1/2 x 17 1/2" (34.3 x 44.5 cm.)

Signed l.r. "E. L. Kirchner"

Provenance:

Karl Nierendorf, New York
Estate of Karl Nierendorf, 1948

Exhibitions:

ART GALLERY OF TORONTO, April 2–May 9, 1954, *A Loan Exhibition of Paintings from The Solomon R. Guggenheim Museum*, no.32

THE SOLOMON R. GUGGENHEIM MUSEUM, New York, October 6, 1954–February 27, 1955, *Selection IV* (Checklist)

THE SOLOMON R. GUGGENHEIM MUSEUM, New York, November 6, 1963–January 5, 1964, *20th Century Master Drawings*, no.52; in collaboration with UNIVERSITY GALLERY, University of Minnesota, Minneapolis, February 3–March 15; and THE FOGG ART MUSEUM, Cambridge, April 6–May 24, 1964

THE SOLOMON R. GUGGENHEIM MUSEUM, New York, June 23–October 23, 1966, *Gauguin and the Decorative Style*

THE SOLOMON R. GUGGENHEIM MUSEUM, New York, April 11–May 26, 1968, *Acquisitions of the 1930's and 1940's*, pp.108–109, ill.

THE SOLOMON R. GUGGENHEIM MUSEUM, New York, July 8–September 14, 1969, *Selected Sculpture and Works on Paper*, p.37, ill.

References:

JOHNSON, UNA E., *20th Century Drawings, Part I: 1900–1940*, New York, 1964, p.45, pl.13

48.1172x454

Ernst Ludwig Kirchner 1880–1938

Ernst Ludwig Kirchner was born May 6, 1880, in Aschaffenburg, Germany. He studied architecture in Dresden from 1901–1905 but in the meantime had decided to become a painter. In 1905, along with Bleyl, Heckel and Schmitt-Rottluff, he helped found the group *Die Brücke* (The Bridge) in Dresden, the artists' goal being to create a "bridge" between traditional art and a new, yet undefined form of expression. *Die Brücke* work was characterized by a kind of voluntary primitivism achieved through schematic drawing and blatantly expressive color. The graphic arts, especially woodcuts, were as much emphasized as painting. Along with *Der Blaue Reiter, Die Brücke* was one of the major groups of early twentieth-century German Expressionism.

The artists broke up in 1913, after which time Kirchner was very active both in painting and printmaking and had several one-man shows, mostly in Germany. In 1915, he suffered a mental and physical breakdown. Subsequent years were spent in and out of sanatoriums. In 1917, he moved to Frauenkirch near Davos, Switzerland, where he was to live and work until 1938 when, during a severe illness and depression, he took his own life on June 15.

Kirchner was a prolific artist both in painting and the graphic arts (drawings in all mediums, watercolors, woodcuts, etchings, lithographs). Although the artist's use of color was extremely expressive, even more so was his manipulation of the drawn line.

Kirchner's mature graphic expression, which began to develop in his work as early as 1910–1911, is characterized by a stiff, dry stroke producing sharp, angular contours. *Nudes* (dated 1908 by W. Grohmann) is clearly an early drawing. The continuous, undulating line and its rich, velvety texture show the influence of one of the fathers of German Expressionism, Edvard Munch.

Paul Klee 1879–1940

Paul Klee was born at Münchenbuchsee near Bern, Switzerland on December 18, 1879. Born into a musical family, the artist's love and knowledge of music (he was an accomplished violinist) provide on important insight into his art.

In 1898 he decided to become an artist and went to Munich to art school, after which, in 1906, he married and settled there. At this time he considered himself primarily a graphic artist, as color presented problems that for the moment he had trouble solving. He traveled extensively in Italy, and exhibited frequently in Germany, including the second *Blaue Reiter* exhibition in 1912. That same year he visited Paris and Delaunay's studio, where he was deeply impressed by that artist's experiments with light, color and abstract form.

In 1914 Klee traveled to Tunis and Kairouan. His exposure to Mediterranean light and color were to radically modify his art: "Color and I are one; I am a painter."

Klee lived in Munich until Gropius called him to the Weimar Bauhaus in 1920. In 1928 a trip to Egypt was to induce another turning point in his art, which became more radically simplified, more abstract and in some cases more ideogrammatic.

Klee left the Bauhaus in 1931 to teach in Düsseldorf for two years. He died after a prolonged illness in a clinic at Muralto-Locarno on June 29, 1940.

The Bavarian Don Giovanni (Der Bayerische Don Giovanni)
1919

Watercolor, $8^7/_8$ x $8^3/_8$″ (22.5 x 21.3 cm.)

Signed u.r. "Klee"
Klee catalogue no.116, 1919

Provenance:

Hans Goltz, Munich, 1920
Karl Nierendorf, New York
Estate of Karl Nierendorf, 1948

Exhibitions:

ART GALLERY OF TORONTO, April 2–May 9, 1954, *A Loan Exhibition of Paintings from The Solomon R. Guggenheim Museum*, no.45

VANCOUVER ART GALLERY, November 16–December 12, 1954, *The Solomon R. Guggenheim Museum, A Selection from the Museum Collection*, no.45

MONTREAL MUSEUM OF FINE ARTS, June 4–July 3, 1955, *A Selection from The Solomon R. Guggenheim Museum, New York*, no.29

THE SOLOMON R. GUGGENHEIM MUSEUM, New York, October 3–November 12, 1961, *Elements of Modern Painting*; circulated by THE AMERICAN FEDERATION OF ARTS, July 1962–September 1963, as *Elements of Modern Art*

THE SOLOMON R. GUGGENHEIM MUSEUM, New York, February 17–April 30, 1967, *Paul Klee 1879–1940: A Retrospective Exhibition*, no.34, ill.; traveled to KUNSTHALLE, Basel, June 3–August 16, 1967

THE SOLOMON R. GUGGENHEIM MUSEUM, New York, May 30–September 2, 1968, *Rousseau, Redon, and Fantasy*

THE SOLOMON R. GUGGENHEIM MUSEUM, New York, July 8–September 14, 1969, *Selected Sculpture and Works on Paper*, p.40, ill.

References:

GROHMANN, WILL, *Paul Klee*, New York, 1954, cat. no.38, p.389, ill.

48.1172x69

Klee was not only a great music lover but a lover of theater and opera as well. Among composers, Mozart and Bach were his favorites, and Grohmann reports that he knew the score of *Don Giovanni* by heart.

The Bavarian Don Giovanni is a study of pictorial structure as well as an imaginary landscape. The flat, rectilinear organization of the surface recalls the artist's earlier experiments with Cubism, as the triangular colored planes – free of contour – are reminiscent of Delaunay's *Windows* which had impressed Klee in 1912.

These planes however are not only prisms of light but theatrical curtains, forcing the viewer to shift from the realm of visual perception to that of the imagination. The ladders evoke the illusionist perspectives of stage settings, as the moon and stars are indications of time. Moreover, all of these motifs recur frequently in Klee's art.

Although it seems evident that the names inscribed are to evoke characters, what is less intelligible is who they are, as they are not those of Mozart's *Don Giovanni*. Whoever they may be, the names have as much vital and satiric presence as the central figure, illustrative of the little distinction made by Klee between the plastic and associative powers of letters and words and those of purely pictorial motifs.

PAUL KLEE

White Blossom in Garden (Weisse Blüte im Garten). 1920

Oil on paper, 7 x 6³/₄″ (17.8 x 17.2 cm.)

Inscribed l.r. "Klee" and on mount "1920/196 Weisse
Blüte im Garten"

Klee catalogue no.196, 1920, as "Gartenbild KL. grüne
ölskizze"

Provenance:
Karl Nierendorf, New York
Estate of Karl Nierendorf, 1948

Exhibitions:
THE SOLOMON R. GUGGENHEIM MUSEUM, New York,
February 17–April 30, 1967, *Paul Klee 1879–1940: A Retro-
spective Exhibition,* no.38, ill.; traveled to KUNSTHALLE,
Basel, June 3–August 16, 1967

THE SOLOMON R. GUGGENHEIM MUSEUM, New York, July 8–
September 14, 1969, *Selected Sculpture and Works on
Paper,* p.41, ill.

48.1172X157

One is struck by the dense opacity of this painting as well
as by its slightly glazed surface, due in part to the medium
and also to the dark tonalities employed. In 1919 Klee
was involved in technical experiments and was using oil
paint more frequently than before.

Although the subject is inspired by nature, there is no
attempt at realism but rather at capturing primordial
rhythms in an essentially formal landscape. In contrast to
the free linear improvisation which characterizes much of
Klee's art, here the emphasis is on rhythmic structure
through color, a direction the artist was to pursue
throughout his life's work.

unner at the Goal (Läufer am Ziel). 1921

atercolor and gouache on paper mounted on paper,
⁷/₈ x 9″ (30.2 x 22.9 cm.)

scribed c.r. "Klee" and on mount "1921 105 Läufer am
el"

ee catalogue no.105, 1921

ovenance:
rl Nierendorf, New York
tate of Karl Nierendorf, 1948

xhibitions:
USEUM OF NON-OBJECTIVE PAINTING, New York, opening
pril 29, 1952, *Evolution to Non-Objectivity*, no.102
E SOLOMON R. GUGGENHEIM MUSEUM, New York, May
–October 11, 1953, *Selection II* (Checklist)
N FRANCISCO MUSEUM OF ART, June 17–July 10, 1955,
rt in the Twentieth Century
TS CLUB OF CHICAGO, February 28–March 31, 1962,
'it and Humor, no.9, ill.

PASADENA ART MUSEUM, February 21–April 2, 1967, *Paul
Klee 1879–1940: A Retrospective Exhibition*, no.42, p.38,
ill.; organized in collaboration with THE SOLOMON R.
GUGGENHEIM MUSEUM, traveled to SAN FRANCISCO MUSEUM
OF ART, April 13–May 14; COLUMBUS GALLERY OF FINE
ARTS, Ohio, May 25–June 25; CLEVELAND MUSEUM OF ART,
Ohio, July 5–August 13; WILLIAM ROCKHILL NELSON
GALLERY, Kansas City, September 1–30; BALTIMORE
MUSEUM OF ART, October 24–November 19; WASHINGTON
UNIVERSITY ART GALLERY, St. Louis, December 3, 1967–
January 5, 1968; PHILADELPHIA MUSEUM OF ART, January
15–February 15, 1968

THE SOLOMON R. GUGGENHEIM MUSEUM, New York, April
11–May 26, 1968, *Acquisitions of the 1930's and 1940's*,
p.105, ill.

THE SOLOMON R. GUGGENHEIM MUSEUM, New York, July
8–September 14, 1969, *Selected Sculpture and Works on
Paper*, p.41, ill.

References:

KINCHELOE, ISABEL M. and COOK, LESTER H., *Adventures in
Value*, New York, 1969, p.655, ill.

48.1172x55

The simultaneous portrayal of successive movements
which is implicit in this work of 1921 is based on the same
pictorial principles as those in Klee's "Fugue" paintings of
the same year (*Fugue in Red, Hanging Fruit, Dream City,
Ceramic-Erotic-Religious*). The chromatic variations of a
single shape correspond to the harmonic variations of a
single melodic line inherent to the structure of the fugue.
The artist's economy of color, as well as the evenly
cadenced articulation of all parts of the surface, unite
figure and ground in a concise polyphonic rhythm.

From the Song of Songs "Let him kiss me with the kisses of his mouth" (II version) (Schriftbild aus dem Hohen Lied "Er küsse mich mit seines Mundes Kuss" [II Fassung]). 1921

Ink and watercolor on paper, 6³/8 x 6⁷/8″ (16.2 x 17.5 cm)

Inscribed l.r. "Klee" and on mount "1921/179 (aus dem Hohen Lied) (II. Fassung)"

Klee catalogue no.179, 1921

Provenance:

Karl Nierendorf, New York
Estate of Karl Nierendorf, 1948

Exhibitions:

THE SOLOMON R. GUGGENHEIM MUSEUM, New York, February 17–April 30, 1967, *Paul Klee 1879–1940: A Retrospective Exhibition*, no.45, ill.; traveled to KUNSTHALLE, Basel, June 3–August 16, 1967

THE SOLOMON R. GUGGENHEIM MUSEUM, New York, July 8–September 14, 1969, *Selected Sculpture and Works on Paper*, p.42, ill.

48.1172x535

In the style of an illuminated manuscript, here script, images and color are mingled in a complex visual statement. The spirit of an illumination is accentuated by the antique color and the graphic motifs which have a primitive vitality (through their seemingly spontaneous line and stylized arabesques) as well as a hieratic quality (through their symmetrical disposition and iconic simplicity).

Klee increases the visual impact of words by endowing them with a poetically plastic presence, without, however, denying them their conventional associations.

This is the second watercolor on this theme done by Klee in 1921. The first version is in the Angela Rosengart Collection in Lausanne.

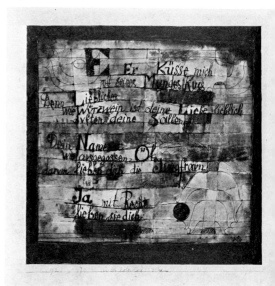

nce, Monster, to my Soft Song! (Tanze Du Ungeheuer zu
nem sanften Lied!). 1922

l transfer with watercolor on gesso-primed gauze,
/8 x 11 1/2″ (35.9 x 29.2 cm.)

cribed on mount, "1922/54 Tanze Du Ungeheuer zu
nem sanften Lied!"

e catalogue no.54, 1922

ovenance: Rudolf Bauer, Berlin, 1938

hibitions:

OMON R. GUGGENHEIM FOUNDATION, New York,
e 1, 1939, *Art of Tomorrow*, (Fifth catalogue of
Solomon R. Guggenheim Collection of Non-
jective Paintings), no.508

CHHOLZ GALLERY and WILLARD GALLERY, New York,
tober 9–November 2, 1940, *Paul Klee*, no.28

E MUSEUM OF MODERN ART, New York, June 30–July 27,
41, *Paul Klee*, p.35, ill. (revised edition, 1945)

SEUM OF NON-OBJECTIVE PAINTING, New York,
ening April 29, 1952, *Evolution to Non-Objectivity*,
103

E SOLOMON R. GUGGENHEIM MUSEUM, New York,
ruary 3–May 3, 1953, *A Selection* (Checklist)

E SOLOMON R. GUGGENHEIM MUSEUM, New York,
y 26–October 9, 1955, *Selection V* (Checklist)

TS CLUB OF CHICAGO, February 28–March 31, 1962,
t and Humor, no.11, ill.

E SOLOMON R. GUGGENHEIM MUSEUM, New York,
bruary 17–April 30, 1967, *Paul Klee 1879–1940: A
trospective Exhibition*, no.51, p.35, ill., traveled to
NSTHALLE, Basel, June 3–August 16, 1967

E SOLOMON R. GUGGENHEIM MUSEUM, New York,
ril 11–May 26, 1968, *Acquisitions of the 1930's and 1940's*,
3, ill.

E SOLOMON R. GUGGENHEIM MUSEUM, New York,
ay 30–September 2, 1968, *Rousseau, Redon, and Fantasy*

E SOLOMON R. GUGGENHEIM MUSEUM, New York,
y 8–September 14, 1969, *Selected Sculpture and Works on
per*, p.43, ill.

ferences:

DION-WELCKER, CAROLA, *Paul Klee*, New York, 1952,
5

SSER, THOMAS M., "Which Klee?" *Arts Magazine*, vol.41,
5, March 1967, p.36, ill.

NASON, H. H., *History of Modern Art*, New York, 1968,
57, pl.430

508

This is another example of the imaginative and playful
aspect of Klee's talent with an implicit reference to music.
The "Monster" – a concoction of arabesques and lines –
like most of Klee's creations is more humorous than
fearful.

Here the artist has dispensed with all conventional spatial
indications such as perspective, scale or horizon lines. The
viewer is thus transported from a basically theatrical
situation (a dancer and accompanist on a stage) to a
weightless, spaceless fantasy world.

A slightly smaller ink drawing, virtually identical except
for a few details, is in the Rosengart Collection, Lucerne.

PAUL KLEE

Aging Venus. 1922

Watercolor, oil transfer drawing and paper collage
mounted on board, 11⅝ x 23⅛" (29.5 x 58.8 cm.)

Signed and dated l.r. "Klee 1922"

Klee catalogue no.8, 1922

Provenance:
Karl Nierendorf, New York
Estate of Karl Nierendorf, 1948

Exhibitions:
GALERIE HANS GOLTZ, Munich, May–June 1925, *Paul Klee
2. Gesamtausstellung*, no.77, ill. (listed as 1923)

MUSEUM OF NON-OBJECTIVE PAINTING, New York,
opening April 29, 1952, *Evolution to Non-Objectivity*,
no.122

THE SOLOMON R. GUGGENHEIM MUSEUM, New York,
March 30–May 5, 1954, *Selection III* (Checklist)

VANCOUVER ART GALLERY, November 16–December 12,
1954, *The Solomon R. Guggenheim Museum, A Selection
from the Museum Collection*, no.35

SAN FRANCISCO MUSEUM OF ART, June 17–July 10, 1955,
Art in the 20th Century

THE SOLOMON R. GUGGENHEIM MUSEUM, New York,
January 24–May 1, 1956, *Selection VI* (Checklist)

THE SOLOMON R. GUGGENHEIM MUSEUM, New York,
August 30–October 8, 1961, *Modern Masters from the
Collection of The Solomon R. Guggenheim Museum*

PHILADELPHIA MUSEUM OF ART, November 2, 1961–
January 7, 1962, *Guggenheim Museum Exhibition, A Loan
Collection of Paintings, Drawings, and Prints from The
Solomon R. Guggenheim Museum, New York*, no.73

ARTS CLUB OF CHICAGO, February 28–March 31, 1962,
Wit and Humor, no.10, ill.

PASADENA ART MUSEUM, February 21–April 2, 1967,
Paul Klee 1879–1940: A Retrospective Exhibition, no.42,
p.38, ill.; organized in collaboration with THE SOLOMON
R. GUGGENHEIM MUSEUM, traveled to SAN FRANCISCO
MUSEUM OF ART, April 13–May 14; COLUMBUS GALLERY OF
FINE ARTS, Ohio, May 25–June 25; CLEVELAND MUSEUM OF
ART, Ohio, July 5–August 13; WILLIAM ROCKHILL NELSON
GALLERY, Kansas City, September 1–30; BALTIMORE
MUSEUM OF ART, October 24–November 19; WASHINGTON
UNIVERSITY ART GALLERY, St. Louis, December 3, 1967–
January 5, 1968; PHILADELPHIA MUSEUM OF ART,
January 15–February 15, 1968

THE SOLOMON R. GUGGENHEIM MUSEUM, New York, April
11–May 26, 1968, *Acquisitions of the 1930's and 1940's*,
pp.106–107, ill.

48.1172x63

One of the artist's more frankly erotic pictures, the
subject portrayal is generally overlooked due to the
humor and delicacy with which the reclining figure is
treated.

The diaphanous quality of the composition is achieved
through the vibrating black line (the technique of oil
transfer drawing, used frequently by the artist between
1920 and 1927) and the evanescent tones of pink, ocher
and some areas of blue which have been sprayed on the
paper with an atomizer, another of Klee's technical
inventions.

The painting, done on paper, has been mounted on
cardboard on which the upper and lower orange bands
were then painted, tightening the structure of the composition and reinforcing its horizontality. This framing of
an image was done often by Klee and is seen in several
other of the works shown here.

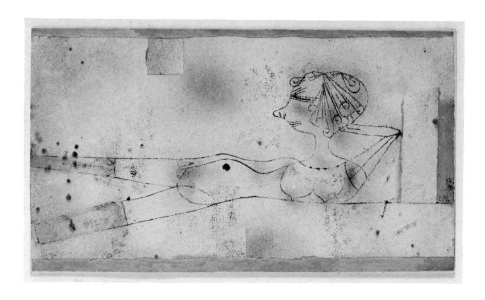

PAUL KLEE

Red Balloon (Roter Ballon). 1922

Oil on chalk-primed muslin mounted on board, 12^1/$_2$ x 12^1/$_4$″ (31.8 x 31.1 cm.)

Inscribed l.l. "Klee" and on reverse mount "1922 VI 179 Roter Ballon Klee"

Klee catalogue no. VI, 179, 1922

Provenance:
Hermann Lange, Krefeld
Karl Nierendorf, New York
Estate of Karl Nierendorf, 1948

Exhibitions:
KUNSTVEREIN FÜR DIE RHEINLANDE UND WESTFALEN, Düsseldorf, June 14–July 6, 1931, *Paul Klee*, no.17

THE SOLOMON R. GUGGENHEIM MUSEUM, New York, May 13–October 11, 1953, *Selection II* (Checklist)

VANCOUVER ART GALLERY, November 16–December 12, 1954, *The Solomon R. Guggenheim Museum, A Selection from the Museum Collection*, no.34

MONTREAL MUSEUM OF FINE ARTS, June 4–July 3, 1955, *A Selection from The Solomon R. Guggenheim Museum, New York*, no.24

THE SOLOMON R. GUGGENHEIM MUSEUM, New York, January 24–June 1, 1956, *Selection VI* (Checklist)

TATE GALLERY, London, April 16–May 26, 1957, *Paintings from The Solomon R. Guggenheim Museum*, no.35; organized by THE SOLOMON R. GUGGENHEIM MUSEUM, traveled to GEMEENTEMUSEUM, The Hague, June 25–September 1, no.35; ATENEIUMIN TAIDEKOKOELMAT, Helsinki, September 27–October 20, no.35; GALLERIA NAZIONALE D'ARTE MODERNA, Rome, December 5, 1957–January 8, 1958, no.52; WALLRAF–RICHARTZ–MUSEUM, Cologne, January 26–March 30, no.36; MUSÉE DES ARTS DÉCORATIFS, Paris, April 23–June 1, 1958, no.15, ill.

THE SOLOMON R. GUGGENHEIM MUSEUM, New York, October 21, 1959–June 19, 1960, *Inaugural Selection* (Checklist)

THE SOLOMON R. GUGGENHEIM MUSEUM, New York, August 30–October 8, 1961, *Modern Masters from the Collection of The Solomon R. Guggenheim Museum*

THE SOLOMON R. GUGGENHEIM MUSEUM, New York, October 3, 1961–January 11, 1962, *Elements of Modern Painting;* circulated by THE AMERICAN FEDERATION OF ART July 1962–September 1963, as *Elements of Modern Art*

PHILADELPHIA MUSEUM OF ART, November 1, 1961–January 7, 1962, *Guggenheim Museum Exhibition, A Loan Collection of Paintings, Drawings, and Prints from The Solomon R. Guggenheim Museum, New York*, no.72

WORCESTER ART MUSEUM, Massachusetts, February 6–April 7, 1963, *Aspects of Twentieth Century Painting Lent by The Solomon R. Guggenheim Museum*, no.19, ill.

THE SOLOMON R. GUGGENHEIM MUSEUM, New York, June 5–October 13, 1963, *Cézanne and Structure in Modern Painting*

THE SOLOMON R. GUGGENHEIM MUSEUM, New York, April 30–September 1, 1965, *Paintings from the Collection of The Solomon R. Guggenheim Museum*, no.52, ill.

THE SOLOMON R. GUGGENHEIM MUSEUM, New York, February 17–April 30, 1967, *Paul Klee 1879–1940: A Retrospective Exhibition*, no.58, ill.

THE METROPOLITAN MUSEUM OF ART, New York, November 15, 1967–April 1, 1968, *Selections from the Collection of The Solomon R. Guggenheim Museum*

THE SOLOMON R. GUGGENHEIM MUSEUM, New York, April 11– May 26, 1968, *Acquisitions of the 1930's and 1940's*, p.112, ill.

THE SOLOMON R. GUGGENHEIM MUSEUM, New York, May 30–September 2, 1968, *Rousseau, Redon, and Fantasy*

References:
ROY, CLAUDE, *Paul Klee aux Sources de la Peinture*, Paris, 1963, p.53, ill.

ARNASON, H. H., *History of Modern Art*, New York, 1968, pl.106

MESSER, THOMAS M., *Paul Klee Exhibition at the Guggenheim Museum: A Post Scriptum*, New York, 1968, p.17, ill.

48.1172x524

he imaginary architectures and illusionary perspectives that were among the artist's major themes are found in his painting. The same geometric (yet allusive) structure and diaphanous color appear in another painting of the same year, *Small Fir Painting*. Although in earlier works the artist made specific references to houses through details such as windows and slanted roofs, here they are reduced to a minimum. The resulting schematic rendering anticipates the purely abstract compositions of colored squares which began the following year.

The translucent color of *Red Balloon* is produced by the open yet stopped weave of the chalk-primed muslin and its resistence to the application of color.

A sphere (balloon or moon) suspended in space was a recurrent motif in the artist's work, seen in paintings such as *Rising of the Moon* (1925), *Balloon through the Window* (1929), *Fantastic Tale* (1929), *Ad Marginem* (1930).

PAUL KLEE

Contact of Two Musicians (Kontakt zweier Musiker). 1922

Oil transfer drawing with watercolor on chalk-primed muslin, 18 x 12″ (45.7 x 30.5 cm.)

Inscribed u.r. "Klee" and on mount "1922 X 93 Kontakt zweier Musiker"

Klee catalogue no.93, 1922

Provenance:
Karl Nierendorf, New York
Estate of Karl Nierendorf, 1948

Exhibitions:
GALERIE HANS GOLTZ, Munich, May–June 1925, *Paul Klee 2. Gesamtausstellung*, no.11

THE SOLOMON R. GUGGENHEIM MUSEUM, New York, February 3–May 3, 1953, *A Selection* (Checklist)

THE SOLOMON R. GUGGENHEIM MUSEUM, New York, July 26–October 9, 1955, *Selection V* (Checklist)

THE SOLOMON R. GUGGENHEIM MUSEUM, New York, October 21, 1959–June 19, 1960, *Inaugural Selection* (Checklist)

THE SOLOMON R. GUGGENHEIM MUSEUM, New York, August 30–October 8, 1961, *Modern Masters from the Collection of The Solomon R. Guggenheim Museum*

THE SOLOMON R. GUGGENHEIM MUSEUM, New York, February 17–April 30, 1967, *Paul Klee 1879–1940: A Retrospective Exhibition*, no.55, ill.; traveled to KUNSTHALLE, Basel, June 3–August 16, 1967

THE SOLOMON R. GUGGENHEIM MUSEUM, New York, June 28–October 1, 1967, *Museum Collection, Seven Decades, A Selection* (Checklist)

THE SOLOMON R. GUGGENHEIM MUSEUM, New York, April 11–May 26, 1968, *Acquisitions of the 1930's and 1940's*, p.114, ill.

THE SOLOMON R. GUGGENHEIM MUSEUM, New York, May 30–September 2, 1968, *Rousseau, Redon, and Fantasy*

References:
GROHMANN, WILL, *Paul Klee Handzeichnungen, 1921–1930*, Berlin, 1934, no.19, p.18

48.1172x527

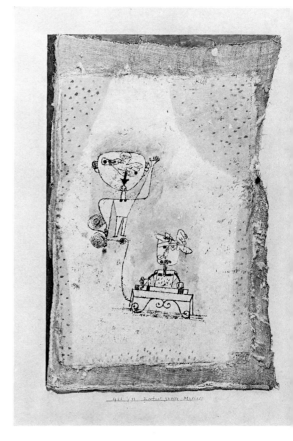

Painted in the same year and in the same mediums, *Contact of Two Musicians* is comparable to *Dance, Monster, to my Soft Song.* Although spatial conventions are no more respected here than in the other work, the allusion is merely theatrical, not fantastic, thanks to the curtains by which the figures are framed.

The torn and ragged edges of the muslin support provide further evidence that, to the artist's mind, traditional pictorial conventions were irrelevant.

PAUL KLEE

Tropical Gardening, VI 55 (Tropische Garten Kultur). 1923

Watercolor and ink, 7³/₈ x 18″ (18.7 x 45.7 cm.)

Inscribed l.r. "Klee" and on mount "1923, VI (55)
Tropische Garten Kultur"

Klee catalogue no.55, 1923

Provenance:
Rudolph Bauer, Berlin
Solomon R. Guggenheim, New York, 1937

Exhibitions:
PHILADELPHIA ART ALLIANCE, February 8–28, 1937, *Solomon
R. Guggenheim Collection of Non-Objective Paintings*,
no.176, p.47 (listed as *Tropical Culture*)

GIBBES MEMORIAL ART GALLERY, Charleston, South Carolina, March 7–April 7, 1938, *Solomon R. Guggenheim
Collection of Non-Objective Paintings,* no.250

SOLOMON R. GUGGENHEIM FOUNDATION, New York,
June 1, 1939, *Art of Tomorrow* (Fifth catalogue of the
Solomon R. Guggenheim Collection of Non-Objective
Paintings), no.509, p.174 (listed as *Tropical Culture*)

THE SOLOMON R. GUGGENHEIM MUSEUM, New York,
February 3–May 3, 1953, *A Selection* (Checklist)

VANCOUVER ART GALLERY, November 16–December 12,
1954, *The Solomon R. Guggenheim Museum, A Selection
from the Museum Collection,* no.36

SAN FRANCISCO MUSEUM OF ART, June 17–July 10, 1955,
Art in The Twentieth Century

THE SOLOMON R. GUGGENHEIM MUSEUM, New York,
July 26–October 9, 1955, *Selection V* (Checklist)

THE SOLOMON R. GUGGENHEIM MUSEUM, New York,
October 21, 1959–June 19, 1960, *Inaugural Selection*
(Checklist)

THE SOLOMON R. GUGGENHEIM MUSEUM, New York,
August 30–October 8, 1961, *Modern Masters from the
Collection of The Solomon R. Guggenheim Museum*

PHILADELPHIA MUSEUM OF ART, November 2, 1961–
January 7, 1962, *Guggenheim Museum Exhibition, A Loan
Collection of Paintings, Drawings, and Prints from The Solo-
mon R. Guggenheim Museum, New York,* no.78

THE SOLOMON R. GUGGENHEIM MUSEUM, New York,
April 30–September 1, 1965, *Paintings from the Collection
of The Solomon R. Guggenheim Museum,* no.53, p.51, ill.

PASADENA ART MUSEUM, February 21–April 3, 1967, *Paul
Klee 1879–1940: A Retrospective Exhibition*, no.113, ill.;
organized in collaboration with THE SOLOMON R. GUGGEN-
HEIM MUSEUM, New York, traveled to SAN FRANCISCO
MUSEUM OF ART, April 13–May 14; COLUMBUS
GALLERY OF FINE ARTS, Ohio, May 25–June 25; CLEVELAND
MUSEUM OF ART, Ohio, July 5–August 13; WILLIAM
ROCKHILL NELSON GALLERY, Kansas City, September 1–30;
BALTIMORE MUSEUM OF ART, October 24–November 19;
WASHINGTON UNIVERSITY ART GALLERY, St. Louis,
December 3, 1967–January 5, 1968; PHILADELPHIA
MUSEUM OF ART, January 15–February 15, 1968

THE SOLOMON R. GUGGENHEIM MUSEUM, New York,
May 30–September 2, 1968, *Rousseau, Redon, and Fantasy*

37.509

The horizontal alignment of motifs, somewhat allusive
to a bar of music, is a compositional device used by Klee
in scenes of gardens and architecture as early as 1923.
Later works, where open-work horizontal bands cover
the entire surface, not only recall hieroglyphics or other
forms of picture-writing but are comparable to a musical
score in their rhythmic repetition and continuity. (eg.
Pastorale, 1927, The Museum of Modern Art, New York).

Aside from the connections to writing and music,
Grohmann suggests that Klee may have been inspired by
lace-work seen in Bauhaus workshops in the development of this flat and delicate open script.

The straight upward thrust of the tropical plants as well
as their radial patterns of growth illustrate Klee's belief in
the essential cosmic order found in nature.

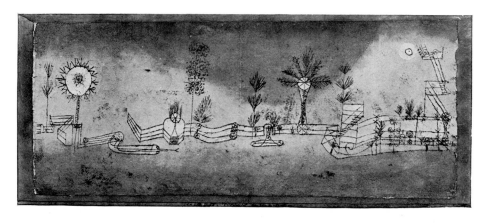

PAUL KLEE

In the Current Six Thresholds (*In der Strömung sechs Schwellen*). 1929

Tempera and oil on canvas, 17 x 17″ (43.2 x 43.2 cm.)

Signed and dated l.r. "Klee 1929"

Klee catalogue no.S.2 (92), 1929

Provenance:
Alfred Flechtheim, Berlin
J. B. Neumann, New York
Klee Estate, Bern
Galerie Louise Leiris, Paris
Curt Valentin, New York
G. David Thompson, Pittsburgh
Galerie Beyeler, Basel
Heinz Berggruen, Paris, 1966

Exhibitions:
GALERIE FLECHTHEIM, Berlin, 1931, *Paul Klee*, no.2
KUNSTVEREIN FÜR DIE RHEINLANDE UND WESTFALEN,
Düsseldorf, 1931, no.69
KUNSTHAUS, Zürich, 1960, *G. David Thompson Collection*,
no.83; traveled to KUNSTMUSEUM, Düsseldorf, 1960–61;
The Hague, 1961; GALLERIA CIVICA D'ARTE MODERNA,
Turin, 1961
THE SOLOMON R. GUGGENHEIM MUSEUM, New York,
February 17–April 30, 1967, *Paul Klee 1879–1940: A Retro-
spective Exhibition*, no.102, ill.
THE METROPOLITAN MUSEUM OF ART, New York, Novem-
ber 15, 1967–April 1, 1968, *Selections from the Collection of
The Solomon R. Guggenheim Museum*

References:
KLEE, PAUL, *Das Bildnerische Denken*, Basel, 1956, p.212,
ill. (Published in English as *The Thinking Eye*, New York,
1961, p.212, ill., listed as "In the Current Six Crescendos")
ARNASON, H. H., *History of Modern Art*, New York, 1968,
pl.107

Upon his return from Egypt in 1928, Klee attacked a series of works which, although not really larger in size than his customary production, are more monumental in scale. These are known as his Egyptian paintings.

The darkly resonant tone of the painting is achieved by overlaying color on a black ground. This technique was devised for specific reasons. According to the artist's words, "We do not have to understand the black, it is the primeval ground."

Completely independent of outer reality, Klee appears to be striving to portray a universal order through the natural logic of the surface structure. The title seems to allude to initiatic thresholds such as found in Egyptian symbolism. In 1929, Klee was also studying mathematics and its application to art. These preoccupations with real and divine measurements create a highly enigmatic painting in which the sense of silence, immutability and mystery is powerfully projected.

66.1842

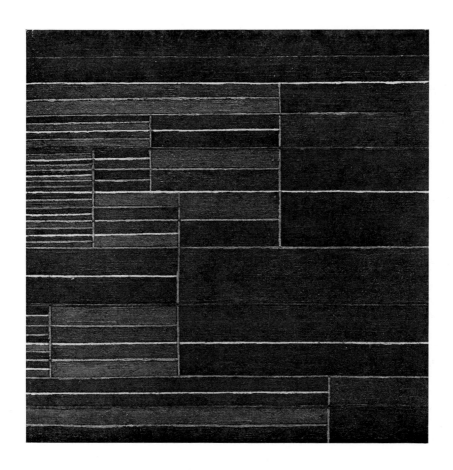

PAUL KLEE

Open Book (Offenes Buch). 1930

Varnished watercolor on white lacquer-primed canvas, 17⁷/₈ x 16³/₄″ (45.4 x 42.6 cm.)

Inscribed l.l. "Klee" and on stretcher "1930. E6 'Offenes Buch' Klee"

Klee catalogue no.E6 (206), 1930

Provenance:
Rolf de Maré, Paris, c. 1931
Karl Nierendorf, New York
Estate of Karl Nierendorf, 1948

Exhibitions:
THE SOLOMON R. GUGGENHEIM MUSEUM, New York, February 3–May 3, 1953, *A Selection* (Checklist)

THE SOLOMON R. GUGGENHEIM MUSEUM, New York, October 6, 1954–February 27, 1955, *Selection IV* (Checklist)

THE SOLOMON R. GUGGENHEIM MUSEUM, New York, July 26–October 9, 1955, *Selection V* (Checklist)

THE SOLOMON R. GUGGENHEIM MUSEUM, New York, January 24–May 1, 1956, *Selection VI* (Checklist)

TATE GALLERY, London, April 16–May 26, 1957, *Paintings from The Solomon R. Guggenheim Museum*, no.36, ill.; organized by THE SOLOMON R. GUGGENHEIM MUSEUM, traveled to GEMEENTEMUSEUM, The Hague, June 25–September 1; ATENEIUMIN TAIDEKOKOELMAT, Helsinki, September 27–October 20; GALLERIA NAZIONALE D'ARTE MODERNA, Rome, December 5, 1957–January 8, 1958, no.53; WALLRAF–RICHARTZ–MUSEUM, Cologne, January 26–March 30, no.37; MUSÉE DES ARTS DÉCORATIFS, Paris, April 23–June 1, 1958, no.16

THE SOLOMON R. GUGGENHEIM MUSEUM, New York, October 21, 1959–June 19, 1960, *Inaugural Selection* (Checklist)

THE SOLOMON R. GUGGENHEIM MUSEUM, New York, August 30–October 8, 1961, *Modern Masters from the Collection of The Solomon R. Guggenheim Museum*

THE SOLOMON R. GUGGENHEIM MUSEUM, New York, June 5–October 13, 1963, *Cézanne and Structure in Modern Painting*

THE SOLOMON R. GUGGENHEIM MUSEUM, New York, April 30–September 1, 1965, *Paintings from the Collection of The Solomon R. Guggenheim Museum*, no.60, ill.

PASADENA ART MUSEUM, February 21–April 2, 1967, *Paul Klee 1879–1940: A Retrospective Exhibition*, no.113, ill.; organized in collaboration with THE SOLOMON R. GUGGENHEIM MUSEUM, traveled to SAN FRANCISCO MUSEUM OF ART, April 13–May 14; COLUMBUS GALLERY OF FINE ARTS, Ohio, May 25–June 25; CLEVELAND MUSEUM OF ART, Ohio, July 5–August 13; WILLIAM ROCKHILL NELSON GALLERY, Kansas City, September 1–30; BALTIMORE MUSEUM OF ART, October 24–November 19; WASHINGTON UNIVERSITY ART GALLERY, St. Louis, December 3, 1967–January 5, 1968; PHILADELPHIA MUSEUM OF ART, January 15–February 15, 1968

THE SOLOMON R. GUGGENHEIM MUSEUM, New York, April 11–May 26, 1968, *Acquisitions of the 1930's and 1940's*, p.113, ill.

THE SOLOMON R. GUGGENHEIM MUSEUM, New York, May 30–September 2, 1868, *Rousseau, Redon, and Fantasy*

COLUMBUS GALLERY OF FINE ARTS, Ohio, October 5, 1968–September 7, 1969, *Paintings from The Solomon R. Guggenheim Museum*, p.32, ill.

References:
EINSTEIN, CARL, *Die Kunst des 20. Jahrhunderts*, Berlin, 1931, 3rd edition, p.553, ill.

ROY, CLAUDE, *Paul Klee aux Sources de la Peinture*, Paris, 1963, p.69, ill.

GROHMANN, WILL, *Paul Klee*, New York, 1967, p.118, ill.

48.1172x526

The complex multiple perspectives – found in other paintings of the same period such as *Opened*, 1933 (Collection F.K., Bern) – evoke an imaginary architecture of infinite space and time, tempting one to interpret this "book" as a symbol of eternal laws or universal knowledge, a hypothesis which is consistent not only with Egyptian symbolism but with Klee's philosophy of life and art.

The mottled surface of the canvas is found in other paintings after 1928 as are the hatched shadows, developed in 1924 and perhaps deriving (although at some distance) from Klee's earlier predilection for etching.

PAUL KLEE

Barbarian Sacrifice (Barbaren-Opfer). 1932

Watercolor. 24³/₄ x 18⁷/₈″ (62.9 x 48 cm.)

Inscribed l.r. "Klee" and on mount "1932 IV Barbaren-Opfer"

Klee catalogue no.12, 1932

Provenance:
Siegfried Rosengart, Lucerne
H. C. Schang, New York, 1969

Exhibitions:
KUNSTMUSEUM, Bern, August 11–November 4, 1956, *Paul Klee,* no.620, p.98
MUSEUM OF FINE ARTS, Boston, October 10–November 17, 1957, *European Masters of our Time,* no.55, p.19, pl.92
M. KNOEDLER & CO., INC., New York, December 5–29, 1967, *Space and Dream,* p.59, ill.
THE SOLOMON R. GUGGENHEIM MUSEUM, New York, July 8–September 14, 1969, *Selected Sculpture and Works on Paper,* p.46, ill.
SAIDENBERG GALLERY, New York, October 14–November 29, 1969, *Paul Klee, a Retrospective Exhibition,* no.39, ill.

References:
COURTHION, PIERRE, *Klee,* Paris, 1953, pl.13

69.1893

The close juxtaposition of small colored dots – characteristic of Klee's brief "divisionist" period of 1930 to 1932 – is reminiscent of Neo-Impressionist "pointillisme", although the methodical alignment and the grey ground are not. Klee's technique, initiated in 1930, was apparently reinforced by a visit to Sicily in the summer of 1931 and his discovery of Sicilian mosaics.

Although an exact reading of the iconography is impossible because of the artist's highly personal poetics, the painting shows Italian or Moslem inspiration in the triple arcade of an imaginary architecture, the pennant, scalloped festoons, and other decorative details.

Severing of the Snake. 1938

Watercolor on chalk-primed burlap, 20$^1/_2$ x 15$^1/_2$"
(52.1 x 39.4 cm.)

Signed u.r. "Klee"

Klee catalogue no.R2 (262), 1938

Provenance:

J. B. Neumann, New York
Nierendorf Gallery, New York
Estate of Karl Nierendorf, 1948

Exhibitions:

NIERENDORF GALLERY, New York, February 1940, *Paul Klee: An Exhibition in Honor of the Sixtieth Birthday of the Artist*, no.8

BUCHHOLZ GALLERY AND WILLARD GALLERY, New York, October 9–November 2, 1940, *Paul Klee*, no.96

THE MUSEUM OF MODERN ART, New York, June 30–July 27, 1941, *Paul Klee*, no.62

CINCINNATI ART MUSEUM, Ohio, April 7–May 3, 1942, *Paintings by Paul Klee and Sculptures by Alexander Calder*

THE SOLOMON R. GUGGENHEIM MUSEUM, New York, April 30–September 1, 1965, *Paintings from the Collection of The Solomon R. Guggenheim Museum*, no.66, ill.

THE SOLOMON R. GUGGENHEIM MUSEUM, New York, April 11–May 26, 1968, *Acquisitions of the 1930's and 1940's*, p.107, ill.

References:

NIERENDORF, KARL, ed., *Paul Klee, Paintings, Watercolors 1913–1939*, New York, 1941, pl.56

48.1172x57

The motif of the snake occurs throughout the artist's career. It appears with greater frequency however after his return from Egypt. Moreover the simplified cipher of the snake and the stylization of the knife suggest that Egyptian painting may have been present in Klee's mind.

Although there is nothing explicitly morbid about this painting, it is probably a symbolic rendering of the premonition of death which haunted the artist throughout his final years.

PAUL KLEE

Rolling Landscape (Wogende Landschaft). 1938

Watercolor on chalk-primed canvas, $15^3/_4$ x $21^3/_8''$
(40 x 54.3 cm.)

Inscribed u.l. "Klee" and on reverse "Wogende Landschaft 1938"

Klee catalogue no.Y9 (409), 1938

Provenance:
Karl Nierendorf, New York
Estate of Karl Nierendorf, 1948

Exhibitions:
ART GALLERY OF TORONTO, April 2–May 9, 1954, *A Loan
Exhibition of Paintings from The Solomon R. Guggenheim
Museum*, no.44

THE SOLOMON R. GUGGENHEIM MUSEUM, New York,
April 20–June 19, 1960, *Inaugural Selection* (exhibition
opened October 21, 1959)

THE SOLOMON R. GUGGENHEIM MUSEUM, New York,
August 30–October 8, 1961, *Modern Masters from the
Collection of The Solomon R. Guggenheim Museum*

PHILADELPHIA MUSEUM OF ART, November 2, 1961–
January 7, 1962, *Guggenheim Museum Exhibition, A Loan
Collection of Paintings, Drawings, and Prints from The
Solomon R. Guggenheim Museum, New York*, no.78

THE SOLOMON R. GUGGENHEIM MUSEUM, New York,
July 3–September 30, 1962, *Summer Selection 1962*

THE SOLOMON R. GUGGENHEIM MUSEUM, New York,
April 30–September 1, 1965, *Paintings from the Collection
of The Solomon R. Guggenheim Museum*, no.65, p.62, ill.

THE SOLOMON R. GUGGENHEIM MUSEUM, New York,
February 17–April 30, 1967, *Paul Klee 1879–1940: A Retrospective Exhibition*, no.162, p.126, ill.

THE SOLOMON R. GUGGENHEIM MUSEUM, New York, June
28–October 1, 1967, *Museum Collection, Seven Decades, A
Selection* (Checklist)

THE SOLOMON R. GUGGENHEIM MUSEUM, New York,
April 11–May 26, 1968, *Acquisitions of the 1930's and 1940's*,
p.115, ill.

References:
MESSER, THOMAS M., "Which Klee?" *Arts Magazine*, vol.41
no.5, March 1967, p.37, ill.

1172X529

After 1935 Klee's pictorial language became increasingly
simplified as he concentrated on only the most essential
statements.

The emphasis on calligraphy as an open rhythmic script
and on color as the basis of an undefinable, yet clearly
articulated surface structure endows the late paintings
such as *Rolling Landscape* with an even, all-over pattern,
making them among the most abstract and compelling
statements of the artist's career.

Yves Klein 1928–1962

Yves (né Raymond) Klein was born in Nice, France on April 28, 1928. In 1946 he met Claude Pascal and Arman (Fernandez) and began to paint seriously. One day the three young men metaphysically divided the world among themselves. Klein claimed the sky as his own poetic symbol and from this point began developing his monochrome theories.

After earning a black belt in Japan in 1953, and teaching judo in Spain in 1954, he moved to Paris and began his various experiments; in 1955 he did his first monochrome paintings. Eleven of these, painted in an intense cobalt blue which he named "International Klein Blue", were exhibited at the Galleria Apollinaire in Milan in 1957; in the same year he wrote his first monotone symphony. In 1958 he first made a painting by pressing onto a canvas a "living brush" (a nude model covered with paint). 1958 was also the year of an exhibition where the Iris Clert Gallery was painted Klein blue on the exterior and white on the empty interior; of the development of his theory of air architecture involving ideas of conditioning and controlling human space; and of the design of his fire fountains. Klein invented his sponge trees in 1959, made paintings using atmospheric conditions such as rain and wind in 1960, and created his planetary reliefs and fire paintings in 1961.

Klein was a founding member of the group *Nouveaux Réalistes* in 1960. He married Rotraut Uecker in 1962. On June 6 of the same year, after the opening at the Cannes Film Festival of *Mondo Cane*, in which Klein appeared, he died of a heart attack.

YVES KLEIN

Stalk. c.1959

Stone, metal, and coral, painted, 39″ (99 cm.) high.

Not inscribed

Provenance:
Gift, Mr. and Mrs. Andrew P. Fuller, New York, 1964.

Exhibitions:
JEWISH MUSEUM, New York, January 25–March 12, 1967, *Yves Klein*, p.63, p.45, ill.
THE SOLOMON R. GUGGENHEIM MUSEUM, New York, July 8–September 14, 1969, *Selected Sculpture and Works on Paper*, p.133, ill.

64.1752

Yves Klein, in his search for a personal means of expression, arrived at IKB (International Klein Blue), a color which symbolized infinite space. His blue sponge reliefs are an extension of this idea in that the sponge itself is a remnant of animal life which becomes part of a blue imaginary landscape. The blue sponges on trunks mounted on natural stones become another aspect of this idea – "a forest of sponges".

Gustav Klimt 1862–1918

Gustav Klimt was born July 13, 1862, in Baumgarten, a suburb of Vienna. He studied art in Vienna from 1876–1883, and started his career painting decorative panels in official public buildings. Although his style was academic and allegorical, it was already characterized by the sensuous surfaces and eroticism of his later work.

In 1897 Klimt helped found the Viennese *Secession*, a group of young Austrian artists intent on breaking with academic traditions. Tending strongly toward the decorative, the mannered and symbolic, Viennese *Secession* style was to become synonymous with Austrian *Art Nouveau*. Their first exhibition was held the following year.

Klimt exhibited regularly with the movement until 1904. As his style matured – the erotic content becoming less equivocal and the luxuriant abstract patterns more defined – his art met with growing public opposition. His last large commission was a frieze in the Palais Stoclet in Brussels, executed between 1904 and 1911. This work marks the culminating point of the artist's *Art Nouveau* style. Klimt died in Vienna on February 6, 1918.

GUSTAV KLIMT

Girl Seated in Chair. c. 1912

Charcoal, $21^5/8$ x $13^3/4''$ (55 x 35 cm.)

Not inscribed

Provenance:
Estate of the artist
Dr. Otto Nierenstein Kallir, Vienna
Galerie St. Etienne, New York, 1967

Exhibitions:
GALERIE ST. ETIENNE, New York, February 4–March 4, 1967, *Drawings by Gustav Klimt*, no.22
THE SOLOMON R. GUGGENHEIM MUSEUM, New York, July 8–September 14, 1969, *Selected Sculpture and Works Paper*, p.47, ill.

67.1835

Although Klimt executed a comparatively small number of oil paintings, he was a prodigious draftsman. His favorite and almost exclusive theme (particularly after 1890) was the female figure.

Girl Seated in Chair seems to date from 1912, the year of another drawing of a girl in a spotted robe sleeping in an arm chair (*Gustav Klimt*, Catalogue V, Vienna: Nebehay 1962, no.41, ill). The Museum's drawing appears to be stylistically slightly later due to a less literal rendering. The light but determined whiplash line – suggesting rather than defining the dynamic contours of the figure and the non-descriptive use of pattern to animate certain areas are characteristic of other drawings of the same period.

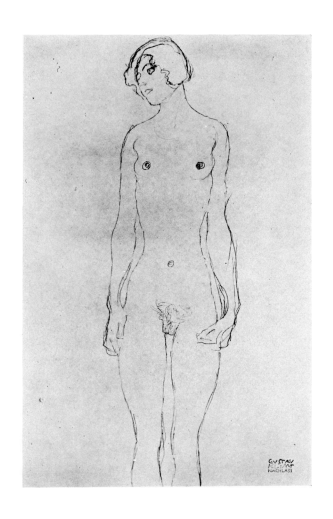

GUSTAV KLIMT

Standing Female Nude, Frontal. c. 1914

Pencil, 22³/₈ x 14³/₄" (57 x 36.5 cm.)

Not inscribed

Provenance:
Estate of the artist
Dr. Otto Nierenstein Kallir, Vienna
Galerie St. Etienne, New York, 1967

Exhibitions:
UNIVERSITY ART GALLERY, Berkeley, California, February 5–
March 10, 1963, *Viennese Expressionism 1910–1924,*
no.16; traveled to PASADENA ART MUSEUM, March 19–
April 21
GALERIE ST. ETIENNE, New York, February 4–March 4,
1967, *Drawings by Gustav Klimt,* no.23
THE SOLOMON R. GUGGENHEIM MUSEUM, New York,
July 8–September 14, 1969, *Selected Sculpture and
Works on Paper,* p.48, ill.

67.1836

The standing and frontal female figure was a frequent
theme of Klimt's from 1891 when he started using it as an
allegory in mural decorations.

This slender, elongated and graceful silhouette is typical
of Klimt's nudes c.1914, in contrast to those of other
periods, which were either heavier or slimmer and more
expressively deformed.

Franz Kline 1910–1962

Franz Kline was born at Wilkes-Barre, Pennsylvania in 1910. He received his art education at the School of Fine and Applied Art of Boston University (1931–35) and at Heatherly's Art School, London (1937–38). In 1938 he settled in New York City, where he was to spend the rest of his life, taking active part in the development of the New York Abstract Expressionist movement.

Kline's early works of the 1940's were mostly city-scapes painted in a fairly realist manner. Around 1946 the first signs of what was to emerge a few years later as his characteristic mature style appeared: a rendering through powerful, painterly gestures of the dynamic and emotional rhythms of the urban environment. Although most of his canvases of the early fifties are restricted to black and white, halfway through the decade he reintroduced color.

Kline had his first one-man show at the Egan Gallery, New York in 1950. His recognition as a major American artist began a few years later and from that time until his death he exhibited frequently, winning both national and international prizes. He died in New York in 1962.

Painting #7. 1952

Oil on canvas, $57\frac{1}{2}$ x $81\frac{3}{4}$" (146 x 207.6 cm.)

Not inscribed

Provenance:
from the artist through Egan Gallery, New York, 1954

Exhibitions:
THE SOLOMON R. GUGGENHEIM MUSEUM, New York, May 12–September 26, 1954, *Younger American Painters*, no.27, ill.; traveled to PORTLAND MUSEUM OF ART, Oregon September 2–October 9, 1955; UNIVERSITY OF WASHINGTON, Seattle, October 16–November 8; SAN FRANCISCO MUSEUM OF ART, November 15, 1955–January 22, 1956; LOS ANGELES COUNTY MUSEUM, February 1–29, 1956; UNIVERSITY OF ARKANSAS, Fayetteville, March 9–April 10, 1956; ISAAC DELGADO MUSEUM OF ART, New Orleans, April 15–May 20, 1956

TATE GALLERY, London, April 16–May 26, 1957, *Paintings from The Solomon R. Guggenheim Museum*, no.37; organized by THE SOLOMON R. GUGGENHEIM MUSEUM, traveled to GEMEENTEMUSEUM, The Hague, June 25–September 1; ATENEIUMIN TAIDEKOKOELMAT, Helsinki, September 27–October 20; GALLERIA NAZIONALE D'ARTE MODERNA, Rome December 5, 1957–January 8, 1958; WALLRAF–RICHARTZ-MUSEUM, Cologne, January 26–March 30; MUSÉE DES ARTS DÉCORATIFS, Paris, April 23–June 1, 1958

THE SOLOMON R. GUGGENHEIM MUSEUM, New York, October 21, 1959–June 19, 1960, *Inaugural Selection* (Checklist)

THE SOLOMON R. GUGGENHEIM MUSEUM, New York, July 1–September 13, 1964, *Van Gogh and Expressionism*

THE SOLOMON R. GUGGENHEIM MUSEUM, New York, April 30–September 1, 1965, *Paintings from the Collection of The Solomon R. Guggenheim Museum*

THE SOLOMON R. GUGGENHEIM MUSEUM, New York, June 28–October 1, 1967, *Museum Collection, Seven Decades, A Selection* (Checklist)

References:
MCBRIDE, HENRY, "Americans Looking East, Looking West", *Art News*, vol.53, no.3, May 1954, p.54

DE KOONING, ELAINE, "Subject: What, How or Who?", *Art News*, vol.54, no.2, April 1955, p.28, ill.

ELSEN, ALBERT E., *Purposes of Art*, New York, 1967, p.431 fig.522

WELLER, ALLEN S., *The Joys and Sorrows of Recent American Art*, Urbana, Illinois, 1968, pl.59

54.1403

round 1950 Kline began to enlarge his brushstrokes into owerful abstract forms. Using a quick-drying, black namel house paint, Kline was able to obtain a remark- ble variety of effects in density, texture, and surface. lthough the term "calligraphy" has often been applied o paintings of Kline's maturity such as this, the artist did ot wholly accept it. He did not consider his paintings as lack figures on a white ground but as studies of dynamic ontrasts between color, energy, and form. Moreover, is predilection for black and white was guided not by a ogmatic decision but by a desire to achieve the simplest

expressive means to describe a rhythm.

Kline was not alone in using black and white. During the late forties – early fifties, a number of other painters, including de Kooning, Newman, Pollock, and Mother-well, were also experimenting with the restriction of color, partly for lack of funds; however, this use continues to be particularly identified with Kline. In the dramatic polarities of black and white, Kline found the best expres-sion for the thrusting diagonals and sweeping brush-strokes that characterize his style.

Oskar Kokoschka 1886–

Oskar Kokoschka was born March 1, 1886, in the small Austrian town of Pöchlarn on the Danube. In 1889 his family moved to Vienna where, after finishing high school, he attended the Arts and Crafts School and became a teacher. Although the prevalent art instruction at the time emphasized ornament, Kokoschka's stand against this aesthetic won him the friendship and patronage of the Viennese architect Adolf Loos. Kokoschka was interested in the vital reality of human expression, a preoccupation which was to mark his life's work.

In 1910 Kokoschka moved to Berlin, where he was a member of the *Der Sturm* group. In the same year he held his first one-man exhibition in Berlin (Paul Cassirer Galerie).

1924–1930 was one of Kokoschka's most productive periods. At that time his expressionist stroke and his impressionist use of color arrived at a culminating point. Not only did he paint extensively but he traveled widely and showed frequently, living intermittently in Paris. In spite of his great activity and growing recognition, he remained extremely poor and was obliged to paint commissioned portraits for a living. In 1937 his works were confiscated by the Nazi regime as "degenerate" art and in 1938 he moved to London, becoming a British subject in 1947. Since 1953 he has been living in Villeneuve, Switzerland.

Knight Errant (Der Irrende Ritter). 1915

Oil on canvas, $35^3/_8$ x $70^7/_8$″ (90 x 180 cm.)

Signed l.r. "OK"

Provenance:
the artist, c.1918
Dr. Oskar Reichel, Vienna, c.1930
Dr. Otto Kallir, New York, 1945
Karl Nierendorf, New York
Estate of Karl Nierendorf, 1948

Exhibitions:
KUNSTHAUS, Zürich, June–July, 1927, *Kokoschka*

GALERIE ST. ETIENNE, Paris, 1939, *Austrian Painting*

BUCHHOLZ GALLERY, New York, October 27–November 15, 1941, *Kokoschka*

GALERIE ST. ETIENNE, New York, March 31–April 24, 1943, *Kokoschka*

INSTITUTE OF CONTEMPORARY ART, Boston, October 16–November 14, 1948, *Oskar Kokoschka Retrospective*, no.24, ill.; traveled to PHILLIPS GALLERY, Washington, D.C., 1948–1949; CITY ART MUSEUM, St. Louis, 1949; M. H. DE YOUNG MEMORIAL MUSEUM, San Francisco, 1949; THE MUSEUM OF MODERN ART, New York, 1949

TATE GALLERY, London, April 16–May 26, 1957, *Paintings from The Solomon R. Guggenheim Museum*, no.38; organized by THE SOLOMON R. GUGGENHEIM MUSEUM, traveled to GEMEENTEMUSEUM, The Hague, June 25–September 1; ATENEIUMIN TAIDEKOKOELMAT, Helsinki, September 27–October 20; GALLERIA NAZIONALE D'ARTE MODERNA, Rome December 5, 1957–January 8, 1958; WALLRAF-RICHARTZ-MUSEUM, Cologne, January 26–March 30; MUSÉE DES ARTS DÉCORATIFS, Paris, April 23–June 1, 1958

TATE GALLERY, London, September 14–November 11, 1962, *Oskar Kokoschka: Retrospective Exhibition*, no.46, pl.16

KUNSTHALLE, Hamburg, 1962–1963, *Oskar Kokoschka*, no.24, ill.

THE SOLOMON R. GUGGENHEIM MUSEUM, New York, July 1–September 13, 1964, *Van Gogh and Expressionism*

GALERIE ST. ETIENNE, New York, October 20–November 20, 1964, *Twenty-fifth Anniversary Exhibition*, no.17, ill.

THE SOLOMON R. GUGGENHEIM MUSEUM, New York, April 30–September 1, 1965, *Paintings from the Collection of The Solomon R. Guggenheim Museum*, no.40, ill.

KUNSTHAUS, Zürich, June 1–July 23, 1966, *Oskar Kokoschka Retrospective*, no.34, fig.9

BADISCHER KUNSTVEREIN, Karlsruhe, August 21–November 20, 1966, *Oskar Kokoschka, Das Porträt*, no.27, ill.

THE SOLOMON R. GUGGENHEIM MUSEUM, New York, June 28–October 1, 1967, *Museum Collection, Seven Decades, A Selection* (Checklist)

E SOLOMON R. GUGGENHEIM MUSEUM, New York,
ril 11–May 26, 1968, *Acquisitions of the 1930's and 1940's,*
.108–109, ill.

LUMBUS GALLERY OF FINE ARTS, Ohio, October 5, 1968–
ptember 7, 1969, *Paintings from the Solomon R. Guggen-
m Museum,* pp.14–15, ill.

ferences:

STHEIM, PAUL, *Oskar Kokoschka,* Potsdam-Berlin, 1918,
38

KOSCHKA, OSKAR, "Vom Bewusstsein der Gesichte",
nius: Zeitschrift für Werdende und alte Kunst, Munich,
19, Bk.1, pp.39–46; p.42, ill. (dated 1916, subtitle
elf-portrait")

STEIN, CARL, *Die Kunst des 20. Jahrhunderts,* Berlin,
28, 2nd ed., p.431, ill.

FFMANN, EDITH, *Kokoschka, Life and Work,* London,
47, no.105, pl.29

ERS, BERNARD S., *The German Expressionists,* New York,
56, p.62

WINGLER, HANS MARIA, *Oskar Kokoschka, The Work of the
Painter,* Salzburg, 1958, no.105, pl.44

HODIN, J. P., *Oskar Kokoschka, the Artist and his Time,*
Greenwich, Connecticut, 1966, pp.58, 134, 145, fig.21

HOFMANN, WERNER, *L'Expressionismo in Austria,* Milan,
1967, p.57, ill.

48.1172X350

"[The artist] saw himself as the *Knight Errant* slung between heaven and earth – between the ghastly smile of
Death and the woman set in a storm-lashed landscape.

The letters of despair, E S, hang flaming in the sky:
'Eloi, Eloi, lama sabachthani' – 'My God, my God, why
hast thou forsaken me?'... In this painting Kokoschka
predicted the nearly fatal wound he was to receive during
the war. The picture was painted before he volunteered
for service [early in 1915]." (quoted from J. P. Hodin,
1966, p.134)

Composition (Abstraction). 1955

Oil enamel and charcoal on canvas, 79¹/₈ x 69¹/₈″
(201 x 175.6 cm.)

Signed l.r. "de Kooning"

Provenance:
from the artist through Martha Jackson Gallery, New
York, 1955

Exhibitions:
THE SOLOMON R. GUGGENHEIM MUSEUM, New York,
July 26–October 9, 1955, *Selection V* (Checklist)

MARTHA JACKSON GALLERY, New York, November 9–11,
1955, *Recent Oils by Willem de Kooning,* no.1
(as *Abstraction*)

PICTURE GALLERY OF SAINT-GAUDENS MEMORIAL, Cornish,
New Hampshire, August 3–September 4, 1956, *Painters c
Today,* no.9 (Organized by THE SOLOMON R. GUGGENHEIM
MUSEUM)

WILLIAMS COLLEGE, Williamstown, Massachusetts,
April 1957, *Selections of American Paintings;* traveled to
WESLEYAN UNIVERSITY, Middletown, Connecticut, May
1957

MUSEUM OF FINE ARTS OF HOUSTON, January 7–
February 8, 1959, *New York-Paris, Paintings of the 50's*

THE SOLOMON R. GUGGENHEIM MUSEUM, New York,
October 21, 1959–June 19, 1960, *Inaugural Selection*
(Checklist)

SALZBURG ZWERGLGARTEN, July 10–August 3, 1961, *Zeigt
Amerikanische Maler Der Gegenwart,* no.36, ill.; organized
by UNITED STATES INFORMATION SERVICE, traveled to
UNITED STATES INFORMATION SERVICE GALLERY, American
Embassy, London, February 28–March 30, 1962 (as
Vanguard American Painting); HESSISCHEN LANDESMUSEUM,
Darmstadt, April 14–May 13, 1962 (as *Abstrakte Ameri-
kanische Malerei*)

WORCESTER ART MUSEUM, Massachusetts, February 6–
April 7, 1963, *Aspects of Twentieth Century Painting Lent l
The Solomon R. Guggenheim Museum,* no.23, ill.

STEDELIJK MUSEUM, Amsterdam, June 29–September 17,
1962, *Dutch Contribution to the International Development
of Art Since 1945,* no.52; organized by NETHERLANDS
MINISTRY OF EDUCATION, ARTS AND SCIENCES, The Hague,
traveled to MONTREAL MUSEUM OF FINE ARTS, October 5–
November 4; NATIONAL GALLERY OF CANADA, Ottawa,
November 15–December 31, 1962

THE SOLOMON R. GUGGENHEIM MUSEUM, New York,
July 1–September 13, 1964, *Van Gogh and Expressionism,* i

THE SOLOMON R. GUGGENHEIM MUSEUM, New York,
April 30–September 1, 1965, *Paintings from the Collection
of The Solomon R. Guggenheim Museum,* no.73, ill.

THE SOLOMON R. GUGGENHEIM MUSEUM, New York,
June 28–October 1, 1967, *Museum Collection, Seven
Decades, A Selection* (Checklist)

Willem de Kooning 1904–

Willem de Kooning was born in Rotterdam April 24, 1904.
From 1916 he worked as an apprentice to a commercial art
firm; at the same time he studied nights at the Rotterdam
Academy of Fine Arts and Techniques. After further study
in Brussels and Antwerp, de Kooning came to the United
States in 1926. He first settled in Hoboken, New Jersey,
supporting himself as a house painter, and later moved to
Manhattan to work as a free-lance commercial artist. He
soon met John Graham, a catalyst in the development of
New York painting, and Arshile Gorky, with whom he
shared a studio in the late thirties.

In 1935 de Kooning was able to commit all his energies to
painting. The works of this period (1935–40) are of two
types: abstractions of simple biomorphic or irregular geometric shapes, often in close-valued, fully saturated color;
and Cubist-derived figure paintings of men. De Kooning,
like Gorky, felt the influence of Picasso. The female figure
became a major preoccupation in the paintings of the
1940's, the decade in which de Kooning achieved his mature style. The first of these women display the strong de-
pendence on draftsmanship, merging of figure with
ground, and Cubist-like planar adjustments which he had
developed in the male figures. By the mid-forties the
women had become more distorted and the space more
tightly interwoven. These were paralleled by colored abstractions, followed by a series of black-and-white "all-
over" paintings which were exhibited at the artist's first
one-man show at the Egan Gallery in 1948. After the sen-
sational fragmented women of 1950–54, he painted a group
of urban and "Parkway" landscape abstractions with
broadened strokes of rich color. Recently de Kooning has
returned to figure-ground painting in which the abstract
space surrounding his women is infused with light.

In 1968–69, de Kooning was honored by a major retrospective exhibition which traveled in Europe and the
United States.

EDELIJK MUSEUM, Amsterdam, September 19–Novem-
er 17, 1968, *Willem de Kooning*, no.68, p.105, ill.;
rganized under the auspices of the International
ouncil of THE MUSEUM OF MODERN ART, New York,
aveled to TATE GALLERY, London, December 5, 1968–
nuary 26, 1969; THE MUSEUM OF MODERN ART, New
ork, March 6–April 27, 1969

NCINNATI ART MUSEUM, Ohio, October 3, 1969–
arch 29, 1970, *Paintings from the Guggenheim Museum,*
Loan Exhibition of Modern Paintings Covering the Period
49–1965, from The Solomon R. Guggenheim Museum*, no.13

References:

HESS, THOMAS B., *Willem de Kooning*, New York, 1959,
pl.139 (as *Untitled Abstraction*)

HUNTER, SAM, *Modern American Painting and Sculpture*,
New York, 1959, pl.30

BANNARD, DARBY, "Willem de Kooning's Retrospective at
The Museum of Modern Art", *Artforum*, vol.VII, no.8,
April 1969, p.43, ill.

55.1419

The complexity and apparent contradictions of de
Kooning's style from the late forties to the early sixties
can best be understood in terms of a conflict between
figure-ground and "all over" painting. This conflict
arose as a result of de Kooning's acute awareness of what
was "good" in current art (Pollock's "drip" paintings at
that time) and his desire to work in that area, as opposed
to the idiom in which he felt most secure – the tradition
of draftsmanship leading from Ingres through Cubism.
After his successful "all over" black-and-white paintings
executed in the late forties, de Kooning turned back to
the figure and painted his famous series of women. These
women (eg., *Woman I*, 1950–52, The Museum of Modern
Art) represent an attempt to reconcile "all over" with a
figure, resulting in an unfocused image which provides a
traditional structure or armature to the painting. *Composition* is one of a series of paintings dating from 1955 in
which a lingering after-image of a woman or women can
be detected or, in other terms, in which the woman has
dissolved into the landscape (eg., *Woman as Landscape*,
private collection). The underlying structure of *Composition*
is composed of side-by-side rectangles, obscured by a thick,
active paint surface. These rectangles tauten the composition through their relationship to the edges of the support.

Planes by Color, Large Nude (Plans par Couleur, Grand Nu
1909

Oil on canvas, 58⅝ x 70″ (149 x 177.8 cm.)

Signed and dated l.r. "Kupka//1909"

Provenance:

Madame Eugénie Kupka, Puteaux, France
Richard Feigen Gallery, Inc., New York
Gift, Mrs. Andrew P. Fuller, New York, 1968

Exhibitions:

SALON D'AUTOMNE, Paris, 1911, no.811

SALON DES INDÉPENDANTS, Paris, 1912, Versions I, II, III,
as nos.1833, 1834, 1835

MUSÉE DU JEU DE PAUME, Paris, 1936, *Kupka – Mucha*

GALERIE S.V.U. MANES, Prague, 1946, *Kupka*

SALON DES INDÉPENDANTS, Paris, 1954.

IV BIENAL DE SÃO PAULO, September–December, 1957,
no.45 (France), p.221

MUSÉE NATIONAL D'ART MODERNE, Paris, May 27–July 13,
1958, *Kupka*, no.5, p.18

References:

DEGAND, LÉON, "Kupka", *Art d'aujourd'hui*, Series 3,
nos.3–4, February–March 1952, pp.54–58, ill.
La Revue des Arts, vol.7, November 1957, opp. p.266, ill
VACHTOVA, LUDMILA, *Frank Kupka, Pioneer of Abstract Art*
New York, 1968, no.87, p.73, ill.

68.1860

František Kupka 1871–1957

František Kupka was born September 23, 1871, at Opocno
in eastern Bohemia. He studied art in Prague (1887–1891)
and in Vienna (1891–94). In 1894 he arrived in Paris, finally
settling in Puteaux outside Paris in 1906.

During the early years in Paris, Kupka worked as an
illustrator. It was not until after 1908 that he could devote
time to the intensive personal research on form and color
which were to characterize his distinctive style and make
him – along with Kandinsky and Malevitch – one of the
pioneers of abstract painting.

Kupka exhibited his first totally abstract paintings at the
Salon d'Automne in 1912. During the pre-World War I
period, he exhibited frequently both at the *Salon d'Automne*
and the *Salon des Indépendants*. He participated briefly in the
Puteaux group *La section d'or* alongside his friend Jacques
Villon in 1912.

From 1914–1918 Kupka was active in the Czech resistance
in France. After the war he continued to paint and teach,
both in Paris and on short trips to Prague. Although he
retained his Czechoslovakian nationality, he considered
himself better understood in France than in his own country. Upon his death June 24, 1957, at Puteaux, a major part
of the artist's work was left to the Musée National d'Art
Moderne in Paris.

1909 marks a decisive turning point in Kupka's style in
his visible orientation towards abstraction. Although the
artist had the opportunity in Paris to become acquainted
with Divisionism, Cubism and Fauvism, he allied himself
to none of these movements. Nevertheless their influence
can be felt in his *Large Nude*, characterized by the division
of the canvas into separate and consecutive planes of
complementary color.

Three black and white preliminary sketches (dated 1909)
exist at the Fogg Art Museum, Cambridge. There are
three pastel studies (dated 1909–1910) at the Musée
National d'Art Moderne, Paris.

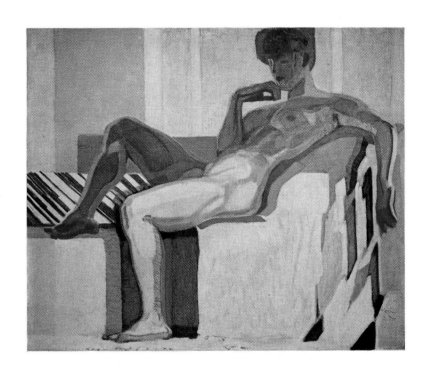

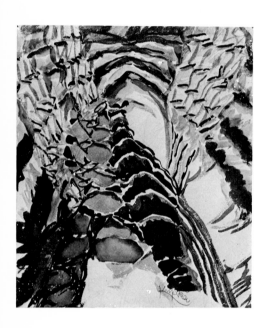

FRANTIŠEK KUPKA

Study for "The Tale of Pistils and Stamens" (Le Conte de Pistils et d'Étamines). 1919

Watercolor, 10³/₄ x 9³/₈″ (27.3 x 23.8 cm.)

Signed l.r. "Kupka"

Provenance:
Galerie Karl Flinker, Paris, 1964

Exhibitions:

GALERIE KARL FLINKER, Paris, May–July 1964, *Kupka, Pastel et Gouaches 1906–1945*, no.40

THE SOLOMON R. GUGGENHEIM MUSEUM, New York, June 28–October 1, 1967, *Museum Collection, Seven Decades, A Selection* (Checklist)

SPENCER A. SAMUELS AND COMPANY, LTD., New York, March 25–April 27, 1968, *Frank Kupka*, no.41, ill.

THE SOLOMON R. GUGGENHEIM MUSEUM, New York, July 8–September 14, 1969, *Selected Sculpture and Works on Paper*, p.50, ill.

References:

CASSOU, JEAN and FÉDIT, DENISE, *Kupka*, Stuttgart, 1964, p.41, ill.

64.1704

This is one of many studies for *Le conte de pistils et d'étamines* which was exhibited at the *Salon d'Automne* in 1919. The theme and its treatment denote the artist's lifelong interest in organic structure and cosmic cycles.

Throughout Kupka's life he was haunted by a native baroque sensibility which he sought to channel in what he wished to be a highly rational art. The tension between these two contradictory facets of the artist's personality and aims is strongly felt in this composition: between the undulating and basically ambiguous concept of space and the meticulous and even rhythm of the chromatic relationships.

FRANTIŠEK KUPKA

The Colored One (La Colorée). 1919–1920

Oil on canvas, 25 1/2 x 21 1/4" (64.8 x 54 cm.)

Signed l.l. "Kupka"

Provenance:
Richard L. Feigen, Inc., New York
Gift, Mrs. Andrew P. Fuller, New York, 1966

Exhibitions:
THE SOLOMON R. GUGGENHEIM MUSEUM, New York,
June 28–October 1, 1967, *Museum Collection, Seven
Decades, A Selection* (Checklist)

SPENCER A. SAMUELS AND COMPANY, LTD., New York,
March 25–April 27, 1968, *Frank Kupka,* no.40, ill.

66.1810

Although by 1919 Kupka rarely reverted to what could
be recognized as a figurative theme, this painting is not as
much a digression as it might seem. The compositional
motif of a large circle intersected by circles of lesser size,
thus creating a rhythmical pattern of sectors and ellipses,
was quite frequent in his art (from *Disks of Newton* 1912,
Philadelphia Museum of Art, to the *Autour d'un point*
series, worked on as late as 1930), and it provides the basic
structure for *The Colored One.*

The colors, characteristically brilliant and translucent and
strictly limited to primary and secondary values, are
graded and related according to their natural occurrence
in the spectrum. Such a simplification intensifies their
power as pure color.

FRANTIŠEK KUPKA

Study for "Le Jaillissement". 1921–22

Gouache, 10³/₄ x 6¹/₂″ (27.3 x 16.5 cm.)

Signed l.r. "Kupka"

Provenance:
Gift, Galerie Karl Flinker, Paris 1964

Exhibitions:

GALERIE KARL FLINKER, Paris, May–July 1964, *Kupka, Pastels et Gouaches 1906–1945,* no.50

THE SOLOMON R. GUGGENHEIM MUSEUM, New York, June 28–October 1, 1967, *Museum Collection, Seven Decades, A Selection* (Checklist)

THE SOLOMON R. GUGGENHEIM MUSEUM, New York, July 8–September 14, 1969, *Selected Sculpture and Works on Paper,* p.51, ill.

64.1705

Two themes are found throughout Kupka's mature work (after 1910). The first, that of circular motion, is visible in the study for *The Tale of Pistils and Stamens.* The second, that of a juxtaposition of vertical planes, is illustrated here. For the artist, both had symbolic meaning: the first, that of the recurring cosmic cycle; the second, that of man's reach for the absolute.

The title of this study (and the several paintings Kupka did on the same theme) could be freely translated "Upward Thrust". Through the juxtaposition of relatively narrow, straight-edged planes, on both vertical and diagonal axes, it would be possible to suppose that the original inspiration came from central European Baroque architecture which Kupka knew well, with its tight vertical groupings of squared-off columns, the diagonal digressions of the molding contours as seen from below, the increased complexity of forms as the eye moves upward, and the mirror images multiplying all effects.

FRANTIŠEK KUPKA

Two Blues, No.2 (Deux Bleus, No.2). 1956

Oil on canvas, 38¹/₄ x 33³/₈″ (97.2 x 84.6 cm.)

Signed and dated l.r. "Kupka//1956"

Provenance:
Madame Eugénie Kupka, Courbevoie, France
Gift, Madame Eugénie Kupka, 1962

Exhibitions:
V BIENAL DE SÃO PAULO, September–December 1957,
no.43 (France), p.221

THE SOLOMON R. GUGGENHEIM MUSEUM, New York,
June 28–October 1, 1967, *Museum Collection, Seven
Decades, A Selection* (Checklist)

62.1618

Two Blues is characteristic of Kupka's late austere style,
emphasizing a dynamic asymmetrical relationship between
a few simple, flat vertical planes of contrasting color.

In 1954, Kupka executed another, slightly smaller and
unsigned but otherwise largely identical painting (Collection Louis Carré, Paris), which, although not numbered
(as is this one) was probably *No.1* in the artist's mind.

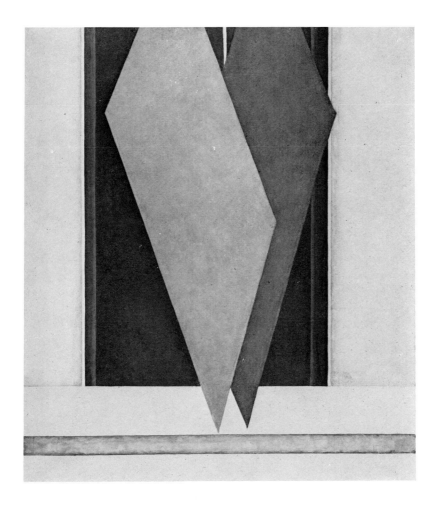

Wifredo Lam 1902–

Wifredo Lam was born on December 8, 1902, in Sagua la Grande, Cuba. After studying at the Beaux-Arts schools of Havana, Madrid and Barcelona, he went to Paris in 1938. There he met Picasso, who introduced him to André Breton, Max Ernst and Victor Brauner. Lam joined the Surrealist movement and had his first major one-man exhibition in Paris at the Galerie Pierre in 1939.

In 1941 Lam returned to the Antilles with Breton, Masson, Lévi-Strauss and others. From 1947–52 he lived in Cuba, New York and Paris, traveling to Italy and England. He left Cuba in 1952 for Paris, to return to America in 1957–58 as a member of the Graham Foundation for Advanced Study in the Fine Arts in Chicago. Lam lived intermittently in New York. He now resides in Paris.

Rumblings of the Earth. (La Rumeur de la Terre). 1950

Oil on canvas, $59^3/_4$ x 112" (151.7 x 284.4 cm.)

Not inscribed

Provenance:
the artist
Gift, Mr. and Mrs. Joseph Cantor, Indianapolis, Indiana, 1959

Exhibitions:
MINISTRY OF EDUCATION, Parque Central, Havana, October 2–15, 1950, *Lam: Obras Recientes*, no.9
ICA GALLERY, London, 1952, *Wifredo Lam*, no.8
THE SOLOMON R. GUGGENHEIM MUSEUM, New York, October 21, 1959–June 19, 1960, *Inaugural Selection* (Checklist)
UNIVERSITY OF NOTRE DAME ART GALLERY, Indiana, January 8–29, 1961, *Wifredo Lam*, pp.18–19, ill.
ART GALLERY/CENTER FOR INTER-AMERICAN RELATIONS, New York, July 2–September 14, 1969, *Latin American Paintings from The Solomon R. Guggenheim Museum*, p.18, p.19, ill.

References:
Cahiers d'art, Paris, 1951, p.181, ill.
Espacio, Havana, November–December 1954, p.38, ill.
Medium, Communication Surréaliste (Wifredo Lam issue), January 1955, ill. facing p.17

59.1525

"This picture took form in 1950 without any definite or literary idea behind it, by emerging, as it were, from the day-to-day strivings of a painter who, faced with a canvas, constructs an organic composition out of the simple elements and complex forms of his language. It was only afterwards that these forms became strictly poetical symbols, such as carnal love, materialized as flames in the right-hand side of the picture. I call this work *Rumblings of the earth* by which I mean the earth and its imperatives, the substances of which it is composed and the forms they assume: unending transmutations, fertilizations, births and deaths." (Statement by Wifredo Lam, May 1969, Center for Inter-American Relations, 1969)

FERNAND LÉGER

*The Great Parade (final version). (La Grande Parade, état
définitif).* 1954

Oil on canvas, $117^3/_4$ x $157^1/_2''$ (299 x 400 cm.)

Not inscribed

Provenance:
the artist
Galerie Maeght, Paris, 1962

Exhibitions:

LA MAISON DE LA PENSÉE FRANÇAISE, Paris, 1954, *Fernand
Léger; Oeuvres récentes, 1953–1954*, no.47, ill.

III BIENAL DE SÃO PAULO, June–October 1955, no.28
(France), p.137

MUSÉE DES ARTS DÉCORATIFS, Paris, June–October 1956,
Fernand Léger, no.157, ill.

STEDELIJK MUSEUM, Amsterdam, December 1956–January
1957, *Wegbereider*, no.78

HAUS DER KUNST, Munich, March-May 1957, *Fernand
Léger*, no.138, ill.

KUNSTHALLE, Basel, May 22–June 23, 1957, *Fernand
Léger*, no.102, ill.

THE SOLOMON R. GUGGENHEIM MUSEUM, New York,
February 28–April 29, 1962, *Fernand Léger, Five Themes
and Variations*, no.111, ill.

THE SOLOMON R. GUGGENHEIM MUSEUM, New York,
April 30–September 1, 1965, *Paintings from the Collection of
The Solomon R. Guggenheim Museum*, no.72, ill.

THE METROPOLITAN MUSEUM OF ART, New York, November 15, 1967–April 1, 1968, *Selections from the Collection of
The Solomon R. Guggenheim Museum*

References:

Cahiers d'art, Paris, 1954, t.2, pp.131–132, 173, ill.
Heures Claires, Paris, 1955, no.123, ill.
VERDET, ANDRÉ, *Fernand Léger*, Geneva, 1955, p.44, pl.54
DESCARGUES, PIERRE, *Fernand Léger*, Paris, 1955, p.160, ill.
JARDOT, MAURICE, *Léger*, Paris, 1956, pl.17
DELEVOY, ROBERT L., *Léger*, Geneva, 1962, p.112, ill.
TADINI, EMILIO, *Fernand Léger*, Milan, 1964, no.XVI, ill.
HAMILTON, GEORGE HEARD, *Painting and Sculpture in
Europe 1880–1940*, Baltimore, 1967, pl.91(B)
ARNASON, H. H., *History of Modern Art*, New York, 1968,
p.204, pl.74
OSMAN, RANDOLPH E., *New York, ein Kunstführer*, Reutlingen, 1969, p.201, fig.99

62.1619

The Great Parade (final version), painted a year before the
artist's death, is considered the definitive work of his
entire career. It is not only the culmination of several
cycles developed over the preceding fifteen years (*Divers,
Cyclists, Constructors, Country Outing*, and the *Circus*
theme) but a synthesis of Léger's distinctive preoccupations with regard to color, form and composition. Here,
"forthright color" is truly an autonomous substance,
circulating freely throughout the canvas. The human
figures, characteristically robust and mechanically articulated, are manipulated as purely formal elements. The
composition is the most elaborate of the artist's career,
not only in its complex tangle of forms but in the
contrapuntal relationship between line and color.

Preparedness. December 1968

Magna on canvas, 3 panels, 120 x 216″ (305 x 549 cm.)

Signed on reverse of third panel, "Roy Lichtenstein 1968"

Provenance: from the artist, through Leo Castelli Gallery, New York, 1969

Exhibitions:

THE SOLOMON R. GUGGENHEIM MUSEUM, New York, September 18–November 9, 1969, *Roy Lichtenstein*, no.55 ill.

69.1885.1–3

Roy Lichtenstein 1923–

Roy Lichtenstein was born in 1923 in New York City. In 1939 he attended the Art Students League and from 1940 to 1943 he studied at Ohio State University. From 1943 to 1946 he served in Europe in the armed forces, returning to Ohio State for a BFA in 1946 and a MFA in 1949. He was an instructor at Ohio State for the following two years, moving to Cleveland in 1951, where he remained, painting and assuming odd jobs for a living, until 1957. After 1957, he taught at New York State University, Oswego (1957–1960) and Rutgers University (1960–1963), moving back to New York City in 1963.

Lichtenstein's paintings of the mid-fifties covered such subjects as treaty signings, cowboys and Indians, and other vintage Americana. Although he abandoned these paintings for a form of Abstract Expressionism which occupied him from 1957–1960, he soon began to introduce comic figures into these paintings and, in 1961, to work with the cartoon alone. Portraying comic strips and the isolated object of common origin, his thematic material grew to include paintings after such masters as Cezanne, Picasso, Mondrian, and Monet; picture post-card landscapes; a series of brush-stroke paintings which made pointed reference to Action Painting; and since 1966, a body of work concerned with the decorative style of the 1930's. He has developed his technical range to include plastics, enamels, silk-screens, ceramics and sculpture.

Lichtenstein has participated in numerous group exhibitions in America and abroad since 1962 and showed in the United States pavilion at the 1966 Venice Biennale. Over the past few years, his work has been honored by several major museum retrospective exhibitions.

In *Preparedness* one finds the consistent features of Lichtenstein's style (primary colors, mechanical line, Ben Day dots) as well as certain determinants of his late 1960's development: the rhythmic repetition of geometric and modular units and a formal design that is reminiscent of the thirties. Lichtenstein intended the painting to be a loaded comment not only about the innocent optimism of the thirties, as reflected in the murals of the period, but also as a statement about the "heroic" nature of that type of composition. The painting recalls, coincidentally, another unique painting of a similar nature, Léger's *The City*. The left-hand panel of *Preparedness*, a study in blue, black, and white, conveys the impression of a factory interior, replete with smoking chimneys, that is reminiscent of Demuth. Lichtenstein accomplishes the transition from the left-hand panel to the center and right-hand panel, predominantly red and yellow in color, by means of a blue quarter-circle and the use of a prominent sequence of diagonals. This arrangement is complemented by a brief pattern of blue Ben Day dots in the second and third panels. The repetition of heads not only reinforces the vigor of his social comment but it creates a striking pattern of receding forms in the lower portion of the middle panel. In terms of both scope and achievement, *Preparedness* can be considered the summation of Lichtenstein's exploration of the thirties as a theme for his recent painting and sculpture.

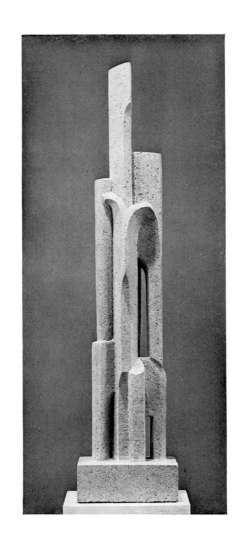

Jacques Lipchitz 1891–

Jacques Lipchitz (né Chaim Jacob) was born in Druskieniki, Lithuania on August 22, 1891. He came to Paris in 1909 to study sculpture at the École des Beaux Arts. Early in his career he became friends with Max Jacob, Modigliani, Soutine, Gris, and Picasso. He did not fully accept the Cubist style until about 1915; from then until 1925, however, Lipchitz was the most prominent sculptor within the Cubist movement. His first one-man exhibition was at the Léonce Rosenberg Gallery in 1920.

1925 was a significant year for Lipchitz. He became a citizen of France and married Berthe Kitrosser. His work, through his discovery of a new way of using the lost wax process, became looser and gradually freed itself from Cubism.

Lipchitz stayed in Paris until 1940, when the war forced him to flee to America where he has remained except for a 7 month return to Paris in 1946. He married Yulla Halberstadt in 1948. After a fire destroyed his Manhattan studio in 1953, Lipchitz moved to Hastings-on-Hudson, where he now lives and works.

Standing Personage (Personnage Debout). 1916

Stone, 42^{1}/$_{2}$″ (108 cm.) high

Incised on base front l.r. "JL 16"

Provenance: from the artist, through Fine Arts Associates, New York, 1958

Exhibitions:

GALERIE DE LA RENAISSANCE, Paris, June 13–June 28, 1930, *Cent Sculptures par Jacques Lipchitz.*

THE MUSEUM OF MODERN ART, New York, May 18–August 1, 1954, *The Sculpture of Jacques Lipchitz,* p. 29, ill.; traveled to WALKER ART CENTER, Minneapolis, October 1–December 12, 1954; CLEVELAND MUSEUM OF ART, Ohio, January 25–March 13, 1965

THE SOLOMON R. GUGGENHEIM MUSEUM, New York, October 21, 1959–June 19, 1962. *Inaugural Selection* (Checklist)

THE SOLOMON R. GUGGENHEIM MUSEUM, New York, July 8–September 14, 1969, *Selected Sculpture and Works on Paper,* p.134, ill.

References:

RAYNAL, MAURICE, *Jacques Lipchitz,* Paris, 1947, p.14, ill.

HAMMACHER, A. M., *Jacques Lipchitz, His Sculpture,* New York, 1960, fig. XXVIII

ROSENBLUM, ROBERT, *Cubism and Twentieth-Century Art,* New York, 1960, pl.210

VAN BORK, BERT, *Jacques Lipchitz, The Artist at Work,* New York, 1966, p.54, ill.

ARNASON, H. H., *History of Modern Art,* New York, 1968, pl.332

58.1526

Around 1915 Lipchitz began working in a new style: organic shapes were replaced by geometric forms and volume was virtually eliminated. These flattened, elongated figures were executed initially in clay and then in wood. *Standing Personage* of 1916 is made of stone, which lends a feeling of greater strength to this Synthetic Cubist sculpture. Lipchitz rapidly discarded the non-representational quality of these works and turned to a style closely allied to Cubist painting, in which his more solid but faceted figures were represented as if seen from many different angles.

Return of the Child. 1941

Granite, 45³/₄″ (116.2 cm.) high

Incised on base top, "J. Lipchitz"

Provenance:
Morton D. May, St. Louis
Fine Arts Associates, New York, 1959

Exhibitions:

THE SOLOMON R. GUGGENHEIM MUSEUM, New York,
October 21, 1959–June 19, 1960, *Inaugural Selection*
(Checklist; withdrawn April 4, 1960)

ARTS CLUB OF CHICAGO, April 19–May 19, 1960,
*Sculpture and Drawings by Sculptors from The Solomon
R. Guggenheim Museum*, no.16, ill.

THE SOLOMON R. GUGGENHEIM MUSEUM, New York,
August 30–October 8, 1961, *Modern Masters from the
Collection of The Solomon R. Guggenheim Museum*

THE SOLOMON R. GUGGENHEIM MUSEUM, New York,
July 8–September 14, 1969, *Selected Sculpture and Works on
Paper*, p.135, ill.

References:

ARNASON, H. H., *History of Modern Art,* New York, 1968,
pl.338

59.1550

Lipchitz had not been able to concentrate on his work
since the start of the war until he got to America in 1941.
He worked furiously upon his arrival in New York,
creating baroque, emotional sculptures. The sculptor
questions the meaning of the child in *Arrival* and *Return
of the Child* both of 1941: "Is it symbolic of my desire to
beget a child? – or is it perhaps my sculpture which I feel
must be saved? (quoted in Alfred Barr, *The Sculpture of
Jacques Lipchitz*, New York, 1954, p.17)

Lipchitz recalled for Alfred Barr the source of the image
of a mother and child which he did not discover until
later: "In 1935 while visiting a sister in Russia, we had
come out of a theater late at night in the rain and hearing
the voice of a woman singing in a loud hoarse voice,
traced it through the darkness until suddenly she appeared
under a street lamp, a legless cripple in a little cart, with
both arms raised and with her wet hair streaming down
her back as she sang". (ibid., p.18) The mother in *Return
of the Child* must be related to this scene.

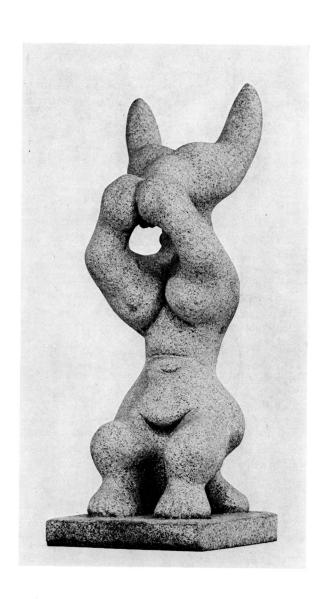

Saraband. 1959

Acrylic resin paint on canvas, 100¹/₂ x 149″ (255.2 x 378.5 cm.)

Signed and dated, l.l. "M. Louis 59"

Provenance:
Mrs. Marcella Louis, Washington, D.C.

Exhibitions:
THE SOLOMON R. GUGGENHEIM MUSEUM, New York, September 25–October 27, 1963, *Morris Louis, 1912–1962* no.10, ill.

LOS ANGELES COUNTY MUSEUM OF ART, February 15–March 26, 1967, *Morris Louis, 1912–1962;* traveled to MUSEUM OF FINE ARTS, Boston, April 13–May 24, 1967; CITY ART MUSEUM, St. Louis, June 16–August 6, 1967

THE METROPOLITAN MUSEUM OF ART, New York, October 18, 1969–February 8, 1970, *New York Painting and Sculpture, 1940–1970,* p.53, no.240; p.222, ill.

References:
ROSENBLUM, ROBERT, "Morris Louis at the Guggenheim Museum", *Art International,* Vol. VII, no.9, December 5, 1963, p.25, pl.3

ROSE, BARBARA, *American Art Since 1900,* New York, 196 p.225, fig.8–11

63.1685

Morris Louis 1912–1962

Morris Louis was born Morris Bernstein November 28, 1912 in Baltimore, Maryland. He studied at the Maryland Institute in Baltimore from 1929–1933 and resided in Baltimore until 1949. In 1952 he moved to Washington, D.C., where he was to remain for the rest of his life, teaching at the Workshop Center for the Arts from 1952–1956.

After painting in an impastoed late Cubist manner, Louis changed his style abruptly, shortly after a visit with Kenneth Noland to Helen Frankenthaler's studio where they saw her "stain" painting, *Mountains and Sea,* of 1952. From that time, Louis devoted himself to experiments in drenched color and open form. The "Veil" paintings of 1954 and 1958–59 are perhaps the most personal examples of this idiom.

In 1961 Louis began the series of "Unfurleds" where his color is concentrated into parallel rivulets which flow diagonally across the lower corners of the canvas. The bright pure hues as well as their increased opacity mark a distinct turning point in Louis's work. This departure evolved into the stripe paintings of the artist's final production (late 1961–1962). Morris Louis died of lung cancer September 7, 1962, in Washington, D.C.

Saraband is a major example of the artist's diaphanous or "Veil" style, in which layers of transparent color are superimposed, each one retaining nonetheless its own identity. The major portion of the canvas is somber, with pure bright colors relegated to the edges of the field. The even rhythm and symmetry of the composition reinforces its lyricism and sobriety. Louis's saturation of the raw canvas with successive veils of paint creates a surface of floating color planes in which foreground and background are indistinguishable. Because Louis did not divulge his working method, his paintings, and the series of "Veils" in particular, appear totally mysterious, seeming to defy any attempt to discern their construction. Of utmost significance, however, is the effect that the "Veils" offer of a run of color that appears to traverse the canvas flowing either from top to bottom or from bottom to top. Large in scale, Louis's paintings are metaphoric, creating a sensation of nature that does not refer to any specific phenomenon such as landscape. Despite a brief career, Louis succeeded in establishing so vital a body of painting as to make him a worthy successor to the New York School of Abstract Expressionism.

No.1–68, 1961–1962

Acrylic resin paint on unprimed canvas, 83 3/4 x 42″ (212.8 x 106.7 cm.)

Not inscribed

Provenance:
Estate of the artist through André Emmerich Gallery, New York, 1968

Exhibitions:

LOS ANGELES COUNTY MUSEUM OF ART, February 15–March 26, 1967, *Morris Louis, 1912–1962*; traveled to MUSEUM OF FINE ARTS, Boston, April 13–May 24; CITY ART MUSEUM, St. Louis, June 16–August 6, 1967, p.66, no.46, ill.

WORCESTER ART MUSEUM, Massachusetts, October 16–November 30, 1969, *The Direct Image in Contemporary American Painting*, no.4, ill.

References:

FRIED, MICHAEL, "The Achievement of Morris Louis", *Artforum*, February 1967, p.38, ill.

68.1846

Apparently influenced by the concentric ring paintings of his friend and neighbor, Kenneth Noland, in late 1961 Louis gradually redistributed his color into parallel bands. The taut ribbons of color, placed vertically, horizontally, and diagonally, present the most unequivocal statement of pure saturated color of the artist's career. Unlike the series of "Unfurled" paintings of 1960–1961, in which Louis opened up the center of the canvas, in paintings such as this, the tight clusters of color bands appear to abandon the "void" in favor of a quasi-symmetrical placement. In most instances the vertical bands of color are anchored at either the top or bottom of the canvas with rivulets of paint occasionally running off at the edges. In the subtle juxtaposition of colors, placement and edge, and in the creation of an atmospheric but non-illusionistic space, Louis proved himself a master, one of the foremost proponents of a new color abstraction.

Kasimir Malevitch 1878–1935

Kasimir Malevitch was born near Kiev on February 11, 1878. He attended the Kiev School of Art and in 1905 worked in Roerburg's private studio in Moscow. Through Roerburg, he met Larionov. He participated in the early Russian avant-garde exhibitions organized by Larionov, *Jack of Diamonds, Donkey's Tail* and *The Target*.

After coming under the influence of Futurism and Cubism, Malevitch arrived at a post-Cubist, non-objective, geometric style of painting called Suprematism. By 1919, he announced that the Suprematist movement was at an end and began to concentrate on writing. His writings include *From Cubism and Futurism to Suprematism* (1916), *On New Systems in Art, The Static and Speed* (1920), and *The Non-Objective World* (1927, *Bauhausbücher*).

In 1927 he visited Berlin where he had an exhibition of his work at the *Grosse Berliner Kunstausstellung*. There he met Bauhaus artists. After his retrospective at the Tretykov Gallery, Moscow, in 1929, he continued to write and paint portraits of his family until 1935 when he died in Leningrad.

KASIMIR MALEVITCH

Morning in the Country After Rain. c.1912

Oil on canvas, 31 1/2 x 31 3/8″ (80 x 79.7 cm.)

Signed l.r. "KM"

Provenance:
the artist, Berlin, c.1924–25
Rose Fried Gallery, New York, 1952

Exhibitions:
Moscow, March 1913, *The Target*
St. Petersburg, November 1913, *Exhibition of the Youth Union* (soyouze Molodeji)
THE SOLOMON R. GUGGENHEIM MUSEUM, New York, May 13–October 11, 1953, *Selection II* (Checklist)
ROSE FRIED GALLERY, New York, December 1952–January 1953
ART GALLERY OF TORONTO, April 2–May 9, 1954, *A Loan Exhibition of Paintings from The Solomon R. Guggenheim Museum*, no.55
THE SOLOMON R. GUGGENHEIM MUSEUM, New York, October 6, 1954–February 27, 1955, *Selection IV* (Checklist)
THE SOLOMON R. GUGGENHEIM MUSEUM, New York, July 26–October 9, 1955, *Selection V* (Checklist)
MONTREAL MUSEUM OF FINE ARTS, June 4–July 3, 1955, *A Selection from The Solomon R. Guggenheim Museum, New York*, no.36
TATE GALLERY, London, April 16–May 26, 1957, *Paintings from The Solomon R. Guggenheim Museum*, no.44; organized by THE SOLOMON R. GUGGENHEIM MUSEUM, traveled to GEMEENTEMUSEUM, The Hague, June 25–September 1; ATENEIUMIN TAIDEKOKOELMAT, Helsinki, September 27–October 20; GALLERIA NAZIONALE D'ARTE MODERNA, Rome, December 5, 1957–January 8, 1958; WALLRAF–RICHARTZ-MUSEUM, Cologne, January 26–March 30; MUSÉE DES ARTS DÉCORATIFS, Paris, April 23–June 1, 1958

THE SOLOMON R. GUGGENHEIM MUSEUM, New York, October 21, 1959–June 19, 1960, *Inaugural Selection* (Checklist)

PHILADELPHIA MUSEUM OF ART, November 2, 1961–January 7, 1962, *Guggenheim Museum Exhibition, A Loan Collection of Paintings, Drawings, and Prints from The Solomon R. Guggenheim Museum, New York*, no.101

THE SOLOMON R. GUGGENHEIM MUSEUM, New York, June 5–October 13, 1963, *Cézanne and Structure in Modern Painting*, ill.

THE SOLOMON R. GUGGENHEIM MUSEUM, New York, April 30–September 1, 1965, *Paintings from the Collection of The Solomon R. Guggenheim Museum*, no.20, ill.

MUSEUM OF FINE ARTS OF HOUSTON, October 21–December 8, 1965, *The Heroic Years: Paris, 1908–1914*

THE SOLOMON R. GUGGENHEIM MUSEUM, New York, June 28–October 1, 1967, *Museum Collection, Seven Decades, A Selection* (Checklist)

References:

ASHTON, DORE, "Fifty-Seventh Street in Review", *Art Digest*, vol.27, no.6, December 15, 1952, p.19, ill.

GRAY, CAMILLA, *The Great Experiment: Russian Art 1863–1922*, New York, 1962, pp.132, 291, pl.92

COURTHION, PIERRE, "Les Grandes Étapes de l'Art Contemporain 1907–1917", *XXe siècle*, no.26, May 1966, p.87, ill.

52.1327

Malevitch's paintings prior to 1913 have been characterized as "Cubo-Futurist" which could be translated as dynamic Cubism. Their geometric and tubular forms are reminiscent of Léger's production of c. 1913. Malevitch himself called the style "Non-sense Realism", relating it to the "Non-sense" poetry of his contemporaries.

White Bull (Stier). 1911

Oil on canvas, 39³/₄ x 53¹/₈″ (101 x 135 cm.)

Inscribed on reverse "Fz. Marc ii/Stier"

Provenance:
the artist
Bernhard Koehler, Berlin
Otto Stangl, Munich, 1951

Exhibitions:
NEUE SECESSION, Munich, 1916, *Franz Marc, Gedächtnis*, no.73

NATIONAL GALERIE, Berlin, 1928, *Neuere Deutsche Kunst aus Berliner Privatbesitz*, no.111

KESTNER-GESELLSCHAFT, Hanover, 1936, *Franz Marc – Gedächtnisausstellung*, no.24

HAUS DER KUNST, Munich, September–October 1949, *De Blaue Reiter*, no.230

THE SOLOMON R. GUGGENHEIM MUSEUM, New York, March 30–May 5, 1954, *Selection III* (Checklist)

VANCOUVER ART GALLERY, November 16–December 12, 1954, *The Solomon R. Guggenheim Museum, A Selection from the Museum Collection*, no.55

MONTREAL MUSEUM OF FINE ARTS, June 4–July 3, 1955, *A Selection from The Solomon R. Guggenheim Museum, New York*, no.37

THE SOLOMON R. GUGGENHEIM MUSEUM, New York, July 26–October 9, 1955, *Selection V* (Checklist)

TATE GALLERY, London, April 16–May 26, 1957, *Paintings from The Solomon R. Guggenheim Museum*, no.46; organized by THE SOLOMON R. GUGGENHEIM MUSEUM, traveled to GEMEENTEMUSEUM, The Hague, June 25–September 1; ATENEIUMIN TAIDEKOKOELMAT, Helsinki, September 27–October 20; GALLERIA NAZIONALE D'ARTE MODERNA, Rom December 5, 1957–January 8, 1958; WALLRAF–RICHARTZ-MUSEUM, Cologne, January 26–March 30; MUSÉE DES ART DÉCORATIFS, Paris, April 23–June 1, 1958

THE SOLOMON R. GUGGENHEIM MUSEUM, New York, August 30–October 8, 1961, *Modern Masters from the Collection of The Solomon R. Guggenheim Museum*

PHILADELPHIA MUSEUM OF ART, November 2, 1961–January 7, 1962, *Guggenheim Museum Exhibition, A Loan Collection of Paintings, Drawings, and Prints from The Solomon R. Guggenheim Museum, New York*, no.104

STÄDTISCHE GALERIE IM LENBACHHAUS, Munich, August 1 October 13, 1963, *Franz Marc*, no.101, pl.26; traveled to KUNSTVEREIN, Hamburg, November 9, 1963–January 1964, no.29, pl.26

THE SOLOMON R. GUGGENHEIM MUSEUM, New York, April 30–September 1, 1965, *Paintings from the Collection of The Solomon R. Guggenheim Museum*, no.19, ill.

THE SOLOMON R. GUGGENHEIM MUSEUM, New York, June 23–October 23, 1966, *Gauguin and the Decorative Style*

Franz Marc 1880–1916

Franz Marc was born in Munich February 8, 1880. Three trips to France between 1903 and 1912 and his acquaintance with Neo-Impressionism, Cubism and Robert Delaunay were decisive factors in liberating the artist from his initial academic training in Munich. Other catalysts in the development of the artist's personal style were his friendship with the colorist August Macke (from 1910) and with Kandinsky (from 1911) with whom he organized the first *Blaue Reiter* exhibition in Munich in 1911. These sucessive encounters increased his awareness of the unlimited possibilities of diagrammatic form and pure non-naturalistic color.

The year 1911 is considered the beginning of Marc's mature style, where forms are reduced to a rhythmic pattern of essential relationships and color is symbolic of a spiritual and natural order. At this time Marc's exclusive source of inspiration was the animal kingdom in which he found a harmony not present in the world of human beings. The artist's work became progressively abstract, attaining a pure abstraction of rhythmic forms in 1914.

With the outbreak of World War I, Marc was called to the front where he was killed at Verdun on March 4, 1916.

THE SOLOMON R. GUGGENHEIM MUSEUM, New York,
June 28–October 1, 1967, *Museum Collection, Seven Decades, A Selection* (Checklist)

References:

KANDINSKY and MARC, eds., *Der Blaue Reiter,* Munich, 1914, 2nd ed., ill. opposite p.91

SCHARDT, ALOIS J., *Franz Marc,* Berlin, 1936, p.163, cat. no.23, 1911; p.89, ill.

HAFTMANN, WERNER, *Painting in the Twentieth Century,* New York, 1965, vol. II, pl.274

1.1312

An essential theme of Marc's was that of animals at rest, exemplary of their "successful submission and adaptation to the laws of nature". In this unusually peaceful study of a bull, the vital tensions are resolved in a single self-contained and unified form.

White Bull was sold soon after it was painted to Bernhard Koehler, a wealthy relative of August Macke. Koehler, who met Marc in 1910, agreed to send the artist a monthly stipend in return for an option on his work and assistance in the development of a personal collection. Through the efforts of Marc and Macke, Koehler acquired some of the best examples of pre-World War I German painting including an important collection of Marcs.

FRANZ MARC

Yellow Cow (Die Gelbe Kuh). 1911

Oil on canvas, 55³/₈ x 74⁷/₈″ (145 x 190.2 cm.)

Signed on reverse "Marc"

Provenance:
Nell Walden, Berlin and Ascona, 1949

Exhibitions:
MODERNE GALERIE, Munich, 1911, *Der Blaue Reiter, die erste Ausstellung,* no.30, ill.

DER STURM, Berlin, 1919, *Sammlung Walden,* no.236

DER STURM, Berlin, 1921, *Leitung: Herwarth Walden, Zehn Jahre Sturm,* no.71

NATIONAL GALERIE, Berlin, 1928, *Neuere Deutsche Kunst aus Berliner Privatbesitz,* no.116

NEW BURLINGTON GALLERIES, London, 1938, *Twentieth-Century German Art,* no.164

KUNSTMUSEUM, Bern, 1944, *Der Sturm: Sammlung Nell Walden aus den Jahren 1912–20,* no.344

THE SOLOMON R. GUGGENHEIM MUSEUM, New York, May 13–October 11, 1953, *Selection II* (Checklist)

THE SOLOMON R. GUGGENHEIM MUSEUM, New York, August 30–October 8, 1961, *Modern Masters from the Collection of The Solomon R. Guggenheim Museum*

GALERIE MAEGHT, Paris, October 26–November 1962, *Der Blaue Reiter,* no.8 (Catalogue published as *Derrière le Miroir,* nos.133–134, October–November 1962)

STÄDTISCHE GALERIE IM LENBACHHAUS, Munich, August 10–October 13, 1963, *Franz Marc,* no.100, pl.25; traveled to KUNSTVEREIN, Hamburg, November 9, 1963–January 5, 1964, no.28, pl.29

THE SOLOMON R. GUGGENHEIM MUSEUM, New York, April 11–May 26, 1968, *Acquisitions of the 1930's and 1940's,* p.119, ill.

References:
MARC, FRANZ, "Die Konstruktiven Ideen der Neuen Malerei", *Pan II,* 1912, p.530

WALDEN, HERWARTH, ed., *Expressionismus die Kunstwende,* Berlin, 1918, p.35, ill.

WALDEN, HERWARTH, ed., *Einblick in Kunst, Expressionismus, Futurismus, Kubismus,* Berlin, 1924, p.31, ill.

DE RIDDER, ANDRÉ, "L'expressionnisme. – sur la déformation", *Le Centaure,* 3rd year, no.6, March 1929, p.143, ill.

SCHARDT, ALOIS J., *Franz Marc,* Berlin, 1936, p.163, cat. no.22, 1911; p.88, ill.

WALDEN, NELL, and SCHREYER, LOTHAR, eds., *Der Sturm, Ein Erinnerungs Buch,* Baden-Baden, 1954, ill. opp. p.48

SELZ, PETER, *German Expressionist Painting,* Berkeley, 1957, pp.203, 263, pl.81, p.16

LANKHEIT, KLAUS, *Franz Marc, Watercolors, Drawings, Writings,* New York, 1959, p.16.

SELZ, PETER, "Der Sturm: The Modern Movement Unfolds", *Art International,* vol. VI, no.9, November 25, 1962, p.22, ill.

49.1210

Yellow Cow, painted in Sindelsdorf in the Bavarian Alps, was shown at the first *Blaue Reiter* exhibition, which opened in Munich, December 18, 1911. The painting is an early example of Marc's mature style. The sculpted yet clearly defined volumes of the cow show a transitional stage between the artist's earlier, more naturalistic treatment of his subject matter and the later stylized flattening into planes. Similarly, the full, rounded contours and arabesques which dominate the composition will soon be replaced by more concise geometric forms.

A sketch for *Yellow Cow* (oil on wood) exists in a private collection in Germany. An almost identical yellow cow appears in a painting of 1912: *Cows, Red, Yellow and Green* (oil on canvas) in the Städtische Galerie, Munich.

FRANZ MARC

The Unfortunate Land of Tyrol (Das arme Land Tirol). 1913

Oil on canvas, 52 x 79″ (132 x 200.6 cm.)

Inscribed l.l. "M" and "Das arme Land Tirol"

Provenance:
William Beffie, Brussels and Brooklyn
Nierendorf Gallery, New York, 1946

Exhibitions:
DER STURM, Berlin, September–November 1913,
Erster Deutscher Herbstsalon, no.274

NEW BURLINGTON GALLERIES, London, 1938, *Twentieth-
Century German Art*, no.15

BUCHHOLZ GALLERY, New York, November 11–December 7, 1940, *Franz Marc*, no.13

THE SOLOMON R. GUGGENHEIM MUSEUM, New York,
May 13–October 11, 1953, *Selection II* (Checklist)

ART GALLERY OF TORONTO, April 2–May 9, 1954, *A Loan
Exhibition of Paintings from The Solomon R. Guggenheim
Museum*, no.57

THE SOLOMON R. GUGGENHEIM MUSEUM, New York,
October 6, 1954–February 27, 1955, *Selection IV*
(Checklist)

MONTREAL MUSEUM OF FINE ARTS, June 4–July 3, 1955,
*A Selection from The Solomon R. Guggenheim Museum,
New York*, no.38, ill.

THE SOLOMON R. GUGGENHEIM MUSEUM, New York,
July 26–October 9, 1955, *Selection V* (Checklist)

TATE GALLERY, London, April 16–May 26, 1957, *Paintings
from The Solomon R. Guggenheim Museum*, no.47; organized by THE SOLOMON R. GUGGENHEIM MUSEUM, traveled
to GEMEENTEMUSEUM, The Hague, June 25–September 1;
ATENEIUMIN TAIDEKOKOELMAT, Helsinki, September 27–
October 20; GALLERIA NAZIONALE D'ARTE MODERNA, Rome,
December 5, 1957–January 8, 1958; WALLRAF-RICHARTZ-
MUSEUM, Cologne, January 26–March 30; MUSÉE DES ARTS
DÉCORATIFS, Paris, April 23–June 1, 1958

THE SOLOMON R. GUGGENHEIM MUSEUM, New York,
October 21, 1959–June 19, 1960, *Inaugural Selection*
(Checklist)

THE SOLOMON R. GUGGENHEIM MUSEUM, New York,
August 30–October 8, 1961, *Modern Masters from the
Collection of The Solomon R. Guggenheim Museum*

STÄDTISCHE GALERIE IM LENBACHHAUS, Munich, August 10
October 13, 1963, *Franz Marc*, no.159; traveled to
KUNSTVEREIN, Hamburg, November 9, 1963–January 5,
1964, no.52, pl.50

THE SOLOMON R. GUGGENHEIM MUSEUM, New York,
July 1–September 13, 1964, *Van Gogh and Expressionism*

References:
DE RIDDER, ANDRÉ, "L'expressionnisme. – sur la valeur du
mot", *Le Centaure*, 3rd year, no.5, February 1929, p.115,
ill.

SADLER, M., *Modern Art and Revolution*, London, 1932, p.1

SCHARDT, ALOIS J., *Franz Marc*, Berlin, 1936, p.165, cat.
no.20, 1913; p.125, ill.

MYERS, BERNARD S., *The German Expressionists, A Generation in Revolt*, New York, 1957, p.226, pl.45

46.1040

Themes of destruction appeared not only in Marc's work of 1912–13 but in Kandinsky's of the same period. Although neither artist admitted to premonitions of World War I, this painting by Marc is expressive of impending disaster. The graveyard, the house on fire, the starved horses and the vulture are unmistakably ominous signs. The sense of doom is reinforced by the agressively jagged black lines and somber colors as well as the chaotic organization of the canvas, symbolic of an order destroyed.

Toward the end of 1913, Marc produced a second version, which he repainted almost beyond recognition in 1914. It is now in the Bayerische Staatsgemäldesammlungen, Munich. A sketch for the first version exists in the Galerie Stangl collection in Munich.

FRANZ MARC

Red Deer (Rotes Reh). 1913

Gouache, 16^1/$_8$ x 13^3/$_8$" (41 x 34 cm.)

Inscribed l.r. "amicalement Fz Marc//I.13"

Provenance:
Hildegarde Prytek, New York, 1948

Exhibitions:

THE SOLOMON R. GUGGENHEIM MUSEUM, New York,
May 13–October 11, 1953, *Selection II* (Checklist)

VANCOUVER ART GALLERY, November 16–December 12,
1954, *The Solomon R. Guggenheim Museum, A Selection
from the Museum Collection,* no.56

MONTREAL MUSEUM OF FINE ARTS, June 4–July 3, 1955,
*A Selection from The Solomon R. Guggenheim Museum,
New York,* no.39

THE SOLOMON R. GUGGENHEIM MUSEUM, New York,
August 30–October 8, 1961, *Modern Masters from the
Collection of The Solomon R. Guggenheim Museum*

STÄDTISCHE GALERIE IM LENBACHHAUS, Munich, August 10–
October 13, 1963, *Franz Marc,* no.166; traveled to
KUNSTVEREIN, Hamburg, November 9, 1963–January 5,
1964, no.77

THE SOLOMON R. GUGGENHEIM MUSEUM, New York,
April 11–May 26, 1968, *Acquisitions of the 1930's and 1940's,*
p.116, ill.

THE SOLOMON R. GUGGENHEIM MUSEUM, New York,
July 8–September 14, 1969, *Selected Sculpture and Works
on Paper,* p.56, ill.

References:

SCHARDT, ALOIS J., *Franz Marc,* Berlin, 1936, p.167, cat.
no.5, 1913

BÜNEMANN, HERMANN, *Franz Marc, Zeichnungen –
Aquarelle,* Munich, 1952, p.53, ill.

48.1180

Red Deer is another example of an animal in repose, in
basic harmony with his surroundings. Characteristic of
the artist's development in 1913 is the more abstract conception, a more angular treatment and a more unified
stable rhythm. The animal's submission to a total cosmic
order is visually emphasized by the intersecting lines and
the broad, overlapping planes of color.

At least two watercolors of *Red Deer* (also dated 1913)
exist in private collections in Düsseldorf and Zürich.

References:

LANKHEIT, KLAUS, *Franz Marc, Watercolors, Drawings, Writings*, New York, 1960, p.38, ill.

FRANZ MARC

Horse Asleep (Träumendes Pferd, Schlafendes Pferd). 1913?

Gouache and charcoal, 15⁷/₈ x 18¹/₂" (40.3 x 47 cm.)

Signed c.r. "M".

Provenance:
Frederick M. Stern, New York
Karl Nierendorf Gallery, New York, 1944

Exhibitions:

THE SOLOMON R. GUGGENHEIM MUSEUM, New York, August 30–October 8, 1961, *Modern Masters from the Collection of The Solomon R. Guggenheim Museum*

PHILADELPHIA MUSEUM OF ART, November 2, 1961–January 7, 1962, *Guggenheim Museum Exhibition, A Loan Collection of Paintings, Drawings, and Prints from The Solomon R. Guggenheim Museum, New York*, no.104

STÄDTISCHE GALERIE IM LENBACHHAUS, Munich, August 10–October 13, 1963, *Franz Marc*, no.168; traveled to KUNSTVEREIN, Hamburg, November 9, 1963–January 5, 1964, no.78

THE SOLOMON R. GUGGENHEIM MUSEUM, New York, July 8–September 14, 1969, *Selected Sculpture and Works on Paper*, p.57, ill.

44.937

The extreme archetypal abstraction of *Horse Asleep* is characteristic of Marc's style in 1913. Although the horses are clearly recognizable, no naturalistic details remain. More than before, the subject has become a pretext – an organizational factor – for a harmonious composition of lines and colored planes.

By this time, forms as material volumes no longer interested the artist. On the contrary, his forms are open and transparent, no different from the ambient space. Color is merely a constellation of colored energy as line is a vector of cosmic forces. All are of the same indivisible and intangible substance, momentarily arrested in their course of flux and change.

Agnes Martin 1912–

Agnes Martin was born in Maklin, Canada, in 1912, and came to the United States in 1932. She received her MFA from Columbia University and has taught at the University of New Mexico and Eastern Oregon College. Her first one-man exhibition was held at the Betty Parsons Gallery, New York, in 1958. The Robert Elkon Gallery has represented her in New York since 1963. The artist resides in New Mexico.

Martin's painting is ascetic, rational and extremely subtle. She restricts herself radically in every sense. Her grounds are large, flat fields of unpainted canvas or neutral color. On these irrevocably two-dimensional surfaces she draws repeated symmetrical patterns, using the most elementary implements and media: draftsman's pencils, neutral stains and simple measuring tools such as T-squares or yardsticks. Within this voluntarily narrow range there are multiple variations: minute differences in interval, an almost invisible irregularity of line, zones of greater and lesser density or intensity. Organized according to definite modular systems, her work may be classified as "Systemic". Paradoxically, it is the strict organizational systems themselves which produce the artist's sensitively modulated surfaces.

AGNES MARTIN

White Flower. 1960

Oil on canvas, 71 7/8 x 72″ (182.6 x 182.9 cm.)

Signed on reverse "M–P"

Provenance:
Anonymous gift, 1963

Exhibitions:

THE SOLOMON R. GUGGENHEIM MUSEUM, New York, July 20–August 29, 1965, *Some Recent Gifts*

THE SOLOMON R. GUGGENHEIM MUSEUM, New York, March 29–April 20, 1969, *American Paintings from the Museum Collection*

63.1653

In *White Flower,* Agnes Martin has created a radically simple format and organizational scheme within which there are myriad, albeit minute and infinitely subtle variations of color, interval and touch. The perception of these variations depends upon intimate and careful investigation. There is a whitish-gray grid of rectangles drawn on a cool, dark-gray stained surface. The rows of rectangles differ infinitesimally in size. Within alternating rectangles, there are two pairs of two small parallel lines. The staccato rhythms of these graphic accents offer, perhaps, within the impersonal whole, the barest hint of a personal handwriting. The thin tracery of continuous lines forming the grid is not rigidly ruled, but lightly drawn and slightly uneven. The two tones are as neutral as possible, thin stains without painterly texture. Nothing sensuous detracts from the cool, detached, even remote impression of the whole.

Untitled. 1948

Pencil and watercolor, 15³/₈ x 11¹/₂″ (38.5 x 29.2 cm.)

Signed l.r. "H.M"

Provenance:
the artist
Le Point Cardinal, Paris

Exhibitions:
THE SOLOMON R. GUGGENHEIM MUSEUM, New York,
July 8–September 14, 1969, *Selected Sculpture and Works
on Paper*, p.61, ill.

65.1772

Henri Michaux 1899–

Henri Michaux was born in Namur, Belgium on May 24,
1899. He grew up in Brussels, where he began preparing for
a medical degree. He later abandoned his medical studies
and in 1924 settled in Paris.

Michaux is better known as an author and poet than as a
painter. He began to write in 1922 and published his first
poetic essay in 1927. His first graphic works date from the
latter period, products of free association transmitted
through the Surrealist technique of automatic writing.

In 1937 Michaux began to draw and paint regularly, parallel to his activity as a writer. In both creative endeavors he
sought to portray subconscious and visionary experiences.
The artist's preferred mediums were gouache and watercolor, perhaps for the freedom and fluidity which they
allow. His first exhibition was held in 1937 at the Galerie
Pierre, Paris.

Michaux's interest in the subconscious workings of the
human mind led him to experiment with hallucinogenic
drugs in 1956. His attempts to transgress the limits of con-
sciousness are recorded in published essays as well as ink
drawings, which have appeared intermittently from that
time to the present. An important retrospective of the
artist's work was held at the Musée National d'Art Moderne, Paris in 1965.

Soon after the loss of his wife in a tragic accident, Michaux executed a series of several hundred watercolors
similar to this in a few weeks' time. The monstrous
organic form, the arid color wash and the fuzzy tentacular
line suggest – through a kind of visionary expressionism –
the artist's sense of desolation.

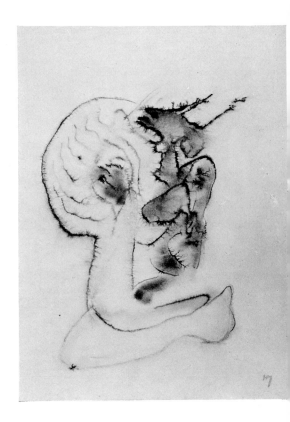

HENRI MICHAUX

Untitled. 1965

Watercolor, 15 x 11¹/₄″ (38 x 28.5 cm.)

Signed l.r. "H.M."

Provenance:
The artist
Le Point Cardinal, Paris, 1965

Exhibitions:
THE SOLOMON R. GUGGENHEIM MUSEUM, New York,
July 8–September 14, 1969, *Selected Sculpture and Works
on Paper*, p.61, ill.

.1775

Although abstract and non-representational, one could
assume from the few frugal lines that this watercolor is an
imaginary portrait. Its mysterious facelessness is both a
frightening and meaningful insight into Michaux's feelings about the essential anonymity of a man's identity.

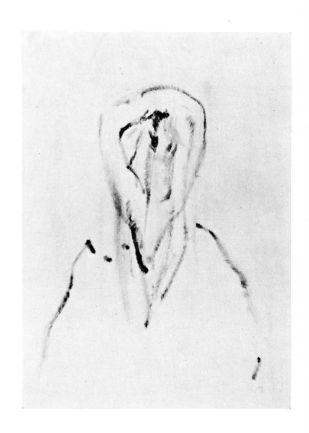

HENRI MICHAUX

Untitled. 1966

Gouache, $12^3/_4$ x $19^3/_4''$ (32.5 x 50.2 cm.)

Signed l.r. "M"

Provenance:
the artist
Le Point Cardinal, Paris, 1969

Exhibitions:
THE SOLOMON R. GUGGENHEIM MUSEUM, New York,
July 8–September 14, 1969, *Selected Sculpture and Works
on Paper*, p.62, ill.

69.1876

Numerous gouaches of this kind were executed by the
artist between 1964 and 1966, characterized by the
disintegration of form into ciphers of pure movement.
Along with a series of drawings in India ink executed
between 1959 and 1964, these works appear as the most
airy, dynamic and spontaneously gestural of the artist's
career to date.

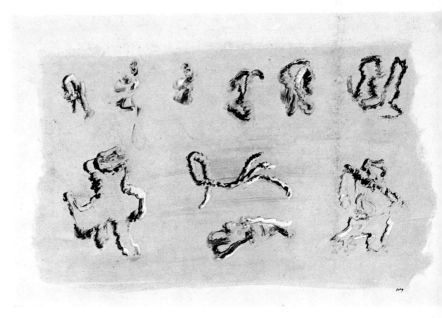

Joan Miró 1893–

Joan Miró was born April 20, 1893, in Barcelona. He attended art schools in Barcelona and was familiar with Cubism and the Dada movement before moving to Paris in 1919. After settling in Paris, he summered at his parents' farm in Montroig (Spain) for many years.

Although he had one-man shows in Barcelona (1919) and in Paris (1921), his first successful exhibition was in Paris in 1925, at the height of Surrealism. The acquaintance with Jean Arp, André Masson and Paul Klee's work encouraged Miró to formulate the world of his imagination through a repertory of spontaneous forms and dream images. However, through the color, texture and plastic presence of his forms, a sensual relationship with reality persists throughout the evolution of his career.

Imaginary images are transformed into more rhythmically patterned compositions in around 1940 and finally into a gestural idiom in the 1950's and 1960's with emphasis on strong color and energetically expressive calligraphy. Moreover in the fifties, Miró turned to ceramics and sculpture, proof of the strongly sensual and tactile side of his nature, so often overlooked due to his powerfully imaginative imagery. The artist resides today in Palma de Mallorca.

Untitled. 1917

Pencil, 7³/₈ x 5⁷/₈″ (18.6 x 13.5 cm.)

Signed and dated l.r. "Miró.//1917"

Provenance:
Galleria d'Arte del Naviglio, Milan, 1959

Exhibitions:
THE SOLOMON R. GUGGENHEIM MUSEUM, New York, July 8–September 14, 1969, *Selected Sculpture and Works on Paper*, p.63, ill.

59.1539

This drawing of a male nude was done in Barcelona, probably at the Sant Lluch circle, where Miró sketched from the model until 1918. That drawing was difficult for him is confirmed by his teachers in Barcelona as well as by his own statement: "I am a colorist, but zero when it comes to form. I can't learn to distinguish a straight line from a curve." (quoted in Michel Leiris, "Joan Miró", *Documents*, October 1929, p.263).

Although at first glance the figure seems heavy and graceless, the dynamic opposition between straight and curved lines, the rhythmic arabesque of the total form, as well as the precise and delicate line rendering infuse the silhouette with vigor and plastic grace.

Figures of similar date and treatment are recorded in Miró's Sant Lluch sketchbooks. Furthermore, in a *Standing Nude* of 1918 (Pierre Matisse Gallery, New York), one finds a comparable but more deliberately exaggerated stylization of form.

JOAN MIRÓ

The Village Prades (View of Montroig). 1917

Oil on canvas, 26¹/₈ x 29″ (66.2 x 76.3 cm.)

Signed l.l. "Miró"

Provenance:

the artist, Barcelona, 1918
Signor Pedro Manach, Barcelona
Signora Pedro Manach, Barcelona, 1951
Mrs. Patricia Kane Matisse, New York, 1969
Gallery Loeb and Krugier, New York, 1969
Robert Elkon Gallery, New York, 1969

Exhibitions:

GALERIES DALMAU, Barcelona, February 16–March 3, 1918, *Exposició Joan Miró*, no.58

THE MUSEUM OF MODERN ART, New York, March 18–May 10, 1959, *Joan Miró*, no.4; traveled to LOS ANGELES COUNTY MUSEUM OF ART, June 10–July 21, 1959

MUSÉE NATIONAL D'ART MODERNE, Paris, June 28– November 1962, *Joan Miró*, no.4

NATIONAL MUSEUM OF MODERN ART, Tokyo, August 26–October 9, 1966, *Joan Miró Exhibition – Japan, 1966*, no.12, ill.; traveled to NATIONAL MUSEUM OF MODERN ART, Kyoto, October 20–November 30, 1966

ROBERT ELKON GALLERY, New York, September 27–October 29, 1969, *New Acquisitions*, no.16, ill.

References:

SOBY, JAMES THRALL, *Joan Miró*, New York, 1959, p.12, ill.

DUPIN, JACQUES, *Joan Miró, Life and Work*, New York, 1962, cat. no.38, ill.

PERUCHO, JUAN, *Joan Miró and Catalonia*, New York, 1968, pl.19

69.1894

1917 was a very productive year for the artist. Although he was living in Barcelona, he took several trips to Montroig and the surrounding villages of Cambrils, Ciurana, and Prades in order to immerse himself in nature, a vital source for his inspiration.

In comparison to his more naturalist production of the previous year, in the landscapes of 1917 the abstract rhythms of nature are more personally and energetically rendered, becoming the dominant theme of the painting. In this landscape of vital rhythms and autonomous expressive color, arcs, zigzags, curves and chevrons collide in a harmonious counterpoint. In contrast to this dynamically pulsating vision of nature, the village in the background appears detached and static.

The contrast is not accidental. At that period, Miró made a distinction between cosmic forces and man-made objects, the former being subject to expressive deformation, the latter retaining its objective appearance.

A similar treatment of nature is found in *The Path, Ciurana* of the same year (Collection M. E. Tappenbeck, Paris).

JOAN MIRÓ

Personage (Painting; Composition; Abstraction). 1925

Oil and tempera on canvas, 51¹/₈ x 38″ (129.7 x 96.5 cm.)

Signed and dated l.l. "Miró//1925"

Provenance:

the artist, Montroig
Pierre Loeb, Paris
Karl Nierendorf, New York
Estate of Karl Nierendorf, 1948

Exhibitions:

THE SOLOMON R. GUGGENHEIM MUSEUM, New York,
May 13–October 11, 1953, *Selection II* (Checklist)

ART GALLERY OF TORONTO, April 2–May 9, 1954, *A Loan
Exhibition of Paintings from The Solomon R. Guggenheim
Museum,* no.59

THE SOLOMON R. GUGGENHEIM MUSEUM, New York,
June 23–October 23, 1966, *Gauguin and the Decorative
Style*

THE SOLOMON R. GUGGENHEIM MUSEUM, New York,
June 28–October 1, 1967, *Museum Collection, Seven
Decades, A Selection* (Checklist)

References:

DUPIN, JACQUES, *Joan Miró, Life and Work,* New York,
1962, p.512, cat. no.139, ill.

GOLDWATER, ROBERT, *Space and Dream,* New York, 1967,
p.68, ill.

48.1172x504

Personage is characteristic of the artist's production in
1925. In contrast to the immediately preceding period
where the fantastic images bear direct reference to
reality, Miró's paintings of 1925 are automatic images in
the Surrealist sense, inspired by hallucinations and dreams

As a group, not only are the paintings similar in feeling
but they are similar in form: a hazy background on which
float one or several enigmatic transparent white shapes.
The meaning of the graphic signs used here can only be
guessed at from their recurrence in other compositions of
the same period: the crossed star pattern was a frequent
representation of the sun; the dotted circle around a
black spot projecting linear rays was used to signify the
moon or a star.

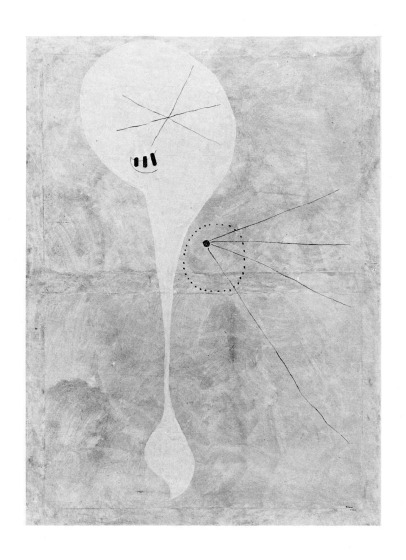

JOAN MIRÓ

Landscape (The Hare; Le Lièvre). 1927

Oil on canvas, 51¼ x 76¾″ (132 x 195 cm.)

Inscribed below and right of center "Miró//1927" and on reverse "Joan Miró//Paysage//1927"

Provenance:
the artist, 1927
Pierre Loeb, Paris
Galerie Maeght, Paris, 1957

Exhibitions:
GEORGES BERNHEIM ET CIE., Paris, May 1–15, 1928, *Miró*

KAISER-WILHELM-MUSEUM, Krefeld, January–February 1954, no.3; traveled to Stuttgart, February 21–March 28; HAUS AM WALDSEE, Berlin, April 7–May 2, 1954

PALAIS DES BEAUX-ARTS, Brussels, January 6–February 7, 1956, *Joan Miró*, no.32, ill.; KUNSTHALLE, Basel, March 24–April 29, 1956, no.22

GALLERIA NAZIONALE D'ARTE MODERNA, Rome, December 5, 1957–January 8, 1958, *Paintings from The Solomon R. Guggenheim Museum*; organized by THE SOLOMON R. GUGGENHEIM MUSEUM, traveled to WALLRAF-RICHARTZ-MUSEUM, Cologne, January 26–March 30; MUSÉE DES ARTS DÉCORATIFS, Paris, April 23–June 1, 1958

THE SOLOMON R. GUGGENHEIM MUSEUM, New York, October 21, 1959–June 19, 1960, *Inaugural Selection* (Checklist; added to exhibition March 30, 1960)

MUSÉE NATIONAL D'ART MODERNE, Paris, June 28–November 1962, *Joan Miró*, no.43

TATE GALLERY, London, August 27–October 11, 1964, *Joan Miró*, no.70; traveled to KUNSTHAUS, Zürich, October 31–November 6, 1964

THE SOLOMON R. GUGGENHEIM MUSEUM, New York, April 30–September 1, 1965, *Paintings from the Collection of The Solomon R. Guggenheim Museum*, no.57, ill.

NATIONAL MUSEUM OF MODERN ART, Tokyo, August 26–October 9, 1966, *Joan Miró Exhibition – Japan 1966*, no.32, ill.; traveled to NATIONAL MUSEUM OF MODERN ART, Kyoto, October 20–November 30, 1966

THE SOLOMON R. GUGGENHEIM MUSEUM, New York, June 28–October 1, 1967, *Museum Collection, Seven Decades, A Selection* (Checklist)

THE SOLOMON R. GUGGENHEIM MUSEUM, New York, May 30–September 2, 1968, *Rousseau, Redon, and Fantasy*

THE COLUMBUS GALLERY OF FINE ARTS, Ohio, October 5, 1968–September 7, 1969, *Paintings from The Solomon R. Guggenheim Museum*, p.30, ill.

References:
GEORGE, WALDÉMAR, "Miró et le miracle ressuscité", *Le Centaure*, vol.3, no.8, May 1, 1928, p.205, ill.

PRÉVERT, JACQUES, and RIBEMONT-DESSAIGNES, G., *Joan Miró*, Paris, 1956, p.116, ill.

KERRIGAN, ANTHONY, "Joan Miró at Son Abrines", *The Critic*, February–March, 1959, p.21, ill.

VALLIER, DORA, "Avec Miró", *Cahiers d'art*, nos.33–35, 1960, p.168

DUPIN, JACQUES, *Joan Miró, Life and Work*, New York, 1962, pp.178–79, 225, cat. no.184, ill.

GOLDWATER, ROBERT, *Space and Dream*, New York, 1967, p.69, ill.

57.1459

Miró spent the summers of 1926 and 1927 at Montroig. Whereas during his winters in Paris he was working on dream landscapes, during the summer months his landscapes reflected his natural surroundings. In contrast to the transparent color and indeterminate space of his winter production, the Montroig paintings mark a return to the earth and nature. This is emphasized by the more brilliant and denser application of paint and the conciseness and clarity of forms, which are not only more earth-bound but better situated, thanks to the distinctly drawn horizon line.

The hare is a simple organic shape, symbolic of primal being. A falling comet with its fiery tail provides a pretext for the familiar dynamic (often circular or spiral) dotted line. The juxtaposition of hare and comet as well as the equality assigned to both earth and heavens express a reconciliation between earthly and cosmic forces, reality and dreams.

JOAN MIRÓ

Painting. 1953

Oil on canvas, 76³/₄ x 148³/₄″ (195 x 377.8 cm.)

Inscribed l.r. "Miró" and on reverse "Miró//1953//peinture"

Provenance:

from the artist through Pierre Matisse Gallery, New York, 1955

Exhibitions:

GALERIE MAEGHT, Paris, June–August 1953, *Miró*, no.15

PIERRE MATISSE GALLERY, New York, November 17–December 12, 1953, *Miró, Recent Paintings*, no.15, ill.

THE SOLOMON R. GUGGENHEIM MUSEUM, New York, July 26–October 9, 1955, *Selection V* (Checklist)

TATE GALLERY, London, April 16–May 26, 1957, *Paintings from The Solomon R. Guggenheim Museum*, no.51, ill.; organized by THE SOLOMON R. GUGGENHEIM MUSEUM, traveled to GEMEENTEMUSEUM, The Hague, June 25–September 1; ATENEIUMIN TAIDEKOKOELMAT, Helsinki, September 27–October 20; GALLERIA NAZIONALE D'ARTE MODERNA, Rome, December 5, 1957–January 8, 1958; WALLRAF-RICHARTZ-MUSEUM, Cologne, January 26–March 30; MUSÉE DES ARTS DÉCORATIFS, Paris, April 23–June 1, 1958

THE MUSEUM OF MODERN ART, New York, March 18–May 10, 1959, *Joan Miró*, no.101a

THE SOLOMON R. GUGGENHEIM MUSEUM, New York, October 21, 1959–June 19, 1960, *Inaugural Selection* (Checklist; added to exhibition April 5, 1960)

PHILADELPHIA MUSEUM OF ART, November 2, 1961–January 7, 1962, *Guggenheim Museum Exhibition, A Loan Collection of Paintings, Drawings, and Prints from The Solomon R. Guggenheim Museum, New York*, no.112

WORCESTER ART MUSEUM, Massachusetts, February 6–April 7, 1963, *Aspects of Twentieth Century Painting Lent by The Solomon R. Guggenheim Museum*, no.29, ill.

THE SOLOMON R. GUGGENHEIM MUSEUM, New York, April 30–September 1, 1965, *Paintings from the Collection The Solomon R. Guggenheim Museum*, no.59, ill.

THE SOLOMON R. GUGGENHEIM MUSEUM, New York, June 28–October 1, 1967, *Museum Collection, Seven Decades, A Selection* (Checklist)

THE SOLOMON R. GUGGENHEIM MUSEUM, New York, May 30–September 2, 1968, *Rousseau, Redon, and Fantasy* ill.

References:

RAYNAL, MAURICE, *Modern Painting*, Geneva, 1953, p.286, ill.

American Abstract Artists, ed., *The World of Abstract Art*, New York, 1957, p.23, ill.

MOTHERWELL, ROBERT, "The Significance of Miró", *Art News*, vol.58, no.4, May 1959, p.33, ill.

SOBY, JAMES THRALL, *Joan Miró*, New York, 1959, p.140, ill.

DUPIN, JACQUES, *Joan Miró, Life and Work*, New York, 1962, pp.389, 434, cat. no.805, ill.

LASSAIGNE, JACQUES, *Miró*, Geneva, 1963, p.100

ARNASON, H. H., *History of Modern Art*, New York, 1968, pl.155

55.1420

Painting of 1953 is a pivotal work in the artist's career. It is situated between the relatively reflective and reserved stage of his art characteristic of the 1940's and the freer, more spontaneous expressivity of the late fifties and sixties. Constant to his total production are the attention to grounds and the whimsical figures. Specific to this particular period of 1953–1954 are the energetic gestural treatment and the voluntary clumsiness of the images, the predominance of bright raw hues and the disconnected dotted lines used to underscore or inflect certain parts of the composition within the total rhythmic pattern.

JOAN MIRÓ (with JOSEPH LLORENS ARTIGAS)

Portico (Portique). April 1956

Ceramic, nine sections, 98″ (248.9 cm.) high

Not inscribed

Provenance:
from the artist through Galerie Maeght, Paris, 1957

Exhibitions:

GALERIE MAEGHT, Paris, June–August 1956, *Terres de Grand Feu*, no.1. (Catalogue published as *Derrière le Miroir*, nos.87–89, June–August 1956)

THE SOLOMON R. GUGGENHEIM MUSEUM, New York, October 21, 1959–June 19, 1960, *Inaugural Selection* (Checklist; remained on exhibition through September 7, 1962)

THE SOLOMON R. GUGGENHEIM MUSEUM, New York, July 8–September 14, 1969, *Selected Sculpture and Works on Paper*, p.138, ill.

References:

BERNIER, ROSAMOND, "Miró céramiste", *L'Oeil*, no.17, May 1956, pp.46–53 (English translation in *The Selective Eye II*, 1956–57, New York, pp.6–13)

KERRIGAN, ANTHONY, "Joan Miró at Son Abrines", *The Critic*, February–March 1959, p.21, ill.

MOTHERWELL, ROBERT, "The Significance of Miró", *Art News*, vol.58, no.4, May 1959, p.32, ill.

SOBY, JAMES THRALL, *Joan Miró*, New York, 1959, p.136, ill.

DUPIN, JACQUES, *Joan Miró, Life and Work*, New York, 1962, pp.472–73

LASSAIGNE, JACQUES, *Miró*, Geneva, 1963, p.107

57.1460

Although Miró began experimenting with ceramics in 1944, it was not until 1954 that he devoted a major part of his activity to that medium. Working with his old friend, the Spanish ceramist Artigas, between February 1954 and May 1956, two hundred and thirty-two pieces went into the kilns in Gallifa. Among them was *Portico*.

The purposely rough surface of *Portico* suggests a primitive hewn-rock construction. This primitive aspect is enhanced by the natural materials (pebbles) embedded in the surface and the broad simple brushed signs (recalling prehistoric sacred symbols), not to mention the imprints of feet. Furthermore the upright and isolated stance of *Portico* endows it with a totemic character.

JOAN MIRÓ (with JOSEPH LLORENS ARTIGAS)

Alicia. 1965–67

Ceramic, 97 x 228¹/₂" (246.4 x 581.4 cm.)

Signed l.r. "Miró Artigas"

Provenance:
Commissioned from the artist, 1965; completed 1967; gift
of Harry F. Guggenheim in memory of his wife Alicia
Patterson Guggenheim, 1967

Exhibitions:
Permanently installed in THE SOLOMON R. GUGGENHEIM
MUSEUM, New York, May 18, 1967

References:
PERUCHO, JUAN, *Joan Miró and Catalonia,* New York, 1967,
pls.111–119
*Selected Sculpture and Works on Paper, The Solomon R.
Guggenheim Museum Collection,* New York, 1969, p.139,
il.

67.1844

Commissioned and presented to the Museum in 1967 by
Harry F. Guggenheim, in memory of his wife Alicia
Patterson Guggenheim, *Alicia* was Miró's second ceramic
mural in the United States (the first is at the Harvard
University Graduate Center, Cambridge, Massachusetts).
Executed by Miró in collaboration with Artigas, the
mural displays the artist's characteristic voluble calligraphy into which letters from Mrs. Guggenheim's first
name have been skillfully integrated. Bright patches of
color light up the subtlety and restraint of the composition.

Head (Tête). 1912?

Limestone, 25″ (63.5 cm.) high

Not inscribed

Provenance:
the artist
Augustus John, London, 1912
J. J. Klejman Gallery, New York, 1955

Exhibitions:
CONTEMPORARY ARTS MUSEUM, Houston, February 26–March 29, 1959, *Totems Not Taboo, An Exhibition of Primitive Art*, ill.

ARTS CLUB OF CHICAGO, April 19–May 19, 1960, *Sculpture and Drawings by Sculptors from The Solomon R. Guggenheim Museum*, no.18, ill.

CLEVELAND MUSEUM OF ART, Ohio, October 4–November 13, 1960, *Paths of Abstract Art*, no.36, ill.

WADSWORTH ATHENEUM, Hartford, Connecticut, April 2‹–May 28, 1961, *Salute to Italy*, p.28, ill.

THE SOLOMON R. GUGGENHEIM MUSEUM, New York, August 30–October 8, 1961, *Modern Masters from the Collection of The Solomon R. Guggenheim Museum*

THE SOLOMON R. GUGGENHEIM MUSEUM, New York, July 8–September 14, 1969, *Selected Sculpture and Works on Paper*, p.141, ill.

References:
PFANNSTIEL, ARTHUR, *Modigliani, L'art et la vie*, Paris, 192‹ p.85

JOHN, AUGUSTUS, *Chiaroscuro, Fragments of Autobiography* New York, 1952, p.131

MODIGLIANI, JEANNE, *Modigliani: Man and Myth*, New York, 1958, pl.67

WERNER, ALFRED, *Modigliani the Sculptor*, New York, 196‹ pls.9–11

CERONI, AMBROGIO, *Amedeo Modigliani, Dessins et Sculptures*, Milan, 1965, p.25, pls.88, 89

WERNER, ALFRED, *Amedeo Modigliani*, New York, 1966, p.25, pl.25

55.1421

Amedeo Modigliani 1884–1920

Amedeo Modigliani was born July 12, 1884, in Leghorn, Italy. The serious illnesses he suffered during his childhood (pleurisy, tuberculosis) were to pursue him throughout his life. He began painting at fourteen; in 1902 he went to Florence to study painting and in 1903 he continued at the School of Fine Arts in Venice.

In late 1905 or early 1906 the artist moved to Paris, settling in Montmartre. His early work was influenced first by turn-of-the-century artists such as Beardsley, Lautrec and Steinlen and shortly afterwards by Cézanne (1909). As a member of the *Société des Indépendants*, he showed in their *Salon* in 1908, 1910 and 1911 as well as in the *Salon d'Automne* in 1912. By this time his mature style was beginning to develop: a concentration on the human face and figure, and a calculated disproportioning of features to personally expressive ends.

Modigliani moved to Montparnasse in 1909 where he became friendly with Brancusi. The latter probably inspired him to take up sculpture in which he was active from late 1909 to 1915. In December 1918 Modigliani had his first and only major one-man show (Galerie Berthe Weill, Paris). Nothing was sold.

In 1917 Modigliani met Jeanne Hébuterne who was to become his companion and model during the last three years of his life. He died of tuberculosis in Paris on January 25, 1920.

a student, Modigliani reportedly desired to become a
sculptor, but finances and poor health did not permit him
to do so. He was nonetheless active in sculpture from 1909
to 1915.

Modigliani's twenty-five catalogued extant sculptures
show a mixture of influences – those of African and
archaic sculpture and Brancusi – which can perhaps be
partly attributed to his aversion for Rodin. His technique
was direct carving in stone (chiefly limestone); only one
modeled work exists.

Modigliani's sculptures are always of the female image –
whether head or figure. The heads such as this are characterized by archaic and hieratic staticity, anonymity,
and formal purity, in which the individual psychology
found in his portrait paintings and sketches is lacking.

AMEDEO MODIGLIANI

Beatrice Hastings. c.1915

Pencil and conté crayon on paper, 12 x 7⁵/₈″ (30.5 x 19.5 cm.)

Inscribed l.r. "BEATRICE"

Provenance:
Hilla Rebay, Greens Farms, Connecticut, 1938
Solomon R. Guggenheim, New York
Gift, Solomon R. Guggenheim, 1941

Exhibitions:
GALERIE ALFRED FLECHTHEIM, Berlin, November 25–December 14, 1930, *Seit Cézanne in Paris*, no.25

GIBBES MEMORIAL ART GALLERY, Charleston, South Carolina, March 1–April 12, 1936, *Solomon R. Guggenheim Collection of Non-Objective Paintings*, no.120

PHILADELPHIA ART ALLIANCE, February 8–February 28, 1937, *Solomon R. Guggenheim Collection of Non-Objective Paintings*, no.185

GIBBES MEMORIAL ART GALLERY, Charleston, South Carolina, March 7–April 7, 1938, *Solomon R. Guggenheim Collection of Non-Objective Paintings*, no.259

SOLOMON R. GUGGENHEIM FOUNDATION, New York, June 1, 1939, *Art of Tomorrow* (Fifth catalogue of the Solomon R. Guggenheim Collection of Non-Objective Paintings), no.534

THE SOLOMON R. GUGGENHEIM MUSEUM, New York, March 30–May 5, 1954, *Selection III* (Checklist)

THE SOLOMON R. GUGGENHEIM MUSEUM, New York, October 6, 1954–February 27, 1955, *Selection IV* (Checklist)

ARTS CLUB OF CHICAGO, April 19–May 19, 1960, *Sculpture and Drawings by Sculptors from The Solomon R. Guggenheim Museum*, no.31, ill.

THE SOLOMON R. GUGGENHEIM MUSEUM, New York, August 30–October 8, 1961, *Modern Masters from the Collection of The Solomon R. Guggenheim Museum*

PHILADELPHIA MUSEUM OF ART, November 2, 1961–January 7, 1962, *Guggenheim Museum Exhibition, A Loan Collection of Paintings, Drawings, and Prints from The Solomon R. Guggenheim Museum, New York*, no.115, ill.

BALTIMORE MUSEUM OF ART, October 23–November 27, 1966, *Twentieth Century Italian Painting and Sculpture*

THE SOLOMON R. GUGGENHEIM MUSEUM, New York, April 11–May 26, 1968, *Acquisitions of the 1930's and 1940's*, p.68, ill.

THE SOLOMON R. GUGGENHEIM MUSEUM, New York, July 8–September 14, 1969, *Selected Sculpture and Works on Paper*, p.65, ill.

References:
LIPCHITZ, JACQUES, *Amedeo Modigliani*, New York, 1954, pl.10

41.534

Beatrice Hastings was an English poetess of South African origin who appeared in Montparnasse in 1914. Introduced to each other by the sculptor Zadkine, the painter and the poetess lived together for two years (1914–1916) during which time he made many paintings and sketches inspired by her beauty.

AMEDEO MODIGLIANI

Nude (Nu Couché, Dormeuse, les Mains derrière la Tête).
1917

Oil on canvas, $28^{3}/_{4}$ x $45^{3}/_{4}$" (73 x 116.2 cm.)

Signed u.r. "Modigliani"

Provenance:
Léopold Zborowski, Paris
Libaude, Paris
H. Bing, Paris
Félix Fénéon, Paris, 1938
Solomon R. Guggenheim, New York
Gift, Solomon R. Guggenheim, 1941

Exhibitions:
GALERIE BING, Paris, October 24–November 15, 1925,
Exposition Rétrospective

LA SOCIÉTÉ DES ARTISTES INDÉPENDANTS, Grand Palais,
Paris, February 20–March 21, 1926, *Trente Ans d'Art
Indépendant*, no.3104

THE SOLOMON R. GUGGENHEIM MUSEUM, New York,
February 3–May 3, 1953, *A Selection* (Checklist)

THE SOLOMON R. GUGGENHEIM MUSEUM, New York,
May 13–October 11, 1953, *Selection II* (Checklist)

THE SOLOMON R. GUGGENHEIM MUSEUM, New York,
March 30–May 5, 1954, *Selection III* (Checklist)

THE SOLOMON R. GUGGENHEIM MUSEUM, New York,
October 6, 1954–February 27, 1955, *Selection IV*
(Checklist)

THE SOLOMON R. GUGGENHEIM MUSEUM, New York,
July 26–October 9, 1955, *Selection V* (Checklist)

THE SOLOMON R. GUGGENHEIM MUSEUM, New York,
January 24–May 1, 1956, *Selection VI* (Checklist)

THE SOLOMON R. GUGGENHEIM MUSEUM, New York,
October 21, 1959–June 19, 1960, *Inaugural Selection*
(Checklist)

THE SOLOMON R. GUGGENHEIM MUSEUM, New York,
August 30–October 8, 1961, *Modern Masters from the
Collection of The Solomon R. Guggenheim Museum*

THE SOLOMON R. GUGGENHEIM MUSEUM, New York,
April 30–September 1, 1965, *Paintings from the Collection
The Solomon R. Guggenheim Museum*, no.44, ill.

THE SOLOMON R. GUGGENHEIM MUSEUM, New York,
June 23–October 23, 1966, *Gauguin and the Decorative Sty*

THE SOLOMON R. GUGGENHEIM MUSEUM, New York,
June 28–October 1, 1967, *Museum Collection, Seven Decade
A Selection* (Checklist)

THE SOLOMON R. GUGGENHEIM MUSEUM, New York,
April 11–May 26, 1968, *Acquisitions of the 1930's and 1940
p.69, ill.

References:

PFANNSTIEL, ARTHUR, *Modigliani et son oeuvre*, Paris, 1956,
p.101, no.141

CERONI, AMBROGIO, *Amedeo Modigliani*, Milan, 1958, cat.
no.122, ill.

CERONI, AMBROGIO, *Amedeo Modigliani, Dessins et Sculptures*, Milan, 1965, pp.18–19, ill.

ARNASON, H. H., *History of Modern Art*, New York, 1968,
p.271, ill.

41.535

Although Modigliani executed paintings and sketches of
female nudes as early as 1912, his greatest concentration
on the nude figure dates from 1917–1918. Shown at
his one-man show in Paris in 1918, the unabashed sensuality
and voluptuousness of reclining nude figures such as this
caused a scandal. At police insistence, five paintings were
removed from the exhibition.

It is interesting to note the stylized treatment of the head
in contrast to the full naturalistic modeling of torso and
limbs. The luminous flesh color of the figure – described
in a languorous arabesque – is set off on one side by the
dark, resonant color of the background and on the other
by the white drapery.

AMEDEO MODIGLIANI

Portrait of a Student (L'Étudiant). 1917?

Oil on canvas, 24^1/$_8$ x 18^1/$_4$" (61.3 x 46.4 cm.)

Signed u.r. "Modigliani"

Provenance:

Dr. Sabouraud, Paris
Harry Stevens, Southam, Rockliffe Park, Ottawa
Dominion Gallery, Montreal, 1943
Fine Arts Associates, New York
Hilla Rebay, Greens Farms, Connecticut, 1945

Exhibitions:

PALAIS DES BEAUX-ARTS, Brussels, November 1933,
Rétrospective Modigliani, no.39

KUNSTHALLE, Basel, January 7–February 4, 1934, Rétrospective Modigliani, no.46

THE SOLOMON R. GUGGENHEIM MUSEUM, New York,
May 13–October 11, 1953, Selection II (Checklist)

ART GALLERY OF TORONTO, April 2–May 9, 1954, A Loan
Exhibition of Paintings from The Solomon R. Guggenheim
Museum, no.60, ill.

VANCOUVER ART GALLERY, November 16–December 12,
1954, The Solomon R. Guggenheim Museum, A Selection
from the Museum Collection, no.63, ill.

MONTREAL MUSEUM OF FINE ARTS, June 4–July 3, 1955,
A Selection from The Solomon R. Guggenheim Museum, no.44

THE SOLOMON R. GUGGENHEIM MUSEUM, New York,
January 24–May 1, 1956, Selection VI (Checklist)

TATE GALLERY, London, April 16–May 26, 1957, Paintings
from The Solomon R. Guggenheim Museum, no.53, ill.;
traveled to GEMEENTEMUSEUM, The Hague, June 25–
September 1, 1957, no. 53; ATENEIUMIN TAIDEKOKOELMAT,
Helsinki, September 27–October 20, 1957, no. 53;
GALLERIA NAZIONALE D'ARTE MODERNA, Rome, December 5, 1957–January 8, 1958, no.32, ill.; WALLRAF-
RICHARTZ-MUSEUM, Cologne, January 26–March 30, 1958,
no.55; MUSÉE DES ARTS DÉCORATIFS, Paris, April 23–June
, 1958; no.37, ill.

THE SOLOMON R. GUGGENHEIM MUSEUM, New York,
August 30–October 8, 1961, Modern Masters from the
Collection of The Solomon R. Guggenheim Museum

THE SOLOMON R. GUGGENHEIM MUSEUM, New York,
October 3–November 12, 1961, Elements of Modern
Painting

THE SOLOMON R. GUGGENHEIM MUSEUM, New York,
April 30–September 1, 1965, Paintings from the Collection of
The Solomon R. Guggenheim Museum, no.45, ill.

THE SOLOMON R. GUGGENHEIM MUSEUM, New York,
June 28–October 1, 1967, Museum Collection, Seven
Decades, A Selection (Checklist)

THE SOLOMON R. GUGGENHEIM MUSEUM, New York,
April 11–May 26, 1968, Acquisitions of the 1930's and 1940's,
p.89, ill.

References:

PFANNSTIEL, ARTHUR, Modigliani et son œuvre, Paris, 1956,
p.106, no.158

45.997

The pristine clarity of form and line as well as the limpid
transparency of the flesh tones set off the sitter's head and
neck from the impressionist treatment of clothes and
background.

A three-quarter-length portrait of the same model, Boy
with Red Hair, is in the collection of Mr. and Mrs.
Theodore E. Cummings, Beverly Hills, California.

317

AMEDEO MODIGLIANI

Yellow Sweater (Portrait of Mme. Hébuterne). 1918

Oil on canvas, 39³/₈ x 25¹/₂" (100 x 64.8 cm.)

Signed u.r. "Modigliani"

Provenance:
Léopold Zborowski, Paris
H. Bing, Paris
Félix Fénéon, Paris
Solomon R. Guggenheim, New York
Gift, Solomon R. Guggenheim, 1937

Exhibitions:
KUNSTHAUS, Zürich, March 18–May 1, 1927, *Italienische Maler*, no.109

GIBBES MEMORIAL ART GALLERY, Charleston, South Carolina, March 1–April 12, 1936, *Solomon R. Guggenheim Collection of Non-Objective Paintings*, no.119

PHILADELPHIA ART ALLIANCE, February 8–28, 1937, *Solomon R. Guggenheim Collection of Non-Objective Paintings*, no.184

GIBBES MEMORIAL ART GALLERY, Charleston, South Carolina, March 7–April 7, 1938, *Solomon R. Guggenheim Collection of Non-Objective Paintings*, no.258

SOLOMON R. GUGGENHEIM FOUNDATION, New York, June 1, 1939, *Art of Tomorrow* (Fifth catalogue of the Solomon R. Guggenheim Collection of Non-Objective Paintings), no.533

THE SOLOMON R. GUGGENHEIM MUSEUM, New York, February 3–May 3, 1953, *A Selection* (Checklist)

SOCIETY OF THE FOUR ARTS, Palm Beach, Florida, January 8–31, 1954, *Amedeo Modigliani 1884–1920*, no.24; traveled to LOWE GALLERY, Miami, February 11–28, 1954

THE SOLOMON R. GUGGENHEIM MUSEUM, New York, March 30–May 5, 1954, *Selection III* (Checklist)

VANCOUVER ART GALLERY, November 16–December 12, 1954, *The Solomon R. Guggenheim Museum, A Selection from the Museum Collection*, no.62, frontispiece

MONTREAL MUSEUM OF FINE ARTS, June 4–July 3, 1955, *A Selection from the Solomon R. Guggenheim Museum*, no.4

THE SOLOMON R. GUGGENHEIM MUSEUM, New York, July 26–October 9, 1955, *Selection V* (Checklist)

TATE GALLERY, London, April 16–May 26, 1957, *Paintings from The Solomon R. Guggenheim Museum*, no.52; traveled to GEMEENTEMUSEUM, The Hague, June 25–September 1, no.52, ill.; ATENEIUMIN TAIDEKOKOELMAT, Helsinki, September 27–October 20, no.52, ill.; GALLERIA NAZIONALE D'ARTE MODERNA, Rome, December 5, 1957–January 8, 1958, no.33, cover ill.; WALLRAF-RICHARTZ-MUSEUM, Cologne, January 26–March 30, no.54, ill.; MUSÉE DES ARTS DÉCORATIFS, Paris, April 23–June 1, 1958, no.38, ill.

CONTEMPORARY ART CENTER, CINCINNATI ART MUSEUM, Ohio, April 18–May 20, 1959, *Amedeo Modigliani; Paintings, Sculpture and Drawings*, no.26, ill.

THE SOLOMON R. GUGGENHEIM MUSEUM, New York, October 21, 1959–June 19, 1960, *Inaugural Selection* (Checklist)

GALLERIA NAZIONALE D'ARTE MODERNA, Rome, July 10–September 10, 1960, *20th Century Italian Art from American Collections* (Organized by The International Program, THE MUSEUM OF MODERN ART, New York), p.98, ill.

WADSWORTH ATHENEUM, Hartford, Connecticut, April 20–May 28, 1961, *Salute to Italy*, pp.31, 32

THE SOLOMON R. GUGGENHEIM MUSEUM, New York, August 30–October 8, 1961, *Modern Masters from the Collection of The Solomon R. Guggenheim Museum*

SAN FRANCISCO MUSEUM OF ART, October 1964–January 1965, *The Human Figure*

THE SOLOMON R. GUGGENHEIM MUSEUM, New York, April 30–September 1, 1965, *Paintings from the Collection of The Solomon R. Guggenheim Museum*, no.48, ill.

THE SOLOMON R. GUGGENHEIM MUSEUM, New York, June 23–October 23, 1966, *Gauguin and the Decorative Style*

THE SOLOMON R. GUGGENHEIM MUSEUM, New York, April 11–May 26, 1968, *Acquisitions of the 1930's and 1940's*, p.27, ill.

COLUMBUS GALLERY OF FINE ARTS, Ohio, October 5, 1968–September 7, 1969, *Paintings from The Solomon R. Guggenheim Museum*, p.24, ill.

References:

PFANNSTIEL, ARTHUR, *Modigliani, L'art et la vie*, Paris, 1929, ill.

PFANNSTIEL, ARTHUR, *Modigliani et son œuvre*, Paris, 1956, p.142, no.268

CERONI, AMBROGIO, *Amedeo Modigliani*, Milan, 1958, no. 151

RUSSOLI, FRANCO, *Modigliani*, London, 1959, pl.30

RUSSOLI, FRANCO, *Amedeo Modigliani*, Milan, 1963, pls.XIV–XV

WERNER, ALFRED, *Amedeo Modigliani*, New York, 1966, ill. opp. p.142

37.533

Modigliani met Jeanne Hébuterne in 1917 when she was nineteen. As his loyal companion until his death, she was the mother of his only child. As his model, she was the subject of twenty inspired portraits executed between 1917 and 1920.

Characteristic of the artist's classic 1919 style are the flat, elongated and evenly oval face, the long curved neck, the empty almond eyes, the simplified planar nose and the small pursed mouth. The body is curved in an S-shaped silhouette, a fluid rhythm which appears particularly in 1918 and 1919 and which was accentuated in portraits of Jeanne, in contrast to the more strict frontality of other sitters or earlier years.

A II. 1924

Oil on canvas, 45 1/2 x 53 1/2" (115.5 x 135.9 cm.)

Signed on reverse, "Moholy-Nagy / A II (1924)"

Provenance:

from the artist, 1943

Exhibitions:

MUSEUM OF NON-OBJECTIVE PAINTING, New York, May 1–
July 10, 1947, *In Memoriam Laszlo Moholy-Nagy*, p.11
MONTREAL MUSEUM OF FINE ARTS, June 4–July 3, 1955, *A
Selection from the Solomon R. Guggenheim Museum*, no.45
TATE GALLERY, London, April 16–May 26, 1957, *Paintings
from The Solomon R. Guggenheim Museum*, no.54; traveled
to GEMEENTEMUSEUM, The Hague, June 25–September 1,
no.54; ATENEIUMIN TAIDEKOKOELMAT, Helsinki, Septem-
ber 27–October 20; GALLERIA NAZIONALE D'ARTE MODERN
Rome, December 5, 1957–January 8, 1958, no.51;
WALLRAF–RICHARTZ–MUSEUM, Cologne, January 26–
March 30, no.58; MUSÉE DES ARTS DÉCORATIFS, Paris,
April 23–June 1, 1958, no.56

THE SOLOMON R. GUGGENHEIM MUSEUM, New York,
October 21, 1959 – June 19, 1960, *Inaugural Selection*
CLEVELAND MUSEUM OF ART, Ohio, October 4–Novem-
ber 13, 1960, *Paths of Abstract Art*, no.33

THE SOLOMON R. GUGGENHEIM MUSEUM, New York,
June 5–October 13, 1963, *Cézanne and Structure in Modern
Painting*, ill.

THE SOLOMON R. GUGGENHEIM MUSEUM, New York,
April 30–September 1, 1965, *Paintings from the Collection
The Solomon R. Guggenheim Museum*, no.54, ill.

PERLS GALLERY, New York, April 26–May 21, 1966, *Seven
Decades 1895–1965, Crosscurrents in Modern Art*, p.85,
no.149, ill. (Organized by the PUBLIC EDUCATION
ASSOCIATION)

THE SOLOMON R. GUGGENHEIM MUSEUM, New York,
June 28–October 1, 1967, *Museum Collection, Seven
Decades, A Selection* (Checklist)

THE SOLOMON R. GUGGENHEIM MUSEUM, New York,
April 11–May 26, 1968, *Acquisitions of the 1930's and 1940's*
pp.78–79, ill.

THE SOLOMON R. GUGGENHEIM MUSEUM, New York,
February 20–April 19, 1970, *Laszlo Moholy-Nagy*, hors
catalogue

References:

BAYER, HERBERT; GROPIUS, WALTER and GROPIUS, ISE, eds.
Bauhaus 1919–1928, Boston, 1952, p.191, ill.

GOLDWATER, ROBERT, *Space and Dream*, New York, 1967,
p.72, ill.

HAFTMANN, WERNER. *Painting in the Twentieth Century*,
New York, 1968, vol.II, p.158, no.342, ill.

Laszlo Moholy-Nagy 1895–1946

Laszlo Moholy-Nagy was born in 1895 in Bacsbarsod,
Hungary. He studied law in Budapest, served in the Aus-
tro-Hungarian army and began drawing and painting extensively in 1917. In 1919 he became acquainted with the
work of Malevitch and El Lissitzky and in 1920 with Berlin
Dada. Both were to have an influence on his art.

In 1923, Moholy-Nagy joined the Bauhaus faculty as a
master of the metal workshop and the Advanced Foundation Course. Truly "Leonardian" as Gropius once wrote,
he collaborated on murals, ballet and stage designs, experimented with photography, light and color and worked in
typography and layout. At the same time his former emphasis on line and collage was replaced by a preoccupation
with colored form in his painting and he began to think of
his work as "Constructivist".

After leaving the Bauhaus in 1928, Moholy-Nagy embarked on a successful career as a stage designer in Berlin.
His growing interest in transparency and planar relationships induced him to experiment with plastics (such as plexiglas) in the execution of "three-dimensional paintings"
(with a projected transparent plane). His interest in light
and movement led to a rotating light sculpture which was
exhibited at the *Internationale Werkbund Ausstellung*, Paris,
in 1930.

The artist worked in Amsterdam in 1934, London in 1935,
and moved to Chicago in 1937, where he opened his own
school of design. He began to work in sculpture in 1941.
Moholy-Nagy died of leukemia November 24, 1946 in
Chicago.

43.900

ainted a year after the artist joined the Weimar Bauhaus,
A II is illustrative of Moholy-Nagy's "Constructivist"
yle. The dynamic unity as well as the spatial ambiguity
f the composition is due to the varied degrees of trans-
arency of both colors and forms. Said Moholy-Nagy:
The passion for transparency is one of the most spectac-
lar features of our time. We might say, with pardonable
nthusiasm, that structure becomes transparency and
ansparency manifests structure." (Moholy-Nagy,
Space-Time Problems in Art", *American Abstract Artists*,
Jew York, 1946)

LASZLO MOHOLY-NAGY

Leuk 4. 1945

Oil on canvas, 49 x 49¹/₄″ (124.5 x 125.1 cm.)

Inscribed on reverse "L. MOHOLY-NAGY//LEUK 4
(45)//Moholy"

Provenance:
from the artist, 1948

Exhibitions:

MUSEUM OF CONTEMPORARY ART, Chicago, May 31–July
12, 1969, *Laszlo Moholy-Nagy*, no.64, p.38, ill.; organized
in collaboration with THE SOLOMON R. GUGGENHEIM
MUSEUM, traveled to SANTA BARBARA MUSEUM OF ART,
California, August 2–September 21; BERKELEY UNIVERSITY
ART MUSEUM, California, October 2–November 2; SEATTL
ART MUSEUM, Washington, November 20, 1969–January 4
1970; THE SOLOMON R. GUGGENHEIM MUSEUM, New York,
February 20–April 10, 1970

48.1124

Painted in 1945 when Moholy-Nagy was suffering from
leukemia, *Leuk 4* is stylistically representative of the last
phase of his life. The nearly square painting combines
characteristic elements, such as transparency, contrast of
line and color, and a clothlike textural quality, which
contribute to an overall tension resulting in spatial
ambivalence. More specifically, the bright yellow arc
serves simultaneously to unify and to dissolve the space
and the compositional structure of the painting as it
intersects both the background and the disc in the foreground. As a summing up of his oeuvre, *Leuk 4* preserves
vestiges of the artist's Constructivist purity along with a
painterly rendering of his concern with the movement
of light and space.

Piet Mondrian 1872–1944

Piet Mondrian was born Pieter Cornelis Mondriaan on March 7, 1872, at Amersfoort, Holland. After studies at the Amsterdam Academy of Fine Arts (1892–97), he embarked on his career as a painter, first in an academic landscape idiom. The period ending in 1908 is marked by the successive influences of Dutch Impressionism, van Gogh, Symbolist and Fauve painting, throughout which the artist retained an essentially realist style.

In about 1909 the artist's work started showing a more personal direction through a stylized simplification which led him quickly and independently to a form of Cubism. This orientation was substantiated by his move to Paris in 1912. By 1913 Mondrian had gone beyond Cubism to a more radical abstraction, where only vestigial references to subject matter (trees, building facades) remained.

Family illness called him home to Holland where he was detained by World War I. During this period he pushed his abstraction even further, arriving at his mature and best known style of vertical and horizontal dissecting lines and flat colored planes (symbolic of universal harmony and balance) in 1917. That same year the Dutch movement *De Stijl* was formed with van Doesburg.

In 1919 Mondrian returned to Paris, there to remain until 1938 when World War II forced him to London. In 1940 he arrived in New York where he resided until his death on February 1, 1944.

PIET MONDRIAN

Chrysanthemum. Undated

Charcoal, 10 x 11 1/4″ (25.5 x 28.5 cm.)

Signed l.r. "PIET MONDRIAAN"

Provenance:
the artist
C. De Boer, Amsterdam
Swetzoff Gallery, Boston, 1961

Exhibitions:
THE SOLOMON R. GUGGENHEIM MUSEUM, New York, August 30–October 8, 1961, *Modern Masters from the Collection of The Solomon R. Guggenheim Museum*

THE SOLOMON R. GUGGENHEIM MUSEUM, New York, October 3–November 12, 1961, *Elements of Modern Painting*

THE SOLOMON R. GUGGENHEIM MUSEUM, New York, April 30–September 1, 1965, *Paintings from the Collection of The Solomon R. Guggenheim Museum*, no.9, ill.

THE SOLOMON R. GUGGENHEIM MUSEUM, New York, July 8–September 14, 1969, *Selected Sculpture and Works on Paper*, p.66, ill.

61.1589

Single flower studies such as the Museum's charcoal drawing *Chrysanthemum* and watercolor *Blue Chrysanthemum* were executed by Mondrian as early as 1901 and episodically through the 1920's. The greater part of those known were executed during the period 1906–1908. Although at first glance *Chrysanthemum* seems a descriptive drawing, upon closer examination one becomes aware of a certain amount of stylization. The heavy angular pencil stroke, the shaded contrasts and the flower's diagonal thrust introduce a kind of expressionist vitality typical of much turn-of-the-century art.

Blue Chrysanthemum. 1906–08

Watercolor and ink, 10⁵/₈ x 8⁷/₈″ (27 x 22.5 cm.)

Signed l.l. "P. MONDRIAAN"

Provenance:
the artist
C. De Boer, Amsterdam
Swetzoff Gallery, Boston, 1961

Exhibitions:

THE SOLOMON R. GUGGENHEIM MUSEUM, New York, August 30–October 8, 1961, *Modern Masters from the Collection of The Solomon R. Guggenheim Museum*, ill.

THE SOLOMON R. GUGGENHEIM MUSEUM, New York, October 3–November 12, 1961, *Elements of Modern Painting*

THE SOLOMON R. GUGGENHEIM MUSEUM, New York, April 30–September 1, 1965, *Paintings from the Collection of The Solomon R. Guggenheim Museum*, no.8, ill.

THE SOLOMON R. GUGGENHEIM MUSEUM, New York, July 8–September 14, 1969, *Selected Sculpture and Works on Paper*, p.67, ill.

References:

ARNASON, H. H., *History of Modern Art*, New York, 1968, p.234, pl.387

61.1588

Blue Chrysanthemum is possibly a later piece than *Chrysanthemum* due to its less literal and less expressionist treatment. Whereas the charcoal study seems to present a more personal relationship between artist and subject – a feeling for the vitality of the chrysanthemum as a peculiar living organism – *Blue Chrysanthemum* is a harmonious synthesis of the form of the flower as a universal species or "the universal manifestation of life" (Mondrian).

This is achieved by a looser, more schematic composition, less emphasis on surface detail in favor of the essential rhythmic structure of the artist's subject, and a frontal and symmetrical distribution of parts following dominant yet equivalent horizontal and vertical axes. A cool, unified coloring destroys the classic opposition between figure and ground.

IET MONDRIAN

Composition 7. 1913

Oil on canvas, 41⁷/₈ x 45″ (121.6 x 114.2 cm.)

Signed l.l. "MONDRIAN"

Provenance:

Sidney Janis Gallery, New York, 1949

Exhibitions:

STEDELIJK MUSEUM, Amsterdam, November 7–December 8, 1913, Third *Moderne Kunst Kring* Exhibition

MUSEUM OF NON-OBJECTIVE PAINTING, New York, May 31–October 1949, *Museum Collection*

SIDNEY JANIS GALLERY, New York, October 10–November 19, 1949, *Mondrian*

MUSEUM OF NON-OBJECTIVE PAINTING, New York, April–May 1952, *Evolution to Non-Objectivity,* no.159 (Checklist)

THE SOLOMON R. GUGGENHEIM MUSEUM, New York, February 3–May 3, 1953, *A Selection* (Checklist)

THE SOLOMON R. GUGGENHEIM MUSEUM, New York, May 13–October 11, 1953, *Selection II* (Checklist)

SIDNEY JANIS GALLERY, New York, September 29–October 31, 1953, *Fifth Anniversary Exhibition,* no.37, ill.

THE SOLOMON R. GUGGENHEIM MUSEUM, New York, March 30–May 5, 1954, *Selection III* (Checklist)

THE SOLOMON R. GUGGENHEIM MUSEUM, New York, October 6, 1954–February 27, 1955, *Selection IV* (Checklist)

THE SOLOMON R. GUGGENHEIM MUSEUM, New York, July 26–October 9, 1955, *Selection V* (Checklist)

THE SOLOMON R. GUGGENHEIM MUSEUM, New York, January 24–May 1, 1956, *Selection VI* (Checklist)

THE SOLOMON R. GUGGENHEIM MUSEUM, New York, December 10, 1957–January 19, 1958, *Piet Mondrian: The Earlier Years;* traveled to SAN FRANCISCO MUSEUM OF ART, February 6–March 23, 1958

THE SOLOMON R. GUGGENHEIM MUSEUM, New York, October 21, 1959–June 19, 1960, *Inaugural Selection* (Checklist)

THE SOLOMON R. GUGGENHEIM MUSEUM, New York, August 30–October 8, 1961, *Modern Masters from the Collection of The Solomon R. Guggenheim Museum*

PHILADELPHIA MUSEUM OF ART, November 2, 1961–January 7, 1962, *Guggenheim Museum Exhibition, A Loan Exhibition of Paintings, Drawings, and Prints from The Solomon R. Guggenheim Museum, New York,* no.117, ill.

WORCESTER ART MUSEUM, Massachusetts, February 6–April 7, 1963, *Aspects of Twentieth Century Painting, Lent by The Solomon R. Guggenheim Museum,* pp.54, 6, ill.

THE SOLOMON R. GUGGENHEIM MUSEUM, New York, June 5–October 13, 1963, *Cézanne and Structure in Modern Painting*

SIDNEY JANIS GALLERY, New York, November 4–30, 1963, *Piet Mondrian,* no.17, ill.

SANTA BARBARA MUSEUM OF ART, January–February 21, 1965, *Piet Mondrian,* no.42, ill.; traveled to DALLAS MUSEUM OF FINE ARTS, March 15–April 15, 1965

THE SOLOMON R. GUGGENHEIM MUSEUM, New York, April 30–September 1, 1965, *Paintings from the Collection of The Solomon R. Guggenheim Museum,* no.32, ill.

M. KNOEDLER & CO., INC., New York, April 26–May 21, 1966, *Seven Decades 1895–1965, Crosscurrents in Modern Art,* p.43, no.52, ill. (Organized by the PUBLIC EDUCATION ASSOCIATION)

THE SOLOMON R. GUGGENHEIM MUSEUM, New York, June 28–October 1, 1967, *Museum Collection, Seven Decades, A Selection* (Checklist)

THE METROPOLITAN MUSEUM OF ART, New York, November 15, 1967–April 1, 1968, *Selections from the Collection of The Solomon R. Guggenheim Museum*

THE SOLOMON R. GUGGENHEIM MUSEUM, New York, April 11–May 26, 1968, *Acquisitions of the 1930's and 1940's,* p.125, ill.

NATIONAL GALERIE, Berlin, September 15–November 20, 1968, *Piet Mondrian,* no.32, ill.; traveled to ORANGERIE DES TUILERIES, Paris, January 18–March 31, 1969, no.42, ill.

References:

SEUPHOR, MICHEL, *Piet Mondrian, Life and Work,* New York, 1956, p.100, no.374, p.254, ill.

ELGAR, FRANK, *Mondrian,* New York, 1968, p.58, no.54, ill.

49.1228

Composition 7 was painted in Paris in the spring or summer of 1913. Although the ocher-gray colors recall Picasso and Braque's Analytical Cubism of 1911–12, this is the only distinct resemblance to Parisian Cubism.

Unlike the latter, Mondrian's point of departure was organic structural form, in this instance a study of trees. His image is subsequently more dynamic – consolidated not only by the contrasts of curves and straight lines but by the swift, uneven, angular and broken strokes – than Braque's and Picasso's basically static compositions.

Mondrian's space is conceived as a close-textured fabric of linear relationships situated on a single plane and organized according to equivalent vertical and horizontal axes. Parisian Cubist space is composed of large irregular (as descriptive) planes which overlap and intersect one another. Furthermore, Mondrian's shading does not create spatial ambiguity as in Parisian Cubism, simply zones of contrasting values.

Finally, the progressive fade-out at the borders which one finds in *Composition 7* is certainly influenced by Braque and Picasso's similar use of this pictorial device. However, whereas the latter employed it to focus attention on a central scaffolded figure or a definitely ovoid composition (which was usually anchored to the bottom edge of the canvas), Mondrian does not. Consistent with his perfect and equivalent relationships between all parts, the artist has created an evenly ordered, all-over pattern recessed equidistantly from all sides.

PIET MONDRIAN

Composition 8. 1914

Oil on canvas, 37$\frac{1}{4}$ x 21$\frac{7}{8}$″ (94.5 x 55.5 cm.)

Signed and dated l.l. "MONDRIAN. 1914"

Provenance:
Sidney Janis Gallery, New York, 1949

Exhibitions:
MUSEUM OF NON-OBJECTIVE PAINTING, New York, May 31–October 1949, *Museum Collection*

SIDNEY JANIS GALLERY, New York, October 10–November 19, 1949, *Mondrian*

THE SOLOMON R. GUGGENHEIM MUSEUM, New York, February 3–May 3, 1953, *A Selection* (Checklist)

THE SOLOMON R. GUGGENHEIM MUSEUM, New York, March 30–May 5, 1954, *Selection III* (Checklist)

VANCOUVER ART GALLERY, November 16– December 12, 1954, *The Solomon R. Guggenheim Museum, A Selection from the Museum Collection*, no.65

SAN FRANCISCO MUSEUM OF ART, June 17–July 10, 1955, *Art in the Twentieth Century*

THE SOLOMON R. GUGGENHEIM MUSEUM, New York, July 26–October 9, 1955, *Selection V* (Checklist)

THE SOLOMON R. GUGGENHEIM MUSEUM, New York, January 24–May 1, 1956, *Selection VI* (Checklist)

THE SOLOMON R. GUGGENHEIM MUSEUM, New York, December 10, 1957–January 19, 1958, *Piet Mondrian: The Earlier Years*; traveled to SAN FRANCISCO MUSEUM OF ART, February 6–March 23, 1958

THE SOLOMON R. GUGGENHEIM MUSEUM, New York, August 30–October 8, 1961, *Modern Masters from the Collection of The Solomon R. Guggenheim Museum*

PHILADELPHIA MUSEUM OF ART, November 2, 1961–January 7, 1962, *Guggenheim Museum Exhibition, A Loan Exhibition of Paintings, Drawings, and Prints from The Solomon R. Guggenheim Museum, New York*

THE SOLOMON R. GUGGENHEIM MUSEUM, New York,
June 5–October 13, 1963, *Cézanne and Structure in Modern Painting*

BALTIMORE MUSEUM OF ART, October 6– November 15, 1964, *"1914"*, no.167, ill.

THE SOLOMON R. GUGGENHEIM MUSEUM, New York,
April 30–September 1, 1965, *Paintings from the Collection of The Solomon R. Guggenheim Museum*, no.35, ill.

THE SOLOMON R. GUGGENHEIM MUSEUM, New York,
June 28–October 1, 1967, *Museum Collection, Seven Decades, A Selection* (Checklist)

THE SOLOMON R. GUGGENHEIM MUSEUM, New York,
April 11–May 26, 1968, *Acquisitions of the 1930's and 1940's,* p.124, ill.

References:

SEUPHOR, MICHEL, *Piet Mondrian, Life and Work*, New York, 1956, cat. no.409, (erroneously ascribed to The Museum of Modern Art, New York), p.259 ill.

JAMES, MARTIN, "The Realism behind Mondrian's Geometry", *Art News,* December 1957, no.7, ill.

59.1227

Composition 8 was probably one of Mondrian's last paintings done in Paris before his return to Holland in 1914. It is thought to be derived from several studies of facades the artist painted in 1913–14 and which provided the predominant theme of his final year in Paris.

Although the space is still unequivocally flat, organized according to a grid of black lines, the grid is larger and more uniform, the lines are more evenly painted, and there is an absence of diagonals.

In *Composition 7* of 1913, color appeared in undetermined zones, whereas here it is more flatly applied and strictly limited to specific grid sections to create a meaningful balance of chromatic relationships. The introduction of pink is a departure from the classic Cubist palette.

THE SOLOMON R. GUGGENHEIM MUSEUM, New York, August 30–October 8, 1961, *Modern Masters from the Collection of The Solomon R. Guggenheim Museum*

PHILADELPHIA MUSEUM OF ART, November 2, 1961–January 7, 1962, *Guggenheim Museum Exhibition, A Loan Collection of Paintings, Drawings, and Prints from The Solomon R. Guggenheim Museum, New York*, no.119

SIDNEY JANIS GALLERY, New York, November 4–30, 1963, *Piet Mondrian*, no.19, ill.

SANTA BARBARA MUSEUM OF ART, January 2–February 21, 1965, *Piet Mondrian*, no.49, ill.; traveled to DALLAS MUSEUM OF FINE ARTS, March 15–April 15, 1965

THE SOLOMON R. GUGGENHEIM MUSEUM, New York, April 30–September 1, 1965, *Paintings from the Collection of The Solomon R. Guggenheim Museum*, no.41, ill.

ART GALLERY OF TORONTO, February 12–March 20, 1966, *Piet Mondrian 1872–1944*, no.80, ill.; traveled to PHILADELPHIA MUSEUM OF ART, April 8–May 9; GEMEENTE-MUSEUM, The Hague, June 15–August 7, 1966

COLUMBUS GALLERY OF FINE ARTS, Ohio, October 5, 1968–September 7, 1969, *Paintings from The Solomon R. Guggenheim Museum*, p.22, ill.

References:

SEUPHOR, MICHEL, *L'art abstrait*, Paris, 1950, p.266, ill.

SEUPHOR, MICHEL, *Piet Mondrian, Life and Work*, New York, 1956, cat. no.424, p.260, ill.

American Abstract Artists, ed., *The World of Abstract Art*, New York, 1957, p.58, ill.

ELGAR, FRANK, *Mondrian*, New York, 1968, pl.80

49.1229

ET MONDRIAN

omposition. 1916

il on canvas and wood strip, 46⁵/₈ x 29¹/₂″ (118.5 x 75 m.)

gned and dated on wood strip l.l. "P. MONDRIAAN-'16"

rovenance:
e artist
ev. H. van Assendelft, Gouda, The Netherlands
rs. Schijvens-van Assendelft, Zeist, The Netherlands
n Nicolas Streep, New York, c.1948
dney Janis Gallery, New York, 1949

xhibitions:
EDELIJK MUSEUM, Amsterdam, November-December 046, *Piet Mondrian Retrospective Exhibition*, no.78; aveled to KUNSTHALLE, Basel, February 6–March 2, 047, no.28

DNEY JANIS GALLERY, New York, October 10–November 12, 1949, *Mondrian*, no.13

IE SOLOMON R. GUGGENHEIM MUSEUM, New York, bruary 3–May 3, 1953, *A Selection* (Checklist)

IE SOLOMON R. GUGGENHEIM MUSEUM, New York, lay 13–October 11, 1953, *Selection II* (Checklist)

RT GALLERY OF TORONTO, April 2–May 9, 1954, *A oan Exhibition of Paintings from The Solomon R. Guggen-im Museum, New York*, no.61

IE SOLOMON R. GUGGENHEIM MUSEUM, New York, ctober 6, 1954–February 27, 1955, *Selection IV* (Checklist)

ONTREAL MUSEUM OF FINE ARTS, June 4–July 3, 1955, *Selection from The Solomon R. Guggenheim Museum, New ork*, no.46, ill.

IE SOLOMON R. GUGGENHEIM MUSEUM, New York, nuary 24–May 1, 1956, *Selection VI* (Checklist)

IE SOLOMON R. GUGGENHEIM MUSEUM, New York, ecember 10, 1957–January 19, 1958, *Piet Mondrian: The arlier Years*; traveled to SAN FRANCISCO MUSEUM OF ART, bruary 6–March 23, 1958

During the years 1915–16, Mondrian began to abandon subject distinctions (such as trees, facades) and concentrated more on purely non-objective compositions. This is the artist's only known work dated 1916. It seems to have evolved from a series of sketches of the Domburg Church facade (dated 1914) and been developed through looser studies in a similar vein: *The Sea* (1913–14) and *Pier and Ocean* (1914–15) inspired by the Domburg seaside.

The work of this period in Holland is characterized by a breakdown of the artist's familiar grid into an empirically improvised cross and line pattern, resulting in a punctuated yet uninterrupted flow of space.

Although the black lines are limited to horizontals and verticals, the areas of color are applied in diagonal cadence. Thus, as was his avowed practice, Mondrian provoked an opposition or duality of pictorial elements, to be resolved through a dynamic balance or "plastic equivalence".

PIET MONDRIAN

Composition 2 (Tableau 2). Paris, 1922

Oil on canvas, $21^7/_8$ x $21^1/_8$" (55.7 x 53.6 cm.)

Signed with monogram and dated l.r. "PM 22"

Provenance:
Jon Nicolas Streep, New York, 1951

Exhibitions:

MUSEUM OF NON-OBJECTIVE PAINTING, New York,
April 29, 1952, *Evolution to Non-Objectivity*, no.160

THE SOLOMON R. GUGGENHEIM MUSEUM, New York,
February 3–May 3, 1953, *A Selection* (Checklist)

ART GALLERY OF TORONTO, April 2–May 9, 1954, *A
Loan Exhibition of Paintings from The Solomon R. Guggenheim Museum, New York*, no.62

VANCOUVER ART GALLERY, November 16–December 12,
1954, *The Solomon R. Guggenheim Museum, A Selection
from the Museum Collection*, no.66, ill.

SAN FRANCISCO MUSEUM OF ART, June 17–July 10, 1955,
Art in the 20th Century, p.15

THE SOLOMON R. GUGGENHEIM MUSEUM, New York,
January 24–May 1, 1956, *Selection VI* (Checklist)

MUSEUM OF FINE ARTS, Boston, October 10–November 17,
1957, *European Masters of Our Time*, no.100, ill.

SOCIETY OF THE FOUR ARTS, Palm Beach, Florida,
March 4–April 5, 1960, *The School of Paris*

CLEVELAND MUSEUM OF ART, Ohio, October 4–
November 13, 1960, *Paths of Abstract Art*, no.25, ill.

THE SOLOMON R. GUGGENHEIM MUSEUM, New York,
August 30–October 8, 1961, *Modern Masters from the
Collection of The Solomon R. Guggenheim Museum*

PHILADELPHIA MUSEUM OF ART, November 2, 1961–
January 7, 1962, *Guggenheim Museum Exhibition, A Loan
Collection of Paintings, Drawings, and Prints from The
Solomon R. Guggenheim Museum, New York*, no.120

WORCESTER ART MUSEUM, Massachusetts, February 6–
April 7, 1963, *Aspects of Twentieth Century Painting Lent by
The Solomon R. Guggenheim Museum, New York*, no.32, ill.

THE SOLOMON R. GUGGENHEIM MUSEUM, New York,
June 28–October 1, 1967, *Museum Collection, Seven
Decades, A Selection* (Checklist)

ALBRIGHT-KNOX ART GALLERY, Buffalo, New York,
March 3–April 14, 1968, *Plus by Minus: Today's Half-
Century*, no.131

NATIONAL GALERIE, Berlin, September 15–November 20,
1968, *Piet Mondrian*, no.50, ill.; traveled to ORANGERIE
DES TUILERIES, Paris, January 18–March 31, 1969, no.73,
cover ill.

References:

KRAUSE, JOSEPH H., *The Nature of Art*, Englewood Cliffs,
New Jersey, 1969, p.306, ill.

51.1309

By 1920, Mondrian had reduced his palette to black,
variations of white, and the three primary colors, and was
composing according to a grid of exclusively horizontal
and vertical black lines. 1922 is a year of simplification
of both color and line relationships, anticipating the
artist's later and generally more austere work.

The format of *Composition 2* is almost square, slightly
higher than it is wide. The central area is almost square in
opposite proportion, slightly wider than high. The large,
central, enclosed non-color core is characteristic of the
artist's early 1920's production, color being reserved to
smaller marginal zones.

As is noticeable here, the artist's non-color areas are
rarely white. Mondrian, during his *De Stijl* period (1917–
1925) habitually mixed small amounts of primary color
pigment into the non-color zones, thus creating different
kinds of chromatic relationships, based not on white but
on off-white variants.

Another standard *De Stijl* practice which is visible here is
that of discontinuing lines before the edge of the canvas.
"According to the late Georges Vantongerloo, the practice originated from a fear that the abstract composition
would lose its organic compactness if all lines were
carried through to the edge of the composition, bisecting
it completely." (Robert P. Welsh, *Piet Mondrian 1872–
1944*, Toronto, 1966, p.170) Mondrian was to abandon
this pictorial principle by the late 1920's.

PIET MONDRIAN

Composition. 1929

Oil on canvas, $17^3/4$ x $17^3/4''$ (45 x 45 cm.)

Signed and dated l.r. "P. M '29"

Provenance:

Katherine S. Dreier, West Redding, Connecticut
Gift, Katherine S. Dreier Estate, 1953

Exhibitions:

THE SOLOMON R. GUGGENHEIM MUSEUM, New York,
May 13–October 11, 1953, *Selection II* (Checklist)

THE SOLOMON R. GUGGENHEIM MUSEUM, New York,
October 6, 1954–February 27, 1955, *Selection IV*
(Checklist)

MONTREAL MUSEUM OF FINE ARTS, June 4–July 3, 1955,
*A Selection from The Solomon R. Guggenheim Museum,
New York,* no.47

TATE GALLERY, London, April 16–May 26, 1957,
*Paintings from The Solomon R. Guggenheim Museum, New
York,* no.55; traveled to GEMEENTEMUSEUM, The Hague,
June 25–September 1; ATENEIUMIN TAIDEKOKOELMAT,
Helsinki, September 27–October 20; GALLERIA NAZIONALE
D'ARTE MODERNA, Rome, December 5, 1957–January 8,
1958; WALLRAF-RICHARTZ-MUSEUM, Cologne, January 26–
March 30; MUSÉE DES ARTS DÉCORATIFS, Paris, April 23–
June 1, 1958

THE SOLOMON R. GUGGENHEIM MUSEUM, New York,
October 3–November 12, 1961, *Elements of Modern
Painting*

THE SOLOMON R. GUGGENHEIM MUSEUM, New York,
April 30–September 1, 1965, *Paintings from the Collection of
The Solomon R. Guggenheim Museum,* no.59, ill.

TAFT MUSEUM, Cincinatti, Ohio, October 22–December 6,
1965, *Color: White to Palette*

THE SOLOMON R. GUGGENHEIM MUSEUM, New York,
June 28–October 1, 1967, *Museum Collection, Seven
Decades, A Selection* (Checklist)

THE METROPOLITAN MUSEUM OF ART, New York, November
15, 1967–April 1, 1968, *Selections from the Collection of
The Solomon R. Guggenheim Museum*

53.1347

Typical of one kind of composition repeatedly used by
the artist between 1928 and 1932 are the perfectly square
format, the large, enclosed, also perfectly square central
zone, as well as the predominance of red over other hues.
Because of the increased simplicity and clarity of relationships, this period is considered that of Mondrian's most
classic style.

In spite of the marginal strips of color, one can observe
the gradual shift of focus from a fairly even grid pattern
to a cruciform axis (such as in the upper left center
portion of the canvas), enclosing or not enclosing planes
of color. This will become a common organizational
theme after 1930.

Henry Moore 1898–

Henry Moore was born July 30, 1898, at Castleford, Yorkshire in England. After secondary school, teaching, and serving in France during World War I, he won scholarships to the Leeds School of Art (1919–1921) and the Royal College of Art, London. He remained at the latter as a teacher until 1931.

While at the Royal College of Art, Moore made frequent visits to the British Museum where he was particularly impressed by Egyptian, Etruscan, Mexican and African sculpture. In 1922 he executed his first direct carvings in stone and wood in which the influence of archaic sculpture as well as that of Gaudier-Brzeska and Epstein is apparent. His first reclining figure dates from 1924.

A solid archaic quality characterizes Moore's production throughout the twenties. After 1930 his sculpture begins to loosen, tending toward a more abstract and organic form of expression. As a founding member of the English Surrealist group (1936), he exhibited in the International Surrealist Exhibition, London, in the same year.

From the late 1930's on, one can identify several recurrent iconographical themes: the half-length figure, the mother and child, the family group, the reclining figure. Constant formal preoccupations include the relationship between internal and external forms, multiple-piece compositions, stringed figures, biomorphic shapes.

Moore has worked in many mediums: wood, stone, concrete, marble, lead, bronze. The artist had his first one-man show in 1928 and his first exhibition in New York in 1943. In 1948 he won the International Sculpture Prize at the Venice Biennale. Among his outstanding commissions are a reclining marble figure for the UNESCO headquarters, Paris (1957) and the two-piece reclining figure at Lincoln Center, New York (1963–1964).

Figure. 1956–60

Elmwood, 111″ (281.9 cm.) high

Not inscribed.

Provenance:
Commissioned from the artist by The Solomon R. Guggenheim Museum, New York, 1956; completed, 1960

Exhibitions:
THE SOLOMON R. GUGGENHEIM MUSEUM, New York, July 8–September 14, 1969, *Selected Sculpture and Works on Paper*, p.142, ill.

References:
GROHMANN, WILL, *Henry Moore*, Berlin, 1960, pl.62
RUSSELL, JOHN, *Henry Moore, Stone and Wood Carvings*, London, 1961, pls.56, 56A
BOWNESS, ALAN, ed., *Henry Moore, Sculpture and Drawing* vol.3, *Sculpture 1955–64*, New York, 1965, pls.33–36
READ, HERBERT, *Henry Moore, A Study of His Life and Work*, New York, 1966, pls.193, 194
HEDGECOE, JOHN, ed., *Henry Spencer Moore*, New York, 1968, pls.282–285 (Text by Henry Moore)
RUSSELL, JOHN, *Henry Moore*, New York, 1968, pls.181, 182

60.1582

Originally intended to be a horizontal sculpture of a reclining figure, this work was transformed by the artist during its execution into a vertical high relief. It is among the largest of Moore's carved wood sculptures completed during his mature years and consequently marks an exception to his usual working methods of making a plaster model for subsequent bronze casting.

Robert Morris 1931–

Robert Morris was born in 1931 in Kansas City, Missouri. He studied art at the University of Kansas City, the Kansas City Art Institute, the California School of Fine Arts, San Francisco, and Reed College, Portland, Oregon. He did graduate work in art history at Hunter College, New York (1961–62). In 1957 he had his first one-man exhibition at the Dilexi Gallery, San Francisco. The artist now resides in New York.

Although Morris's early paintings of the 1950's were in an Abstract Expressionist idiom, in 1960 he gave up painting to concentrate on making objects. His first object – an eight-inch cubic wooden box – dates from 1961. Simultaneously (after 1963) he experimented with non-structured materials, such as rope.

In 1964, Morris exhibited his objects at the Greene Gallery, New York. By this time the physical relationship of an object to its ambient space and ultimately to the viewer had become one of his primary preoccupations.

In 1967, the artist started working with series of identical units in order to create a "field situation". In 1969, his continuing experiments with unstructured materials and "fields" led to works in earth and peat moss, or rooms of mixed soft and hard materials. In all cases, the artist manipulates the viewer's response to a real spatial situation.

As a thinker, articulate speaker and writer, Morris has had a broad influence on younger artists. He is generally considered one of the originators of Minimal Art as well as of "Poor Art" or the art of informal distributions.

Untitled. 1967

Steel, 36 x 180 x 180″ (91 x 457.2 x 457.2 cm.) 9 units, each 36 x 36 x 36″ (91 x 91 x 91 cm.)

Made to the artist's specifications by an industrial fabricator

Not inscribed

Provenance:
the artist; Purchase Award, Guggenheim International Exhibition, through Leo Castelli Gallery, New York, 1967

Exhibitions:
THE SOLOMON R. GUGGENHEIM MUSEUM, New York, October 20, 1967–February 4, 1968, *Guggenheim International Exhibition, 1967: Sculpture from Twenty Nations*, p.155, ill.; traveled to ART GALLERY OF ONTARIO, Toronto, February 23–March 24; NATIONAL GALLERY OF CANADA, Ottawa, April 26–June 9; MONTREAL MUSEUM OF FINE ARTS, June 20–August 18, 1968

THE SOLOMON R. GUGGENHEIM MUSEUM, New York, July 8–September 14, 1969, *Selected Sculpture and Works on Paper*, p.143, ill.

References:
NAKAHARA, YUSUKE, "Guggenheim International Exhibition", *Mizue*, no.755, December 1967, p.64, ill.
ARNASON, H. H., *History of Modern Art*, New York, 1968, pl.1081

67.1865

One of a small series of modular works executed by the artist, this sculpture exemplifies many of Robert Morris's fundamental attitudes and stylistic preoccupations during the middle 1960's, immediately prior to his experiments with soft materials. The sculpture was made by an industrial fabricator to Morris's, specifications; its gray, untreated steel surfaces demonstrate the artist's aversion to color for its own sake and his predilection for a neutral yet perceptually resistant tonality.

The composition itself is a series of variations on the number three: three rows of three units each, with each unit separated from those adjacent to it by aisles three feet in width; each unit occupies a spatial cube of three feet on a side, and is composed of three sheets of steel each of which is three feet square.

Despite its rational, mathematical structure this work of seemingly Constructivist derivation is nevertheless removed from a Constructivist rationality by its very scale. Morris has deliberately avoided any clear relationship to the perceptual scale either of the human body or of architecture, thereby creating a sculptural style in opposition not only to Constructivism but to all previous twentieth-century styles.

Edvard Munch 1863–1944

Edvard Munch was born December 12, 1863, in Loiten, Norway. His father was a doctor who practiced in the poorest sections of Oslo. His mother and two sisters died when he was very young. These tragedies no doubt influenced Munch's overwhelming interest in themes relating to life-death cycles.

After art school in Oslo (1882–83), Munch settled there, notwithstanding frequent prolonged visits to Paris where he was exposed to French Neo-Impressionist painting which influenced his work.

Munch's first one-man show in Berlin in 1892 created an unprecedented scandal and was closed after a few days. The reasons given are varied but the closing is generally attributed to the high-keyed expressionism and overt eroticism which shocked a public accustomed to the academic painting reigning in Germany at that time.

In 1894 Munch began to work in various graphic media. His use of sharp contrast and extremely expressive line contribute to his excellence in printmaking; Munch's production in the graphic arts is of exceptional quality. He continued to paint, exhibiting frequently all over Europe, and undertook a series of large mural paintings for Oslo University (1909–1915) and the Freia chocolate factory in Oslo (1912). The Guggenheim Museum held a major exhibition of his work in 1965.

Munch died January 23, 1944 on his estate at Ekely near Oslo.

EDVARD MUNCH

Portrait of Erik Pedersen. 1944

Pastel, $9^1/_2$ x $17^5/_8''$ (24.1 x 44.7 cm.)

Signed l.l. of center "Edv. Munch"

Provenance
the artist
Erik Pedersen
Estate of Erik Pedersen
Mr. and Mrs. R. Tyler Day, Princeton, New Jersey, 1967

Exhibitions:

THE SOLOMON R. GUGGENHEIM MUSEUM, New York, June 28–October 1, 1967, *Museum Collection, Seven Decades, A Selection* (Checklist)

THE SOLOMON R. GUGGENHEIM MUSEUM, New York, July 8–September 14, 1969, *Selected Sculpture and Works on Paper*, p.68, ill.

67.1837

The man portrayed in this pastel was a former director of the Freia chocolate factory, and thus closely connected with Munch through his involvement with the Freia decorations. Erik Pedersen himself recorded Munch's comments at the time the artist executed the portrait: "Isn't it funny today, I am so weak and feel so bad, I can hardly stand on my feet and then I'm so sensitive that I can make the finest thing." An Oslo art magazine article, undated, mentioned Munch signing three sketches of Pedersen on January 14, 1944, nine days before he died. Two sketches were small pencil drawings and the third was a color portrait known as "His Last Work".

Robert Natkin 1930–

Robert Natkin was born in Chicago in 1930. He graduated from the Art Institute in 1952 and was a founder of the Wells Street Gallery in Chicago in 1957. The first of his numerous one-man shows was held at the Wells Street Gallery in 1957. He has exhibited regularly at the Poindexter Gallery, New York, since 1959.

Natkin is essentially a hedonistic painter, concerned with subtle harmonies and gradations of light and color. His early work was, to a certain degree, influenced by Abstract Expressionism. However, in more recent years the rich and complicated detail of his elaborately structured surfaces and color relationships has revealed his individuality.

The artist lives in New York City.

ROBERT NATKIN

They are Singing in Olive Land. 1963

Oil on canvas, 72 x 72$^1/8$″ (182.9 x 183 cm.)

Signed and dated l.c. "Natkin 1963"

Provenance:
Poindexter Gallery, New York, 1964

Exhibitions:
SAN FRANCISCO MUSEUM OF ART, September 25–November 9, 1969, *Robert Natkin*, no.10; traveled to LAGUNA BEACH ART ASSOCIATION GALLERY, California, February 1–28, 1970

64.1696

Reminiscent of both Bonnard and Matisse in the intensity of color juxtapositions, the complexity of spatial relationships between the surface and slightly receding planes, and the diffusion of light, the effect of this painting is joyous and sensuous. The essential organization of the canvas into vertical bands of color as well as the impressionist treatment of the central portion forecast Natkin's later work where the whole surface of the canvas is divided into gossamer ribbons of pastel color.

Ben Nicholson 1894–

Ben Nicholson was born April 10, 1894, at Denham, Bucks, England. After attending the Slade School of Art, London, for one term (1910–1911), he spent several years traveling in France, Italy, Madeira and California. In 1920 he settled in Cumberland and London, wintering in Italy. During the following years he made frequent trips to Paris. The discovery of Cézanne and Cubism inspired him to start painting seriously.

Around 1926, Nicholson began his semi-abstract still lifes. Their characteristic spareness of form and surface was apparently influenced by the direct carving practiced by the sculptress Barbara Hepworth with whom he shared a studio in London (and who was to become his second wife). In 1933 a superimposition of geometrical and non-referential planar figures, slightly in relief, heralded the beginning of his mature style.

A visit to Mondrian's studio in Paris in 1934 produced a lasting impression on the artist. His palette became more astringent, and his formal relationships became at the same time more determined and more discrete. In that same year he exhibited his first white reliefs in wood.

Except for the period 1947 to 1956, Nicholson has preferred to work in wood relief because of the particular kind of surface relationships the medium allows. His works are shallow in depth, and asymmetrical in composition. His forms are ideal, inspired by landscape, architecture and still-life motifs.

Nicholson won the first prize for painting in the Carnegie International in 1952, the Guggenheim International Award in 1956 and the international prize for painting at São Paulo in 1957. The artist moved in 1957 to Ticino in southern Switzerland where he now resides.

Night Façade. December 1955

Oil on pressed wood, 42 1/2 x 45 3/4" (108 x 116.2 cm.)

Inscribed on reverse "Dec 55//Ben Nicholson//(night façade)"

Provenance:
from the artist through Galerie de France, Paris, 1957

Exhibitions:
THE SOLOMON R. GUGGENHEIM MUSEUM, New York, October 21, 1959–June 19, 1960, *Inaugural Selection* (Checklist)
PHILADELPHIA MUSEUM OF ART, November 2, 1961– January 7, 1962, *Guggenheim Museum Exhibition, A Loan Collection of Paintings, Drawings, and Prints from The Solomon R. Guggenheim Museum, New York*, no.124
DALLAS MUSEUM OF FINE ARTS, April 15–May 17, 1964, *Ben Nicholson Retrospective Exhibition*, no.43

References:
READ, HERBERT, *Ben Nicholson: Work Since 1947*, vol.2, London, 1956, pl.129
ARNASON, H. H., *History of Modern Art*, New York, 1968, p.504, pl.887
RUSSELL, JOHN, *Ben Nicholson*, New York, 1969, pl.64

57.1461

Executed during a period of his career when the artist worked in oil paint, the rich and textured colors of this work are unusual in his production. The iconography is nonetheless characteristic – a composite image of architectural and still life motifs. The spare linear outlines of forms and the contrasting planes of color create a complex and spatially ambiguous composition.

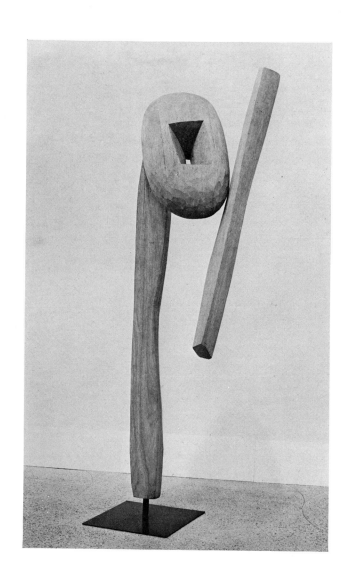

Isamu Noguchi 1904–

Isamu Noguchi was born in Los Angeles on November 17, 1904, of an American mother and a Japanese father, a poet. After twelve years in Japan he returned to America, where he attended high school in Indiana and two years of medical school at Columbia University. He began studying art in 1924 at the Leonardo da Vinci School.

In 1926, Noguchi saw Brancusi's exhibition at the Brummer Gallery and was profoundly impressed. With the aid of a Guggenheim fellowship, he spent the following two years in Paris working in Brancusi's studio. Upon his return to New York, he made his living by making portrait heads, notably of Martha Graham, with whom he would begin a long and successful collaboration in 1935, and of Buckminster Fuller. During a trip to China and Japan, he studied brush drawing and ceramics.

Noguchi's sculptures of the 1940's, related formally to the Surrealist vocabulary, were made from flat marble slabs locked together in a tripod fashion. A concern throughout the artist's career has been to integrate sculpture with man's life and environment as in sets for dance and theater, playgrounds, gardens and fountains.

ISAMU NOGUCHI

The Cry. 1959

Balsa wood on steel base, 84″ (210 cm.) high

Not inscribed

Provenance:
from the artist through Cordier & Ekstrom, Inc., New York, 1966

Exhibitions:

DANIEL CORDIER & MICHEL WARREN, INC., New York, May 16–June 17, 1961, *Isamu Noguchi, Weightlessness*

WHITNEY MUSEUM OF AMERICAN ART, New York, April 17–June 16, 1968, *Isamu Noguchi*, no.33, ill.

THE SOLOMON R. GUGGENHEIM MUSEUM, New York, July 8–September 14, 1969, *Selected Sculpture and Works on Paper*, p.144, ill.

THE METROPOLITAN MUSEUM OF ART, New York, October 18, 1969–February 1, 1970, *New York Painting and Sculpture: 1940–1970*, no.275, p.246, ill.

References:

NOGUCHI, ISAMU, *Isamu Noguchi, A Sculptor's World*, New York, 1968, pl.94

66.1812

Preoccupied with the sense of contrast between New York and Europe, Noguchi, on his return from Paris in 1958, determined to find new ways of capturing the city's newness and crystalline monumentality. For him this search meant the temporary abandonment of his usual working methods in stone and experiments with lighter and less traditional materials. *The Cry*, in balsa – one of the lightest woods known – is one example of this turn in the artist's work; the choice of material is reinforced by Noguchi's composition, which conveys a sense of the effortless floating of biomorphic forms in space.

ISAMU NOGUCHI

Lunar. 1959–60

Anodized aluminum, 70^1/$_2$" (179 cm.) high

Not inscribed

Provenance:

from the artist through Daniel Cordier & Michel Warren, Inc., New York, 1961

Exhibitions:

DANIEL CORDIER & MICHEL WARREN, INC., New York, May 16–June 17, 1961, *Isamu Noguchi, Weightlessness*

WHITNEY MUSEUM OF AMERICAN ART, New York, April 17–June 16, 1968, *Isamu Noguchi,* no.13. (Erroneously dated 1945 in catalogue)

THE SOLOMON R. GUGGENHEIM MUSEUM, New York, July 8–September 14, 1969, *Selected Sculpture and Works on Paper,* p.145, ill.

References:

NOGUCHI, ISAMU, *Isamu Noguchi, A Sculptor's World,* New York, 1968, frontispiece

61.1596

As in *The Cry*, Noguchi's intention with this work was to convey a sense of lightness and weightlessness. In a series of works executed at this period, the artist turned to sheet aluminum as his medium, avoiding the sense of heavy volume by retaining the flatness of his material and merely bending or cutting to arrive at his final image.

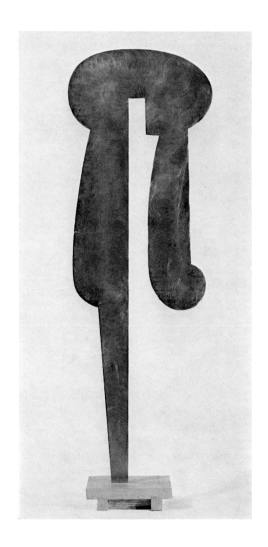

Kenneth Noland 1924–

Kenneth Noland was born in Ashville, North Carolina in 1924. From 1946 to 1948, he studied with Ilya Bolotowsky at nearby Black Mountain College. In 1948–49 he studied with Ossip Zadkine in Paris, after which he moved to Washington, D.C. to teach at the Institute of Contemporary Art and later at Catholic University. In Washington he was the neighbor and friend of Morris Louis, who had a decisive influence on his art. After his first one-man shows in New York (he had shown earlier in Paris) at the Tibor de Nagy Gallery in 1957–58, he was included in the series of exhibitions organized by Clement Greenberg at French & Co. Noland now teaches at Bennington College and lives in South Shaftsbury, Vermont.

Noland's first wholly personal paintings date from 1958–59 and employ the stain technique. The impetus was Louis's stain paintings, themselves deriving ultimately from Pollock's work of 1951 via Helen Frankenthaler's *Mountains and Sea*, 1952, which Louis and Noland had seen together on a trip to New York in 1953. The stain technique, or the soaking of paint into an unprimed canvas, created not a tactile (relief) but a purely optical space. Noland made his breakthrough by appropriating the precise center of the field as the axis around which his pictorial structure would deductively evolve. The first of these paintings were the "pinwheels", concentric colored rings of which the outer has a centrifugal surge, making the image appear to spin. From that time, Noland's career can be seen as a systematic elimination of whatever was not essential to a lucid deductive structure: the "bull's-eyes"; the off-center elliptical "tiger's-eyes" on colored fields; the chevrons, beginning in 1962; the diamond-shaped canvases with diagonal stripes; and finally the horizontally extended canvases with bands of color. The extremely logical structure of Noland's work has produced a radical freedom of expression for color painting.

KENNETH NOLAND

April Tune. 1969

Acrylic emulsion on canvas, $65^3/4''$ x $104^1/8''$ (167 x 620.5 cm.)

Signed on reverse "APRIL TUNE//1969//Kenneth Noland// 65 3/4 x 104" "

Provenance:

from the artist through Lawrence Rubin Gallery, New York, 1969

References:

BANNARD, DARBY, "Notes on American Painting of the Sixties", *Artforum*, vol.XIII, no.5, January 1970, p.44, ill.

69.1915

Around 1967, Noland moved from a diamond-shaped to a horizontal format articulated by bands of color of extreme variation in width. The horizontal extension of the canvas results in an elimination of the vertical edge as a structural element, draws the viewer toward the center of the picture and dramatically explodes the image, giving an illusion of speed and infinite openness. In the most recent of these horizontal band paintings, of which *April Tune* is an example, a large area of color is framed above and below by relatively thin stripes. Although this area is in fact a rectangle, the framing bands insist that it be read not as area but simply as a wider band of color. B keeping the value difference at a minimum, Noland has reduced the isolation of hues, encouraging them to relate to one another despite their explicit chromatic distinctions.

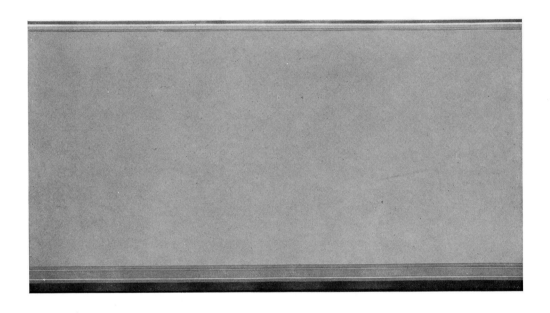

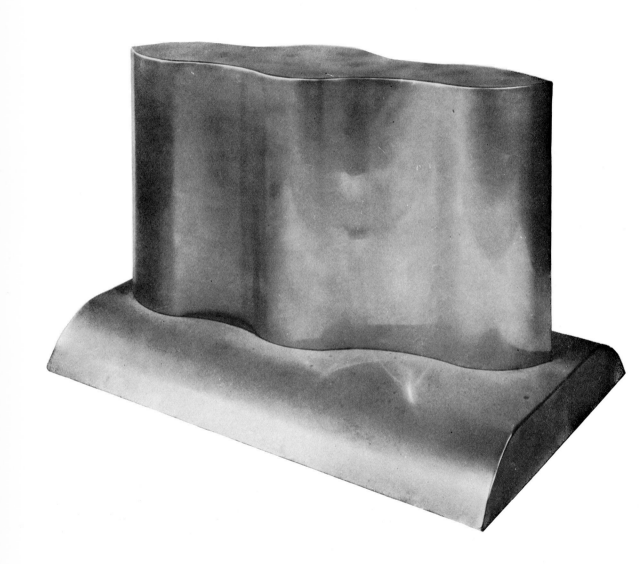

Inversion (Umkehrung). 1966

Chrome plated steel, 29^1/$_4$ x 49^3/$_4$ x 29^3/$_4$" (74.3 x 126.4 x 75.6 cm.)

Not inscribed

Provenance:
the artist; Purchase Award, Guggenheim International Exhibition, through Pace Gallery, New York, 1967

Exhibitions:
THE SOLOMON R. GUGGENHEIM MUSEUM, New York, October 20, 1967–February 4, 1968, *Guggenheim International Exhibition, 1967: Sculpture from Twenty Nations*, p.95, ill.; traveled to ART GALLERY OF ONTARIO, Toronto, February 23–March 24; NATIONAL GALLERY OF CANADA, Ottawa, April 26–June 9; MONTREAL MUSEUM OF FINE ARTS, June 20–August 18, 1968

THE SOLOMON R. GUGGENHEIM MUSEUM, New York, July 8–September 14, 1969, *Selected Sculpture and Works on Paper*, p.147, ill.

67.1866

Eduardo Paolozzi 1924–

Eduardo Paolozzi was born March 7, 1924, in Edinburgh, Scotland, of Italian parents. He studied at the Edinburgh College of Art (1943) and the Slade School of Art, London (1944–1947). He had his first one-man exhibition at the Mayor Gallery, London, in 1947, an exhibition of animal heads in cement which, in their open framework and pitted surfaces, were a powerful refutation of the prevailing English modern tradition of neat forms, clean surfaces and truth to materials. This was the first of a succession of exhibitions by young British sculptors which led to their recognition as a new school at the 1952 Venice Biennale.

Paolozzi spent 1947–1950 in Paris where he exhibited in a group show at the Galerie Maeght, visited Giacometti's studio and was exposed to and impressed by the works of Paul Klee, Dada and Surrealism. His sculpture thereafter, using cast-off objects assembled according to an indisputably human framework, presents anguished images of the identity (or anonymity) of modern man.

Since 1961, Paolozzi's sculptures, although still governed by the principle of assemblage, comprise more simply structured monumental components, incorporated with technological precision into quite different icons of modernity.

Paolozzi was given his first one-man show in New York in 1960 at the Betty Parsons Gallery. He taught at the Hamburg Hochschule from 1960–1962 and had a one-man sculpture exhibition at the Museum of Modern Art, New York, in 1964. In recent years he has executed several series of silk-screen prints which have been widely exhibited both in Europe and America.

Like many leading artists of his generation who had already achieved prominence during the previous decade, Paolozzi during the early 1960's modified his style in response to a new artistic and cultural sensibility that was rapidly emerging. This new sensibility was characterized in art by an impersonality, logic, austerity, elegance, and technological voluptuousness – all qualities that, to a greater or lesser degree, are reflected in *Inversion*.

Using the facilities of the Rolls Royce factory for plating the surfaces of his forms, the artist completed this work as part of a series of closely related sculptures. Although it is among the most austere and symmetrical of the series, *Inversion* nevertheless retains, in its curvilinear rhythms, the incipiently baroque expansiveness characteristic of Paolozzi's style as a whole.

Antoine Pevsner 1886–1962

Antoine Pevsner was born January 18, 1886, in Orel, Russia. After attending the School of Fine Arts in Kiev, and the Academy of Fine Arts in St. Petersburg, he went to Paris (1912, 1913–1914) where, although exposed to Cubism, he was more impressed by the Eiffel Tower.

During a sojourn in Oslo (1915–1916) with his younger brother Naum Gabo, Pevsner turned from painting to sculpture. Both brothers were interested in creating a sculptural form emphasizing the void rather than the compact mass and this was to remain the guiding principle of Pevsner's art throughout his lifetime. In the 1950's his aesthetic attitude was that sculpture is made of space, not concrete materials. It is a "spatial construction" in which time – the other dimension of human existence – should be integrated through dynamic tensions and rhythms.

Pevsner returned to Russia in 1917 where he taught at the Moscow Academy of Fine Arts, with Kandinsky and Malevitch. In 1920 he and Gabo wrote their *Realistic Manifesto* in which they expressed their revolutionary aesthetic. In October 1923 Pevsner left Russia for Paris, becoming a French citizen in 1930. He joined the *Abstraction-Création* group with Mondrian, Herbin and Kupka in 1931 and was a co-founder of the group *Réalités Nouvelles* in 1946.

Pevsner had a large retrospective with Gabo at the Museum of Modern Art, New York in 1948 and a large personal retrospective in Paris (Musée National d'Art Moderne) in 1957. After receiving the French Légion d'honneur in 1961, he died in Paris in 1962.

Twinned Column (Colonne Jumelée). 1947

Bronze, 40^1/$_2$″ (102.9 cm.) high

Inscribed on face l.l. "AP 47" and reverse l.r. "A/P/A"

Provenance:
from the artist, 1954

Exhibitions:
KUNSTHAUS, Zürich, October 15–November 13, 1949, *Pevsner, Vantongerloo, Bill*, no.25

THE SOLOMON R. GUGGENHEIM MUSEUM, New York, March 30–May 5, 1954, *Selection III* (Checklist)

THE SOLOMON R. GUGGENHEIM MUSEUM, New York, October 6, 1954–February 27, 1955, *Selection IV* (Checklist)

NEWARK MUSEUM, New Jersey, April 27–June 10, 1956, *Abstract Art, 1910 to Today*, no.54

MUSÉE NATIONAL D'ART MODERNE, Paris, December 21, 1956–March 10, 1957, *Antoine Pevsner*, no.45, pl.XVII

THE SOLOMON R. GUGGENHEIM MUSEUM, New York, October 21, 1959–June 19, 1960, *Inaugural Selection* (Checklist; withdrawn from exhibition April 4, 1960)

ARTS CLUB OF CHICAGO, April 19–May 19, 1960, *Sculpture and Drawings by Sculptors from The Solomon R. Guggenheim Museum*, no.20

CLEVELAND MUSEUM OF ART, Ohio, October 4–November 13, 1960, *Paths of Abstract Art*, no.108, ill.

PHILBROOK ART CENTER, Tulsa, Oklahoma, October 1–23, 1962, *Twentieth Century Sculpture*, no.43

THE SOLOMON R. GUGGENHEIM MUSEUM, New York, July 8–September 14, 1969, *Selected Sculpture and Works on Paper*, p.149, ill.

References:
GIEDION-WELCKER, CAROLA, *Contemporary Sculpture, An Evolution in Volume and Space*, New York, 1955, p.203, ill.

READ, HERBERT, *Icon and Idea*, Cambridge, Massachusetts, 1955, pl.84

MASSAT, RENÉ, *Antoine Pevsner et le Constructivisme*, Paris, 1956, ill.

PEISSI, PIERRE and GIEDION-WELCKER, CAROLA, *Antoine Pevsner*, Neuchâtel, Switzerland, 1961, pl.104

54.1397

y the mid- or late 1940's Pevsner, living and working
Paris, had arrived at a mature style and technique
hich he would maintain until his death. In this important
ample may be seen his previously developed means of
ploiting symmetry, the interchangeability of solid and
id, and the topological ambiguities of planar surfaces.
evsner's working methods by this time had shifted to
e use of bronze rods, brazed together into the desired
nfiguration. In addition to being more suitable to the
ear continuities within his compositions, this technique
as probably also a reflection of that used by Naum
abo, his older brother, during the 1930's and 1940's in
orks constructed of plastic or nylon filaments.

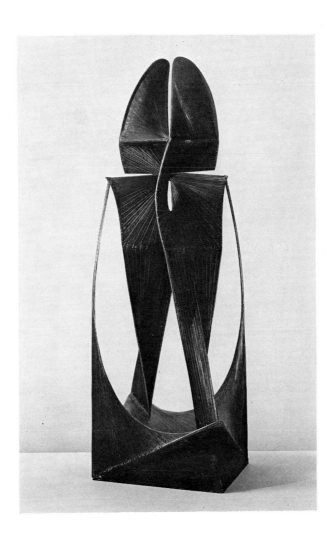

Francis Picabia 1879–1953

Francis Picabia was born January 22, 1879, in Paris of a Spanish father and a French mother. After preliminary schooling, he began art lessons in 1894 and had his first one-man show in 1905 at the age of twenty-six.

As an Impressionist painter Picabia was highly successful. But in 1909 he abandoned his earlier career to elaborate a new style. His self-avowed goal was to capture an impression of movement, simultaneity and an abstract reality. In 1911, Picabia met Marcel Duchamp and joined the Puteaux group which would become the *Section d'Or*. Apollinaire applied the term "Orphisme" to his subsequent work (until 1916). These paintings (of which the *Udnie* series is the best example) are characterized by the dynamic succession of planar forms.

Picabia made his first visit to the United States for the Armory Show in 1913. His renewed contact with Duchamp and his encounter with Stieglitz provided an increased impetus for his native proto-Dada tendencies. From 1916 to 1921 he participated in Dada manifestations and contributed both writings and drawings to Dada publications in Europe and New York. During this period, imaginary living machines ("mécanomorphes") are his most frequent theme.

This period, whether or not it was the artist's most prolific, was that from which his best-known style emerged. After 1927, Picabia continued to show regularly in Paris Salons as well as with the Surrealists with whom he was loosely allied. He died in Paris on November 30, 1953.

FRANCIS PICABIA

Portrait of Mistinguett. 1907

Oil on canvas, 24 x 19³/₄″ (61 x 50.2 cm.)

Signed and dated l.c. "Francis Picabia 1907"

Provenance:
Pierre Granville, Paris, 1966

Exhibitions:
THE SOLOMON R. GUGGENHEIM MUSEUM, New York, June 28–October 1, 1967, *Museum Collection, Seven Decades, A Selection* (Checklist)

66.1801

Portrait of Mistinguett is an unusual painting in the artist's production. Officially, at this time, Picabia was an Impressionist landscape painter. We know however that, although he seldom exhibited them, he did some figure painting, frequently at the request of friends. Madame Gabrielle Buffet-Picabia, the artist's wife from 1909 to 1931, has confirmed that Picabia knew Mistinguett, the famed Cabaret performer, during this period.

The painting shows an eclecticism typical of the artist at this time. The thick expressive contours, the asymmetrical spatial organization and the sharp contrasts of masses are reminiscent of turn-of-the-century French painting (not only Nabi but Toulouse-Lautrec). The brightly colored shadows show a definite Fauve influence. The predominance of line over color which is characteristic of the artist throughout his varied career is already manifest here.

FRANCIS PICABIA

Child Carburetor (L'Enfant Carburateur). c.1919

Mixed media on wood, 49³/₄ x 39⁷/₈″ (126.4 x 101.3 cm.)

Signed l.r. "FRANCIS PICABIA"

Provenance:
Lucien Lefebvre-Foinet, Paris
Art of this Century, New York
Matta, New York
Rose Fried Gallery, New York, 1955

Exhibitions:
SALON D'AUTOMNE, Paris, 1919, no.1533
THE MUSEUM OF MODERN ART, New York, December 7, 1936–January 17, 1937, *Fantastic Art, Dada, and Surrealism*, no.462, pl.461
ROSE FRIED GALLERY, New York, November–December 1954, *Duchamp, Picabia*, no.11

THE SOLOMON R. GUGGENHEIM MUSEUM, New York, July 26–October 9, 1955, *Selection V* (Checklist)
NEWARK MUSEUM, New Jersey, April 27–June 10, 1956, *Abstract Art, 1910 to Today*, no.55
THE SOLOMON R. GUGGENHEIM MUSEUM, New York, June 28–October 1, 1967, *Museum Collection, Seven Decades, A Selection* (Checklist)
THE SOLOMON R. GUGGENHEIM MUSEUM, New York, May 30–September 2, 1968, *Rousseau, Redon, and Fantasy*, ill.
THE MUSEUM OF MODERN ART, New York, November 25, 1968–February 9, 1969, *The Machine as Seen at the End of the Mechanical Age*, p.96, ill.; traveled to UNIVERSITY OF ST. THOMAS, Houston, March 25–May 18; SAN FRANCISCO MUSEUM OF ART, June 23–August 24, 1969

References:
The Little Review, Picabia Number, Spring 1922, insert before p.16, ill.
SEUPHOR, MICHEL, *L'Art Abstrait, ses origines, ses premiers maîtres*, Paris, 1950, p.308
CAMFIELD, WILLIAM A. "The machine style of Francis Picabia", *The Art Bulletin*, vol.XLVIII, nos.3–4, September–December 1966, p.320, note 58
ARNASON, H. H., *History of Modern Art*, New York, 1968, pl.535

55.1426

This is an excellent example of Picabia's "Mécanomorphic" style which lasted approximately from 1915 to 1921. Typical of Picabia's form of Dada expression are the mixture of materials (oil paint, gouache, gold leaf, chalk, pencil on board), the abandonment of traditional "painterly" qualities, the interspersion of satirical texts (sometimes plays on words, sometimes verbal collage), and the subject of the not only "humanized" but humorous machine.

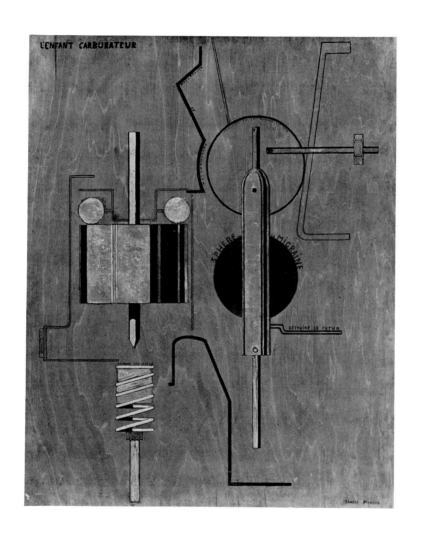

Still Life (Carafon, Pot et Compotier). 1909

Oil on canvas, 28³/₄ x 25⁷/₈″ (72.5 x 65.8 cm.)

Provenance:
Collection Reber, Lausanne
Zwemmer Gallery, London, 1936
Gift, Solomon R. Guggenheim, New York, 1937

Exhibitions:

THE SOLOMON R. GUGGENHEIM MUSEUM, New York,
February 3–May 3, 1953, *A Selection* (Checklist)

THE SOLOMON R. GUGGENHEIM MUSEUM, New York,
May 13–October 11, 1953, *Selection II* (Checklist)

THE SOLOMON R. GUGGENHEIM MUSEUM, New York,
October 6, 1954–February 27, 1955, *Selection IV*
(Checklist)

MONTREAL MUSEUM OF FINE ARTS, June 4–July 3, 1955, *A
Selection from The Solomon R. Guggenheim Museum,* no.49,
ill.

THE SOLOMON R. GUGGENHEIM MUSEUM, New York,
July 26–October 9, 1955, *Selection V* (Checklist)

ARTS CLUB OF CHICAGO, October 3–November 4, 1955,
*An Exhibition of Cubism on the Occasion of the Fortieth
Anniversary of the Arts Club of Chicago,* no.14

THE SOLOMON R. GUGGENHEIM MUSEUM, New York,
January 24–May 1, 1956, *Selection VI* (Checklist)

TATE GALLERY, London, April 16–May 26, 1957, *Paintings
from The Solomon R. Guggenheim Museum,* no.59; orga-
nized by THE SOLOMON R. GUGGENHEIM MUSEUM, traveled
to GEMEENTEMUSEUM, The Hague, June 25–September 1;
ATENEIUMIN TAIDEKOKOELMAT, Helsinki, September 27–
October 20; GALLERIA NAZIONALE D'ARTE MODERNA, Rome,
December 5, 1957–January 8, 1958; WALLRAF–RICHARTZ-
MUSEUM, Cologne, January 26–March 30; MUSÉE DES ARTS
DÉCORATIFS, Paris, April 23–June 1, 1958

THE SOLOMON R. GUGGENHEIM MUSEUM, New York,
October 21, 1959–June 19, 1960, *Inaugural Selection*
(Checklist)

CLEVELAND MUSEUM OF ART, Ohio, October 4–
November 13, 1960, *Paths of Abstract Art,* no.18

THE SOLOMON R. GUGGENHEIM MUSEUM, New York,
August 30–October 8, 1961, *Modern Masters from the
Collection of The Solomon R. Guggenheim Museum*

THE SOLOMON R. GUGGENHEIM MUSEUM, New York,
June 5–October 13, 1963, *Cézanne and Structure in Modern
Painting*

THE SOLOMON R. GUGGENHEIM MUSEUM, New York,
April 30–September 1, 1965, *Paintings from the Collection
of The Solomon R. Guggenheim Museum,* no.12, ill.

MUSEUM OF FINE ARTS OF HOUSTON, October 21–
December 8, 1965, *The Heroic Years: Paris 1908–1914*

THE SOLOMON R. GUGGENHEIM MUSEUM, New York,
June 28–October 1, 1967, *Museum Collection, Seven
Decades, A Selection* (Checklist)

Pablo Picasso 1881–

Pablo Ruiz Picasso was born October 25, 1881, in Malaga,
Spain. After 1895 he resided in Barcelona. A precocious
artist, his works prior to 1901 (signed P. Ruiz Picasso) were
largely scenes of local life and figure studies done in a
virtuoso turn-of-the-century style. 1901 marks the beginning of his more somber Blue Period which was to last
until 1904.

From 1904 to 1948, Picasso lived in Paris, after which he
moved to the south of France. During that time his painting
underwent successive and radical changes: the Rose Period
(1905), Cubism (on which he and Braque collaborated
after 1907), a monumental neo-Classicism (early 1920's), a
marginal Surrealism (1925 through the 1930's) and the
monochromatic and diagrammatic style of Guernica
(1937). Such is Picasso's prolific production that styles,
themes and their variants recur at different stages of his
career, making it difficult to pinpoint his chronological
progression. Still lifes and figure studies predominate, the
artist's inspiration revolving around several often-repeated
themes such as bullfights, women, mythological scenes, the
artist and his model. Since the 1940's his paintings have
become progressively more loosely constructed with
greater emphasis on arbitrary color.

Through his long and varied career and his mastery of all
mediums – painting, sculpture, the graphic arts, ceramics –
Picasso has become the legendary giant of twentieth-
century art.

THE SOLOMON R. GUGGENHEIM MUSEUM, New York,
April 11–May 26, 1968, *Acquisitions of the 1930's and 1940's,*
p.28, ill.

References:

ZERVOS, CHRISTIAN, *Pablo Picasso, œuvres de 1906 à 1912,*
Paris, 1942, vol.2*, pl.81, no.164, ill.

SABARTES, JAIME, *Picasso, Documents iconographiques,*
Geneva, 1954, pl.187

VALLIER, DORA, *L'art abstrait,* Paris, 1967, p.32, no.9, ill.

37.536

Picasso's experiments leading to Cubism began as early
as 1905–1906. During this proto-Cubist period, he was
impressed by Cézanne as well as by Spanish pre-Roman
and African sculpture. Hence volume is a major preoccupation.

1909 marks the first articulate stage of Picasso and
Braque's Analytical Cubism. In *Still Life* the forms are
not yet flattened into intersecting planes but retain an
illusion of volume through the shaded contours, contrasted modeling and a shortened yet not totally obliterated
perspective.

Recorded by Zervos as having been painted in the spring
of 1909, *Still Life* appears stylistically closer to Picasso's
work at Horta de San Juan in the summer of that same
year. Furthermore, in Sabartès's reproduction of the
artist's summer studio, the left side of this picture is
clearly visible on the wall.

PABLO PICASSO

Accordionist (Pierrot). 1911

Oil on canvas, 51¼ x 35¼" (127.5 x 89.5 cm.)

Signed l.l. "Picasso"

Provenance:
Valentine Gallery, New York, 1936
Gift, Solomon R. Guggenheim, New York, 1937

Exhibitions:
MUSEUM OF MODERN ART, New York, 1939, *Picasso: Forty Years of his Art*, p.76, no.97, ill.

THE SOLOMON R. GUGGENHEIM MUSEUM, New York, February 3–May 3, 1953, *A Selection* (Checklist)

THE SOLOMON R. GUGGENHEIM MUSEUM, New York, May 13–October 11, 1953, *Selection II* (Checklist)

THE SOLOMON R. GUGGENHEIM MUSEUM, New York, March 30–May 5, 1954, *Selection III* (Checklist)

THE SOLOMON R. GUGGENHEIM MUSEUM, New York, October 6, 1954–February 27, 1955, *Selection IV* (Checklist)

MUSÉE DES ARTS DÉCORATIFS, Paris, June-October, 1955, *Picasso*, no.24, ill.

ARTS CLUB OF CHICAGO, October 3–November 4, 1955, *An Exhibition of Cubism on the Occasion of the Fortieth Anniversary of the Arts Club of Chicago*, no.15, ill.

THE SOLOMON R. GUGGENHEIM MUSEUM, New York, January 24–May 1, 1956, *Selection VI* (Checklist)

TATE GALLERY, London, April 16–May 26, 1957, *Paintings from The Solomon R. Guggenheim Museum*, no.60; organized by THE SOLOMON R. GUGGENHEIM MUSEUM, traveled to GEMEENTEMUSEUM, The Hague, June 25–September 1; ATENEIUMIN TAIDEKOKOELMAT, Helsinki, September 27–October 20; GALLERIA NAZIONALE D'ARTE MODERNA, Rome, December 5, 1957–January 8, 1958; WALLRAF–RICHARTZ–MUSEUM, Cologne, January 26–March 30; MUSÉE DES ARTS DÉCORATIFS, Paris, April 23–June 1, 1958

THE SOLOMON R. GUGGENHEIM MUSEUM, New York, October 21, 1959–June 19, 1960, *Inaugural Selection* (Checklist)

THE SOLOMON R. GUGGENHEIM MUSEUM, New York, August 30–October 8, 1961, *Modern Masters from the Collection of The Solomon R. Guggenheim Museum*

PHILADELPHIA MUSEUM OF ART, November 2, 1961–January 7, 1962, *Guggenheim Museum Exhibition, A Loan Collection of Paintings, Drawings, and Prints from The Solomon R. Guggenheim Museum, New York*, no.128, ill.

SAIDENBERG GALLERY, New York, April 24–May 15, 1962, *Picasso: An American Tribute*, no.5, ill.

THE SOLOMON R. GUGGENHEIM MUSEUM, New York, June 5–October 13, 1963, *Cézanne and Structure in Modern Painting*

THE SOLOMON R. GUGGENHEIM MUSEUM, New York, April 30–September 1, 1965, *Paintings from the Collection of The Solomon R. Guggenheim Museum*, no.22, ill.

THE SOLOMON R. GUGGENHEIM MUSEUM, New York, April 11–May 26, 1968, *Acquisitions of the 1930's and 1940's*, pp.28–29, ill.

References:

ZERVOS, CHRISTIAN, *Picasso, œuvres de 1906 à 1912*, Paris, 1942, vol.2★, pl.135, no.277, ill.

BARR, ALFRED H., JR., *Picasso, Fifty Years of his Art*, New York, 1946, pp.74–75, ill.

BOECK, WILHELM and SABARTES, JAIME, *Picasso*, New York, 1955, p.152, p.377, ill.

ROSENBLUM, ROBERT, *Cubism and Twentieth-Century Art*, New York, 1960, pl.33

PALAU I FABRE, JOSEP, *Picasso en Cataluna*, Barcelona, 1966, p.164, no.125, ill.

HAMILTON, GEORGE HEARD, *Painting and Sculpture in Europe 1880–1940*, Baltimore, 1967, pl.87

ARNASON, H. H., *History of Modern Art*, New York, 1968, p.128, pl.211

37.537

Picasso spent the summer of 1911 with Braque in Céret in the French Pyrenees. Together the artists brought Analytical Cubism to its culminating point: the almost complete abstraction of the figurative image. Through the original figure's schematization into geometric and transparent planes, the traditional figure/ground relationship was destroyed and replaced by a unified fabric of scaffolded forms.

The pyramidal structure which one finds here and in other paintings of the same period ("*Ma Jolie*", The Museum of Modern Art, New York; *The Aficionado*, Basel) is not only inspired by the preliminary figure's verticality but is an attempt to avoid the classic perspectival organization imposed by the rectangular canvas. As in the oval format paintings, introduced by Braque and Picasso at approximately the same time, a self-contained two-dimensional unity of the surface is attained. The articulation of the canvas is dictated by the inner structure, not by the arbitrary edges of the canvas.

In spite of descriptive details – vestigial references to the original image – this period of Picasso's and Braque's Cubism came to be known as Hermetic Cubism, in view of its relatively difficult legibility.

PABLO PICASSO

Bottle and Glass (Bouteille et Verre: Le Percolateur). 1911–12

Oil on paper mounted on canvas, $25^5/8$ x $19^3/4''$ (65 x 50.2 cm.)

Signed l.r. "Picasso"

Provenance:
Max Pellequer, Paris
Pierre Loeb, Paris, 1938

Exhibitions:
THE SOLOMON R. GUGGENHEIM MUSEUM, New York, February 3–May 3, 1953, *A Selection* (Checklist)

THE SOLOMON R. GUGGENHEIM MUSEUM, New York, March 30–May 5, 1954, *Selection III* (Checklist)

VANCOUVER ART GALLERY, November 16–December 12, 1954, *The Solomon R. Guggenheim Museum, A Selection from the Museum Collection*, no.69, ill.

MONTREAL MUSEUM OF FINE ARTS, Montreal, June 4–July 3, 1955, *A Selection from The Solomon R. Guggenheim Museum*, no.51

THE SOLOMON R. GUGGENHEIM MUSEUM, New York, July 26–October 9, 1955, *Selection V* (Checklist)

ARTS CLUB OF CHICAGO, October 3–November 4, 1955, *An Exhibition of Cubism on the Occasion of the Fortieth Anniversary of the Arts Club of Chicago*, no.16

NEWARK MUSEUM, New Jersey, April 27–June 10, 1956, *Abstract Art, 1910 to Today*, no.57

TATE GALLERY, London, April 16–May 26, 1957, *Paintings from The Solomon R. Guggenheim Museum*, no.62; organized by THE SOLOMON R. GUGGENHEIM MUSEUM, traveled to GEMEENTEMUSEUM, The Hague, June 25–September 1; ATENEIUMIN TAIDEKOKOELMAT, Helsinki, September 27–October 20; GALLERIA NAZIONALE D'ARTE MODERNA, Rome, December 5, 1957–January 8, 1958; WALLRAF–RICHARTZ-MUSEUM, Cologne, January 26–March 30 ; MUSÉE DES ARTS DÉCORATIFS, Paris, April 23–June 1, 1958

THE SOLOMON R. GUGGENHEIM MUSEUM, New York, August 30–October 8, 1961, *Modern Masters from the Collection of The Solomon R. Guggenheim Museum*

DALLAS MUSEUM OF FINE ARTS, October 6–December 31, 1962, *The Arts of Man*

WORCESTER ART MUSEUM, Massachusetts, February 6–April 7, 1963, *Aspects of Twentieth Century Painting Lent by The Solomon R. Guggenheim Museum*, no.35, ill.

THE SOLOMON R. GUGGENHEIM MUSEUM, New York, April 30–September 1, 1965, *Paintings from the Collection The Solomon R. Guggenheim Museum*, no.23, ill.

THE SOLOMON R. GUGGENHEIM MUSEUM, New York, June 28–October 1, 1967, *Museum Collection, Seven Decades, A Selection* (Checklist)

THE SOLOMON R. GUGGENHEIM MUSEUM, New York, April 11–May 26, 1968, *Acquisitions of the 1930's and 1940'* p.46, ill.

References:
ZERVOS, CHRISTIAN, *Pablo Picasso, œuvres de 1906 à 1912*, Paris, 1942, vol.2★, no.299, pl.145

GOLDING, JOHN, *Cubism*, London, 1959, p.113, pl.12A

38.539

Bottle and Glass, completed in Paris in the winter of 1911–1912, is an even more abstract composition than *The Accordionist*. The planes are flatter, the contrasts less descriptive and the structural organization less easy to define.

To counterbalance this unprecedented emphasis on purely formal structure, not only have the vestigial references to reality been maintained but they are reinforced by the introduction of printed letters (used by Picasso and Braque as early as 1910). The latter, within the abstract reality of the painted canvas, appear as islands of concrete reality.

Glass and Bottle of "Bass" (Verre et Bouteille de Bass). 1913

Pencil, gouache, sawdust and collage, 18⁷/₈ x 24³/₄″
(48 x 63 cm.)

Signed l.r. "Picasso"

Provenance:
Max Pellequer, Paris
Pierre Loeb, Paris, 1938

Exhibitions:

ART GALLERY OF TORONTO, April 2–May 9, 1954, *A Loan
Exhibition of Paintings from The Solomon R. Guggenheim
Museum, New York*, no.65

VANCOUVER ART GALLERY, November 16–December 12,
1954, *The Solomon R. Guggenheim Museum, A Selection
from the Museum Collection*, no.70

THE SOLOMON R. GUGGENHEIM MUSEUM, New York,
April 11–May 26, 1968, *Acquisitions of the 1930's and 1940's,*
p.47, ill.

THE SOLOMON R. GUGGENHEIM MUSEUM, New York,
July 8–September 14, 1969, *Selected Sculpture and Works on
Paper*, p.71, ill.

References:

ZERVOS, CHRISTIAN, *Pablo Picasso, œuvres de 1912 à 1917,*
Paris, 1942, vol.2**, no.441, pl.206

38.540

In 1912 Picasso and Braque invented the "collage", the
technique of integrating bits of paper or other extraneous
materials (wood, sand, sawdust, oilcloth, newspaper,
printed labels) into a composition. Cubism emphasized
the flatness of the canvas; collage served to strengthen
that awareness.

The juxtaposition of realities thus attained – the pictorial
reality of the artist's medium and imaginary structure,
and the concrete reality of fragments from the outer
world – force the eye to shift from one plane of surface
reality to another. Flatness becomes a highly ambiguous
notion, constantly modified from one plane to the next.
For example, in this collage, the sawdust background has
more relief and texture than the foreground figures
themselves.

The glass and bottle are no longer fragmented according
to internal structure but reduced to their simplest outer
forms. Their strictly two-dimensional silhouettes (in
spite of surface shading) are characteristic of Synthetic
Cubism.

Picasso executed several still lifes on this theme (1913–
1914), identifiable through the lettering of the Bass
label. Zervos dates this collage 1913.

Woman With Guitar (Femme à la Guitare). 1914

Pencil, 25 x 18³/₄" (63.5 x 47.5 cm.)

Not inscribed

Provenance:
the artist, 1914
Daniel-Henry Kahnweiler, Paris
Fourth Kahnweiler Sale, Hôtel Drouot, Paris, May 7,
1923, no.94
Galerie Simon, Paris, 1923
Collection Kelekian
Walt Kuhn, New York
Walt Kuhn Estate, 1957

Exhibitions:
THE SOLOMON R. GUGGENHEIM MUSEUM, New York,
August 13–October 5, 1958, *Selections* (Checklist)

THE SOLOMON R. GUGGENHEIM MUSEUM, New York,
August 30–October 8, 1961, *Modern Masters from the
Collection of The Solomon R. Guggenheim Museum*

PHILADELPHIA MUSEUM OF ART, Philadelphia, November 2,
1961–January 7, 1962, *Guggenheim Museum Exhibition,
A Loan Collection of Paintings, Drawings, and Prints from
The Solomon R. Guggenheim Museum, New York*, no.129

PENNSYLVANIA STATE UNIVERSITY, University Park,
October 6–November 16, 1963, *Aspects of the Apollonian
Ideal*

THE SOLOMON R. GUGGENHEIM MUSEUM, New York,
July 8–September 14, 1969, *Selected Sculpture and Works on
Paper*, p.72, ill.

57.1488

This pencil drawing of 1914 is characteristic of Synthetic
Cubism (after 1912) in the economy and simplicity of its
forms and the strict two-dimensionality of the composition. Although the shading suggests a superimposition of
planes, there is no illusion of volume or depth. Again
Picasso emphasizes the essential ambiguity of Cubist space
through planes which, while seeming behind one another,
simultaneously seem flush with the surface plane.

The even repartition of rounded and rectilinear contours
is found in many sketches and sculpted reliefs of the same
year, often on the theme of the guitar (See Zervos,
Picasso, œuvres de 1912 à 1917, Paris, 1942, vol.2★★)

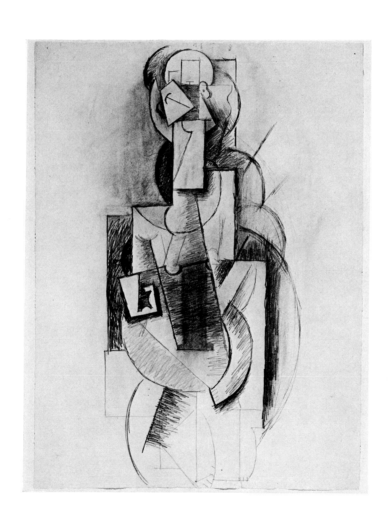

PABLO PICASSO

Mandolin and Guitar. Juan-les-Pins. 1924

Oil with sand on canvas, 56¹/₈ x 79³/₄″ (142.5 x 207.6 cm.)

Signed and dated l.l. "Picasso // 24″

Provenance:

Collection Reber, Lausanne
Jon Nicolas Streep, New York, 1953

Exhibitions:

GALERIES GEORGES PETIT, Paris, June 16–July 30, 1932,
Picasso, p.53, no.156, ill. (as *Nature morte devant la fenêtre*)

KUNSTHAUS, Zürich, September 9–October 30, 1932,
Picasso, p.149, ill.

THE SOLOMON R. GUGGENHEIM MUSEUM, New York,
May 13–October 11, 1953, *Selection II* (Checklist)

THE SOLOMON R. GUGGENHEIM MUSEUM, New York,
March 30–May 5, 1954, *Selection III* (Checklist)

THE SOLOMON R. GUGGENHEIM MUSEUM, New York,
October 6, 1954–February 27, 1955, *Selection IV* (Checklist)
MUSÉE DES ARTS DÉCORATIFS, Paris, June–October 1955,
Picasso, pl.57

THE SOLOMON R. GUGGENHEIM MUSEUM, New York,
January 24–May 1, 1956, *Selection VI* (Checklist)

TATE GALLERY, London, April 16–May 26, 1957, *Paintings
from The Solomon R. Guggenheim Museum*, no.64, ill.; orga-
nized by THE SOLOMON R. GUGGENHEIM MUSEUM, traveled
to GEMEENTEMUSEUM, The Hague, June 25–September 1;
ATENEIUMIN TAIDEKOKOELMAT, Helsinki, September 27–
October 20; GALLERIA NAZIONALE D'ARTE MODERNA, Rome,
December 5, 1957–January 8, 1958; WALLRAF-RICHARTZ-
MUSEUM, Cologne, January 26–March 30; MUSÉE DES ARTS
DÉCORATIFS, Paris, April 23–June 1, 1958

THE SOLOMON R. GUGGENHEIM MUSEUM, New York,
October 21, 1959–June 19, 1960, *Inaugural Selection*
(Checklist)

THE SOLOMON R. GUGGENHEIM MUSEUM, New York,
August 30–October 8, 1961, *Modern Masters from the
Collection of The Solomon R. Guggenheim Museum*, ill.

PHILADELPHIA MUSEUM OF ART, November 2, 1961–
January 7, 1962, *Guggenheim Museum Exhibition, A Loan
Collection of Paintings, Drawings, and Prints from The Solo-
mon R. Guggenheim Museum, New York*, no.130, ill.

THE SOLOMON R. GUGGENHEIM MUSEUM, New York,
October 3, 1961–February 25, 1962, *Elements of Modern
Painting*, circulated by THE AMERICAN FEDERATION OF ARTS,
July 1962–September 1963 as *Elements of Modern Art* and
March 1964–March 1965 as *Elements of Modern Art II*, ill.

PAUL ROSENBERG & CO., New York, April 25–May 12,
1962, *Picasso, An American Tribute*, no.35, ill. Organized
by the PUBLIC EDUCATION ASSOCIATION, New York
WORCESTER ART MUSEUM, Massachusetts,
February 6–April 7, 1963, *Aspects of Twentieth Century
Painting Lent by The Solomon R. Guggenheim Museum*,
p.65, ill.

THE SOLOMON R. GUGGENHEIM MUSEUM, New York,
April 30–September 1, 1965, *Paintings from the Collection
of The Solomon R. Guggenheim Museum*, no.55, ill.

GRAND PALAIS, Paris, November 18, 1966–February 13,
1967, *Hommage à Pablo Picasso*, p.133, ill.

STEDELIJK MUSEUM, Amsterdam, March 4–April 30, 1967,
Picasso, pl.62

THE SOLOMON R. GUGGENHEIM MUSEUM, New York,
June 28–October 1, 1967, *Museum Collection, Seven
Decades, A Selection* (Checklist)

THE METROPOLITAN MUSEUM OF ART, New York, November 15, 1967–April 1, 1968, *Selections from the Collection
of The Solomon R. Guggenheim Museum*

References:

ZERVOS, CHRISTIAN, *Pablo Picasso, œuvres de 1923 à 1925,*
Paris, 1952, vol.5, no.220, pl.107

ELGAR, FRANK, *Picasso*, Paris, 1955, ill. (as *Mandoline et
guitare ou La fenêtre ouverte*)

PENROSE, ROLAND, *Picasso; His Life and Work*, New York,
no.4, pl.XI

JAFFE, HANS L. C., *Pablo Picasso*, New York, 1964, p.110, ill.

DAIX, PIERRE, *Picasso*, New York, 1965, p.128, ill.

ARNASON, H. H., *History of Modern Art*, New York, 1968,
p.334, pl.141

53.1358

Between 1924 and 1926 Picasso executed a series of large
colorful still lifes with an essentially similar thematic
organization: an arrangement of objects on a centrally
situated table in front of an open window. This basic
theme appears for the first time in a group of drawings
and watercolors done at Saint-Raphael in 1919.

Through the two-dimensional volumes, spaces and
perspective, the interlocking planes, the simultaneously
described points of view as well as the arbitrary use of
color and the "cut-out" patterned shapes, *Mandolin and
Guitar* can be defined as a Cubist work.

The almost baroque quality achieved through the predominantly curved contours, the strong involvement with
pattern and the flat application of bright, pure colors are
characteristic of Picasso's last Cubist works.

PABLO PICASSO

Nude. 1941

Ink, $15^7/_8$ x 12″ (40.5 x 30.5 cm.)

Signed and dated l.r. "Picasso // 28.11.41"

Provenance:
Delius Gallery, New York, 1955

Exhibitions:

THE SOLOMON R. GUGGENHEIM MUSEUM, New York,
January 24–May 1, 1956, *Selection VI* (Checklist)

THE SOLOMON R. GUGGENHEIM MUSEUM, New York,
August 30–October 8, 1961, *Modern Masters from the
Collection of The Solomon R. Guggenheim Museum*

PHILADELPHIA MUSEUM OF ART, November 2,
1961–January 7, 1962, *Guggenheim Museum Exhibition,
A Loan Collection of Paintings, Drawings, and Prints from
The Solomon R. Guggenheim Museum, New York*, no.131

THE NEW GALLERY, New York, April 25–May 12, 1962,
Picasso, An American Tribute, no.41, ill.

THE SOLOMON R. GUGGENHEIM MUSEUM, New York,
July 8–September 14, 1969, *Selected Sculpture and Works on
Paper*, p.73, ill.

55.1433

In October and November of 1941, Picasso executed a
series of studies of seated female nudes and a number of
paintings of seated (clothed) female figures. The strangely
deformed image evolved from the study of a nude looking
in a mirror: a contraction of her profile silhouette and a
frontal reflection. Although the drawings of early
October were flat, linear, and without shading, those of
late November show increased attention to volume.

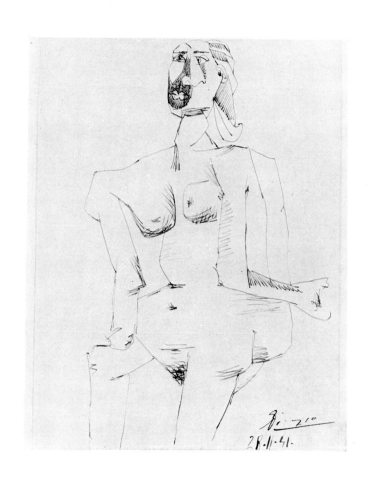

Serge Poliakoff 1906–1969

Serge Poliakoff was born in Moscow in 1906. In 1918 he left Russia to travel, finally settling in Paris in 1923. There he began to paint, studying at the Académie Frochot and the Académie de la Grande Chaumière. In 1935 he moved to London where he attended the Slade School. Upon his return to Paris in 1937, he became friendly with Sonia and Robert Delaunay, Otto Freundlich and Kandinsky. Kandinsky, who influenced him greatly, said of him at this time, "As far as the future is concerned I put my money on Poliakoff". In 1937 he abandoned figurative for abstract painting, and began to exhibit in Europe. After the war he took part in avant-garde exhibitions at the *Salle du Centre des Recherches*, Paris, as well as many international group and one-man shows. He received the Kandinsky Prize in 1947, and was given a one-man show at the Venice Biennale in 1962.

His work is characterized by a Russian feeling for opulent color and rich surface, always existing, however, within a carefully structured and controlled abstract framework.

Poliakoff died in Paris in 1969.

Composition. 1950

Oil on plywood, $51^3/_8$ x $38^1/_4''$ (130.5 x 97.2 cm.)

Signed l.r. "SERgE POLiAKOFF"

Provenance:
Maer Calatchi, Paris, 1954

Exhibitions:
THE SOLOMON R. GUGGENHEIM MUSEUM, New York, December 2, 1953–May 2, 1954, *Younger European Painters*, no.23, ill.; traveled to WALKER ART CENTER, Minneapolis, August 8–September 24; PORTLAND ART MUSEUM, Oregon, October 8–November 14; SAN FRANCISCO MUSEUM OF ART, November 26, 1954–January 25, 1955; THE DALLAS MUSEUM OF FINE ARTS, February 1–March 1; UNIVERSITY OF ARKANSAS, Fayetteville, March 7–April 9; THE DAYTON ART INSTITUTE, Ohio, April 15–May 13; ADDISON GALLERY OF AMERICAN ART, Phillips Academy, Andover, Massachusetts, October 1–31; CARPENTER ART GALLERIES, Dartmouth College, Hanover, New Hampshire, November 5–December 31, 1955; DWIGHT ART MEMORIAL, Mount Holyoke College, South Hadley, Massachusetts, January 3–31, 1956; DAVISON ART CENTER, Wesleyan University, Middletown, Connecticut, February 6–March 18, 1956

THE SOLOMON R. GUGGENHEIM MUSEUM, New York, October 21, 1959–June 19, 1960, *Inaugural Selection* (Checklist)

PHILADELPHIA MUSEUM OF ART, November 2, 1961–January 7, 1962, *Guggenheim Museum Exhibition, A Loan Collection of Paintings, Drawings, and Prints from The Solomon R. Guggenheim Museum, New York*, no.132

References:
ALVARD, JULIEN, "Serge Poliakoff", *XXe Siècle*, no. VII, June 1956, p.46, ill.

American Abstract Artists, ed., *The World of Abstract Art*, New York, 1957, p.3, ill.

VALLIER, DORA, *Serge Poliakoff*, Paris, 1959, pl.18

ARNASON, H. H., *History of Modern Art*, New York, 1968, pl.965

54.1395

In *Composition*, color – a harmony of warm oranges – and a dense physical surface of thick impasto and visible brushwork predominate. Typical of Poliakoff, this rich surface is controlled by the formal structure of the painting. The sweetness of the oranges is tempered by the sharp contrast of the two large, central shapes: one a deep, dark blue, the other a cold gray, steel-like both in texture and color. Tightly interlocking, sharp-edged forms press down into the center of the composition.

Jackson Pollock 1912–1956

Jackson Pollock was born January 28, 1912, in Cody, Wyoming. He grew up in Arizona and California and began studying painting at the Manual Arts High School in Los Angeles. In 1929 he came to New York where he continued to study art under Thomas Hart Benton at the Art Students' League. He settled permanently in New York in 1935, working from 1938 to 1942 on the Federal Arts Project.

Peggy Guggenheim gave Pollock his first one-man show in 1943 at her Art of This Century Gallery in New York. She also gave him a contract which lasted until 1947, permitting him to devote all his time to painting. Prior to 1947, Pollock's work showed the influence of Surrealism in its depiction of mythical or totemic figures as archetypes of the human subconscious. 1947 marks the beginning of his mature style: the monumental unprimed canvases covered with multicolored skeins of dripped paint, evoking the meanderings of the subconscious mind while emphasizing the primacy of paint, not as a medium but as an end in itself. This period lasted until 1951 when Pollock's paintings, while remaining dynamically fluid, became more sparse and austere, limited to black and white.

Pollock exhibited at the 25th Venice Biennale in 1950 and was subsequently shown all over Europe and the United States. He was killed in an automobile accident August 11, 1956.

Ocean Greyness. 1953

Oil on canvas, 57³/₄ x 90¹/₈″ (146.7 x 101.8 cm.)

Signed and dated l.r. "53 Jackson Pollock"

Provenance:

from the artist through Sidney Janis Gallery, New York, 1954

Exhibitions:

THE SOLOMON R. GUGGENHEIM MUSEUM, New York, May 12–September 26, 1954, *Younger American Painters*, no.41, ill. (withdrawn from exhibition September 8, 195 for exhibition, THE ART INSTITUTE OF CHICAGO, following entry); traveled to PORTLAND ART MUSEUM, Oregon, September 2–October 9, 1955; HENRY GALLERY, University of Washington, Seattle, October 16–November 13; SAN FRANCISCO MUSEUM OF ART, November 15, 1955– January 22, 1956; LOS ANGELES COUNTY MUSEUM OF ART, February 1–29; UNIVERSITY OF ARKANSAS, Fayetteville, March 9–April 10; ISAAC DELGADO MUSEUM OF ART, New Orleans, April 15–May 20, 1956

ART INSTITUTE OF CHICAGO, October 21–December 5, 1954, *Sixty-first American Exhibition, Paintings and Sculpture*

PICTURE GALLERY OF SAINT-GAUDENS MEMORIAL, Cornish, New Hampshire, August 3–September 4, 1956, *Painters of Today*, no.14; organized by THE SOLOMON R. GUGGENHEIM MUSEUM, New York

THE MUSEUM OF MODERN ART, New York, December 18, 1956–February 3, 1957, *Jackson Pollock*, no.35, ill.

TATE GALLERY, London, April 16–May 26, 1957, *Paintings from The Solomon R. Guggenheim Museum, New York*, no.65, pl.10; organized by THE SOLOMON R. GUGGENHEIM MUSEUM, New York, traveled to GEMEENTEMUSEUM, The Hague, June 25–September 1, no.65; ATENEIUMIN TAIDE-KOKOELMAT, Helsinki, September 27–October 20, no.65; GALLERIA NAZIONALE D'ARTE MODERNA, Rome, December 5, 1957–January 8, 1958, no.68, pl.68

WHITNEY MUSEUM OF AMERICAN ART, New York, January 14–March 16, 1958, *Nature in Abstraction*, p.17, ill.

THE SOLOMON R. GUGGENHEIM MUSEUM, New York, October 21, 1959–June 19, 1960, *Inaugural Selection* (Checklist)

PHILADELPHIA MUSEUM OF ART, November 2, 1961– January 7, 1962, *Guggenheim Museum Exhibition, A Loan Collection of Paintings, Drawings, and Prints from The Solomon R. Guggenheim Museum, New York*, no.133

SEATTLE WORLD'S FAIR, April 21–October 21, 1962, *Art Since 1950, American and International*, no.53, ill.; traveled in part to THE POSES INSTITUTE OF FINE ARTS, Brandeis University, Waltham, Massachusetts, November 21– December 23, 1962, as *American Art Since 1950*

WORCESTER ART MUSEUM, Massachusetts, February 7– April 7, 1963, *Aspects of Twentieth Century Painting Lent by The Solomon R. Guggenheim Museum*, no.37

NATIONAL GALLERY OF SOUTH AUSTRALIA, Adelaide, *The Adelaide Festival of Arts, 1964: Contemporary American Painting*, no.41

THE SOLOMON R. GUGGENHEIM MUSEUM, New York, July 1–September 13, 1964, *Van Gogh and Expressionism*

THE SOLOMON R. GUGGENHEIM MUSEUM, New York, April 30–September 1, 1965, *Paintings from the Collection of The Solomon R. Guggenheim Museum*, no.70, ill.

CLEVELAND MUSEUM OF ART, Ohio, June 6–July 31, 1966, *50 Years of Modern Art*

THE MUSEUM OF MODERN ART, New York, June 4–September 15, 1967, *Jackson Pollock*, no.77, ill.

References:

BAUR, JOHN I. H., ed., *New Art in America, Fifty Painters of the 20th Century*, Greenwich, Connecticut, 1957, p.239, ill.

O'HARA, FRANK, *Jackson Pollock*, New York, 1959, pl.70

ROBERTSON, BRYAN, *Jackson Pollock*, New York, 1960, pl.162

PELLEGRINI, ALDO, *New Tendencies in Art*, New York, 1966, ill. opp. p.158

ARNASON, H. H., *History of Modern Art*, New York, 1968, color pl.206

54.1408

Following a period of austerity (1951–1952) when Pollock restricted his palette to black and white, in 1953 he returned to a more sensuous handling of paint such as one sees in this example. Moreover, in contrast to the dynamic and delicate labyrinths of paint which are characteristic of the artist's best-known work, in *Ocean Greyness* one finds a heavily impastoed surface and latent images which are reminiscent of the totemic imagery and wild brooding seascapes of his paintings of the mid-forties.

The now-famous drip paintings were executed on the floor, not on the wall. Moving in all directions, Pollock poured or dripped paint on raw canvas, creating a type of all-over structure that avoided a single focal point. This concept of all-over painting, together with a significantly increased scale, represented a dramatic break not only with the traditions of easel painting familiar from the Renaissance but with the spatial interplays of Cubism as well. Pollock created a radically new body of painting; environmental in effect, seemingly without beginning or end. His configurations appeared to extend even beyond the perimeters of the canvas. The act of painting, too, became a significant factor in the evolution of a painting. The movement of the body, rather than just the manipulation of the hand, and such marks of the painter's activity as his footprints, were manifestations of the creative act in process. In the evolution of his drip technique, derived in part from Surrealist automatism, Pollock found the perfect means of expression for the multiple facets of his art.

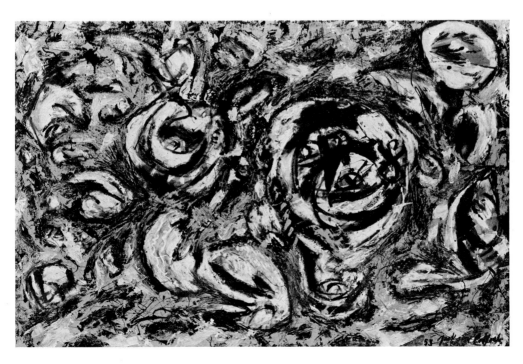

Red Painting (Untitled). 1953

Combine painting on canvas with wood, 79 x 33 1/8″ (200.1 x 84.2 cm.)

Not inscribed

Provenance:
the artist, 1955
Walter K. Gutman, New York
Gift, Walter K. Gutman, 1963

Exhibitions:
JEWISH MUSEUM, New York, March 31–May 8, 1963, *Robert Rauschenberg*, no.6
THE SOLOMON R. GUGGENHEIM MUSEUM, New York, June 28–October 1, 1967, *Museum Collection, Seven Decades, A Selection* (Checklist)

References:
FORGE, ANDREW, *Rauschenberg*, New York, 1969, p.174, ill.

63.1688

Robert Rauschenberg 1925–

Robert Rauschenberg was born October 22, 1925, in Port Arthur, Texas. From 1946–1947 he attended the Kansas City Art Institute, moving to Paris in 1947 where he studied at the Académie Julian under the G.I. Bill.

He returned from Paris in 1948 and went to Black Mountain College in North Carolina to study with Josef Albers whom he credits with being "the most important teacher I've ever had... what he taught had to do with the entire visual world". At Black Mountain he studied not only painting, but photography, music and modern dance. From 1949–1950 he studied at the Art Student's League in New York with Vytlacil and Kantor. In 1951 he had his first one-man show at the Betty Parsons Gallery in New York. In 1952 he produced all black and white paintings and started theater work with Merce Cunningham and Paul Taylor.

In 1953 Rauschenberg began his series of red paintings using comic strips as color ground, sometimes including lights and reflectors in the work. Between 1955 and 1958 Rauschenberg worked on his "combines", using stuffed animals, beds, and other evocative fragments from life which he juxtaposed with purely painterly passages. At this time, he lived in the same building with Jasper Johns who, with John Cage, provided encouragement for his work.

In 1961 he began his "Time" paintings and worked with Universal Limited Art Editions on lithography, a technique that would have a subsequent influence on his paintings. In 1964 Rauschenberg began a world tour with Merce Cunningham and won First Prize at the Venice Biennale. In 1966 he co-founded the organization "EAT" (Experiments in Art and Technology). He was honored by a retrospective exhibition in Amsterdam, Cologne, and Paris in 1968.

Rauschenberg's "red paintings" immediately followed his "white paintings" and "black paintings" of 1952. As the artist stated in an interview (recorded by Billy Klüver, published on disc by the Washington Gallery of Modern Art, Washington D.C. 1963): "I became disturbed by the outside assumptions, the prejudices around the colors being black and white... people thought that the black was about 'old' and 'burned' and 'tarred', and they thought that the white was about 'negation' and 'nothing – some philosophy of nothing... The next move was obvious – to pick some other color. So I picked the hardest color I found to work with which was red."

From 1952 to 1955 he extended the potential of the picture surface to include attached objects and dripping paint which he combined with rectangular passages of color. In the incorporation of found objects Rauschenberg's work reflects the influence of Picasso's collage techniques and Dada, in particular the work of Schwitters. But in altering the traditional role of materials, Rauschenberg, like Jasper Johns, showed new insight into the question of the appropriateness of both new techniques and banal subjects for art. Rauschenberg's work represents a unique crossroad, a vital link between Abstract Expressionism and the subsequent developments including Pop Art, of the 1960's.

Artillerymen (Les Artilleurs). c.1895

Oil on canvas, 31³/₄ x 39¹/₂″ (80.7 x 100.4 cm.)

Signed l.r. "H. Rousseau"

Provenance:
Galerie van Leer, Paris
Galerie Louis Carré, Paris, 1938

Exhibitions:

ARTHUR TOOTH AND SONS, London, February 17–March 12, 1938, *Les maîtres populaires de la réalité,* no.3

ART INSTITUTE OF CHICAGO, January 22–February 23, 1942, *Henri Rousseau;* traveled to THE MUSEUM OF MODERN ART, New York, March 18–May 3, 1942

THE SOLOMON R. GUGGENHEIM MUSEUM, New York, May 13–October 11, 1953, *Selection II* (Checklist)

THE SOLOMON R. GUGGENHEIM MUSEUM, New York, October 6, 1954–February 27, 1955, *Selection IV* (Checklist)

MONTREAL MUSEUM OF FINE ARTS, June 4–July 3, 1955, *A Selection from The Solomon R. Guggenheim Museum,* no.53

THE SOLOMON R. GUGGENHEIM MUSEUM, New York, July 26–October 9, 1955, *Selection V* (Checklist)

THE SOLOMON R. GUGGENHEIM MUSEUM, New York, January 24–March 1, 1956, *Selection VI* (Checklist)

TATE GALLERY, London, April 16–May 26, 1957, *Paintings from The Solomon R. Guggenheim Museum,* no.67; organized by THE SOLOMON R. GUGGENHEIM MUSEUM, traveled to GEMEENTEMUSEUM, The Hague, June 25–September 1; ATENEIUMIN TAIDEKOKOELMAT, Helsinki, September 27–October 20; GALLERIA NAZIONALE D'ARTE MODERNA, Rome, December 5, 1957–January 8, 1958; WALLRAF-RICHARTZ-MUSEUM, Cologne, January 26–March 30; MUSÉE DES ARTS DÉCORATIFS, Paris, April 23–June 1, 1958

THE SOLOMON R. GUGGENHEIM MUSEUM, New York, October 21, 1959–June 19, 1960, *Inaugural Selection* (Checklist)

THE SOLOMON R. GUGGENHEIM MUSEUM, New York, August 30–October 8, 1961, *Modern Masters from the Collection of The Solomon R. Guggenheim Museum*

WILDENSTEIN & CO., INC., New York, April 17–May 25, 1963, *Henri Rousseau,* no.9, ill.

MUSEUM BOYMANS-VAN BEUNINGEN, Rotterdam, July 10–September 6, 1964, *Le monde des naïfs,* no.4, ill.; traveled to MUSÉE NATIONAL D'ART MODERNE, Paris, October 14–December 6, 1964

THE SOLOMON R. GUGGENHEIM MUSEUM, New York, April 30–September 1, 1965, *Paintings from the Collection of The Solomon R. Guggenheim Museum,* no.5, ill.

PAUL ROSENBERG & CO., New York, April 26–May 21, 1966, *Seven Decades 1895–1965; Crosscurrents in Modern Art,* p.36, no.43, ill. (Organized by the PUBLIC EDUCATION ASSOCIATION, New York)

Henri Rousseau 1844–1910

Henri Julien Félix Rousseau was born May 21, 1844, in Laval, France. In 1869 he married, settled in Paris and entered the toll service as a second-class clerk. It was this function which earned him the name "Le Douanier" (the Customs Official), bestowed upon him by Guillaume Apollinaire.

In 1884, at the age of forty, he retired to devote himself to painting, exhibiting for the first time at the *Salon des Indépendants* in 1886. His most frequent subject was landscape, although he painted still lifes and portraits as well, executed in a naive folk-art style. The first of many exotic landscapes – the wild beasts and jungle vegetation for which he was to achieve reknown – was painted in 1891.

Although Rousseau's deliberately unsophisticated style and manners made him a frequent object of ridicule, he enjoyed the friendship and respect of a group of his contemporaries to whom he incarnated the primitive soul. These included Picasso, Delaunay, Apollinaire, Alfred Jarry and Max Jacob. Rousseau died in Paris September 2, 1910.

THE SOLOMON R. GUGGENHEIM MUSEUM, New York,
April 11–May 26, 1968, *Acquisitions of the 1930's and 1940's,*
p.48, ill.

THE SOLOMON R. GUGGENHEIM MUSEUM, New York,
May 30–September 2, 1968, *Rousseau, Redon, and Fantasy*

References:

Der Querschnitt, Berlin, 1926, ill. following p.688

BASLER, ADOLPHE, *Henri Rousseau, sa vie, son œuvre,*
New York, 1927, p.31, pl.14

COURTHION, PIERRE, *Henri Rousseau, le Douanier*, Geneva,
1944, pl.30

RICH, DANIEL CATTON, *Henri Rousseau*, New York,
revised ed., 1946, p.29, ill.

SHATTUCK, ROGER, *The Banquet Years, The Arts in France
1885–1918,* London, 1958, p.81, no.21a

BOURET, JEAN, *Henri Rousseau*, New York, 1961, p.190,
pl.86

VALLIER, DORA, *Henri Rousseau*, New York, 1962, p.51, ill.

SALMON, ANDRÉ, *Henri Rousseau*, New York, 1963,
pp.44–45, ill.

38.711

Nature was an important source of inspiration for the
Douanier Rousseau. His landscape production however is
divided into two diametrally opposed styles. The first,
visible in his tropical scenes, shows a dramatic synthesis
of nature through broad, flat stylized forms and a daring
use of rich contrasting colors. The second, reserved for
views of the French countryside, was relatively naturalistic, with painstaking attention to detail and chromatic
nuance. *Artillerymen* is representative of the latter style.

The frontal alignment of the soldiers leads one to suppose
that the artist was working from a group photograph to
which he either added or adjusted the landscape to repeat
the formal rhythms of the group. The perspective of
superimposed horizontal planes is a common device in
naive painting.

In spite of his so-called primitivism, Rousseau had an
infallible color sense. In *Artillerymen* the infinite variations
of green anticipate the painter's life-long predilection for
that color. The blacks and whites not only establish a
clearly cadenced sequential articulation of the canvas but
show the artist's accomplishment in creating bright, pure
contrasts.

Between 1893 and 1895, Rousseau executed three known
paintings on military themes: *The Last of the 51st* of 1893
(now lost), *War* of 1894 and *Artillerymen*.

HENRI ROUSSEAU

Football Players (Les Joueurs de Football). 1908

Oil on canvas, 39 $^{1}/_{2}$ x 31 $^{5}/_{8}$″ (100.4 x 80.3 cm.)

Signed and dated l.r. "Henri Rousseau//1908"

Provenance:
Suermondt Collection, Drove (Düsseldorf)
Paul Rosenberg Collection, Paris
Mrs. Murray S. Danforth
Mrs. Henry D. Sharpe, Providence, by auction, Sotheby
& Co., Inc., London, 1960

Exhibitions:
24th SALON DES INDÉPENDANTS, Paris, March 20–May 2,
1908

29th SALON DES INDÉPENDANTS, Paris, April 20–June 13,
1911 (Salle Rousseau)

GALERIE FLECHTHEIM, Berlin, March 1926, *Rousseau
Ausstellung*, p.12, ill.

GALERIE PAUL ROSENBERG, Paris, March 3–31, 1937, no.15

ARTHUR TOOTH & SONS, London, February 17–March 12,
1938, *Les maîtres populaires de la réalité*, no.2

ART INSTITUTE OF CHICAGO, January 22–February 23,
1942, *Henri Rousseau;* traveled to THE MUSEUM OF MODERN
ART, New York, March 18–May 3, 1942

WILDENSTEIN & CO., INC., New York, April 8–May 8,
1948, *Six Masters of Post-Impressionism*, p.54, no.41, ill.

XXV BIENNALE INTERNAZIONALE D'ARTE VENEZIA, Venice,
1950, *Salle Rousseau*

SIDNEY JANIS GALLERY, New York, November 5–
December 22, 1951, *Henri Rousseau*, no.17

XXVII BIENNALE INTERNAZIONALE D'ARTE VENEZIA, Venice,
1954, *Loan Exhibition*

CASINO COMMUNAL, Knokke-Le-Zoute, Belgium, June 29–
August 31, 1958, *Les peintres naïfs du douanier à nos jours*,
p.7, no.2, ill.

THE SOLOMON R. GUGGENHEIM MUSEUM, New York, August 30–October 8, 1961, *Modern Masters from the Collection of The Solomon R. Guggenheim Museum*, ill.

PHILADELPHIA MUSEUM OF ART, Philadelphia, November 2, 1961–January 7, 1962, *Guggenheim Museum Exhibition, A Loan Collection of Paintings, Drawings, and Prints from The Solomon R. Guggenheim Museum, New York*, no.135, ill.

WILDENSTEIN & CO., INC., New York, April 17–May 25, 1963, *Henri Rousseau*, no.49

MUSEUM BOYMANS-VAN BEUNINGEN, Rotterdam, July 10–September 6, 1964, *Le monde des naïfs*, no.22; traveled to MUSÉE NATIONAL D'ART MODERNE, Paris, October 14–December 6, 1964

THE SOLOMON R. GUGGENHEIM MUSEUM, New York, April 30–September 1, 1965, *Paintings from the Collection of The Solomon R. Guggenheim Museum*, p.22, no.13, ill.

THE SOLOMON R. GUGGENHEIM MUSEUM, New York, May 30–September 2, 1968, *Rousseau, Redon, and Fantasy*, ill.

References:

UHDE, WILHELM, *Henri Rousseau*, Paris, 1911, p.64

UHDE, WILHELM, *Henri Rousseau*, Düsseldorf, 1914, pl.15

UHDE, WILHELM, *Henri Rousseau*, Dresden, 1921, p.42, ill.

ZERVOS, CHRISTIAN, *Rousseau*, Paris, 1927, pl.76

SOUPAULT, PHILIPPE, *Le Douanier*, Paris, 1927

RICH, DANIEL CATTON, *Henri Rousseau*, New York, 1942, p.51, ill.

GREY, ROCH, *Henri Rousseau*, Paris, 1943, pl.31

COURTHION, PIERRE, *Henri Rousseau, le Douanier*, Geneva, 1944, pl.XI

UHDE, WILHELM, *Rousseau*, Bern, 1948, pl.47

GAUTHIER, MAXIMILIEN, *Henri Rousseau*, Paris, 1949, p.20, ill.

DUCA, L., *Henri Rousseau dit le Douanier*, Paris, 1951, pl.XIV

KUH, KATHERINE, *Léger*, Urbana, 1953, pl.80

ROSENBERG, PAUL, *Masterpieces Recalled*, 1957, ill.

SHATTUCK, ROGER, *The Banquet Years, The Arts in France 1885–1918*, Garden City, 1961, pl.VIII

BIHALJI-MERIN, OTO, *Modern Primitives: Masters of Naïve Painting*, New York, 1961, p.53, ill.

BOURET, JEAN, *Henri Rousseau*, New York, 1961, p.133, pl.37

CERTIGNY, HENRI, *La vérité sur le Douanier Rousseau*, Paris, 1961, p.315

VALLIER, DORA, *Henri Rousseau*, New York, 1962, p.111, ill.

SALMON, ANDRÉ, *Rousseau*, New York, 1963, p.67, ill.

60.1583

Football Players, in the artist's attempt to depict a group in movement, is an unusual painting in his basically static production.

The symmetrical borders of trees and the horizontal division of the canvas create a sturdy perspective framework within which the players visually interact with one another through their alternating gestures and coloring. This central arabesque endows the canvas with a rare dynamic quality which the comparatively frozen stances of the figures fail to project of themselves. The stiffness of rhythm is echoed by the four trees in the background.

The foliage is of Rousseau's Ile-de-France style, executed with meticulous detail. Furthermore, *Football Players* shows an inhabitual palette for the artist, of light pastel and golden tones.

Egon Schiele 1890–1918

Egon Schiele was born June 12, 1890, at Tulln near Vienna. A precocious draftsman, he received little sympathy from his teachers or his parents. In 1906, against the wishes of his guardian uncle (Schiele's father had died insane the previous year), he enrolled in the Vienna Academy of Fine Arts. The next year he met Gustav Klimt, whose art offered Schiele a welcome alternative to the stifling academism of his professors. In 1909 Schiele and a group of students left the Vienna Academy and formed the *Neukunstgruppe,* and at Klimt's invitation he showed four paintings at the second *Kunstschau* exhibition.

By 1910 Schiele had grown independent of the decorative, elegant mannerisms of Klimt's Art Nouveau style, to emerge as an expressionist, a painter of psychic explorations. His subjects were the traditional portrait, nude, landscape, townscape, to which he showed a singularly ambivalent attitude: erotic revulsion, achieved with a sensitive, quivering line. Draftsmanship is the dominant formal feature of Schiele's style; his oeuvre includes thousands of magnificent drawings.

Schiele's art met with open hostility from the conservative Austrian public; he was forced to leave Krumau, his mother's native town, because of his "pornographic" drawings; he was jailed on charges of "immorality" and "seduction" and his drawings confiscated in the town of Neulengbach. There followed a period of embittered isolation and poverty. In 1914 he began to exhibit again and received commissions enabling him, in 1915, to marry Edith Harms. The blatant expressionism of his earlier work was attenuated in his late and final style.

At the Vienna *Secession* exhibition of 1918, Schiele was represented by 19 oils, all of which sold. But his turn of luck was perverse: during the epidemic of influenza which spread over most of Europe in that year following the war, Edith died on October 28; Egon died three days later.

Portrait of an Old Man (Johann Harms). 1916

Oil on canvas, $55^5/_8$ x $43^5/_8''$ (141.3 x 110.8 cm.)

Signed and dated in monogram "EGON//SCHIELE// 1916"

Provenance:
Karl Grünwald, Vienna
Dr. and Mrs. Otto Kallir, New York
Partial gift, Dr. Otto Kallir, 1969

Exhibitions:

GLASPALAST, Munich, 1917, *Secession*

WIENER SECESSION, Vienna, March 1918, XLIX *Secession Wien,* no.6

NEUE GALERIE, Vienna, 1923, *Egon Schiele, Gemälde und Handzeichnungen,* no.6

Dresden, 1926, *Internationale Kunstausstellung,* no.262

HAGENBUND, Vienna, 1928, *Gedächtnisausstellung zum 10. Todestag,* no.62

GALERIE ST. ETIENNE, New York, November 1941, *Egon Schiele*

GALERIE ST. ETIENNE, New York, April 5–May 1, 1948 *Egon Schiele,* no.8, ill.

INSTITUTE OF CONTEMPORARY ART, Boston, October 6–November 6, 1960, *Egon Schiele 1890–1918,* no.52; traveled to GALERIE ST. ETIENNE, New York, November 15–December 15, 1960; J. B. SPEED MUSEUM, Louisville, Kentucky, January 3–31; CARNEGIE INSTITUTE, Pittsburgh, March 1–April 2; MINNEAPOLIS INSTITUTE OF ARTS, April 19–May 21, 1961

GALERIE ST. ETIENNE, New York, October 17–November 14, 1964, *Twenty-fifth Anniversary Exhibition,* no.43

THE SOLOMON R. GUGGENHEIM MUSEUM, New York, February 5–April 25, 1965, *Gustav Klimt and Egon Schiele,* no.40, ill.

References:

ROESSLER, ARTHUR, *Kritische Fragmente, Aufsätze über Österreichische Neukünstler,* Vienna, 1918, p.66, f.n.

KARPFEN, FRITZ, *Das Egon-Schiele-Buch,* Vienna, 1921, pl.20

FAISTAUER, ANTON, *Neue Malerei in Österreich, Betrachtungen eines Malers,* Vienna, 1923, pl.5

NIERENSTEIN, OTTO, *Egon Schiele, Persönlichkeit und Werk,* Vienna, 1930, p.67, cat. no.153, pl.114

KALLIR, OTTO, *Egon Schiele, Oeuvre, Catalogue of the Paintings,* New York, 1966 (second edition of Nierenstein, 1930), p.420, cat. no.213, ill.

69.1884

The only recorded portrait of 1916, *Portrait of an Old Man* depicts Schiele's father-in-law Johann Harms. As is typical of his portraits, there are no props used as clues to the sitter's personality or occupation; in some cases even the chair, included here, is omitted. The color is somber, almost monochromatic (rare in the context of Expressionist painting). The color value is used in a hierarchical fashion, building up from the dark, inexpressive background to the median gray of the body's soft diagonal and reaching its height in the more vibrant head and hands, the constant focal points of Schiele's figure paintings. These small areas succinctly embody his exploration of the sitter's character. In this case the rough skeletal hands and deeply furrowed brow express a weariness of old age. But the pose of the figure, seemingly draped over the chair because of the low viewpoint, and the tenderness with which the head rests on the left hand, soften the image and suggest a melancholy peace.

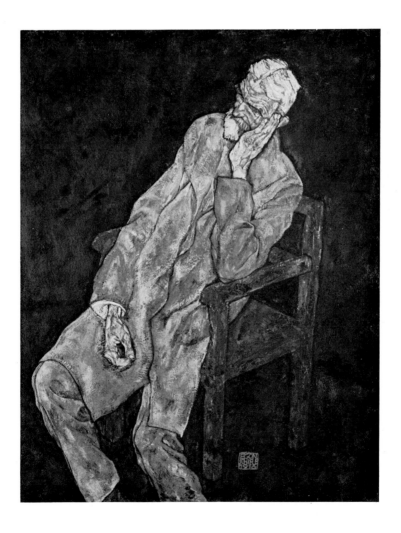

Kurt Schwitters 1887–1948

Kurt Schwitters was born June 20, 1887, in Hanover, Germany. Except for art schooling in Dresden and Berlin (1909–1914), he was to reside in Hanover the greater part of his life. Schwitters began his career as an academic painter, but by 1918 his painting had become more abstract and he began experimenting with collage from which was to evolve his classic collage style. His abstract oils and collages were shown at the *Der Sturm* Gallery, Berlin in 1918.

Immediately thereafter (1919), Schwitters formulated the concept of MERZ which was to dominate his life's work: the use of any and all materials to support the act of creation ("I called my new way of creation with any material MERZ"). He later extended the term MERZ to include his poetry and all other relevant activities. Foremost among the latter was a MERZbau or a fantastic spatial structure of both Dada and Constructivist inspiration which occupied four rooms of Schwitters's Hanover house and on which the artist worked for seventeen years, ever integrating new elements of disparate origins and associations.

Traditionally considered a Dada theorist and practitioner Schwitters's relationship to the Dada group was complex. Due to his association with *Der Sturm*, he was first refused membership to the Dada Club but he attended and participated in Dada manifestations and wrote and lectured on phonetic poetry.

Until his departure from Hanover in 1937, Schwitters was active in the publication of his "Merz" magazine (1923–1932) as well as in advertizing and typography. His contacts with Neo-Plasticism led to a stricter, more formalist composition in his collages between 1923 and 1937.

From 1937 to 1940 Schwitters lived in Norway and after 1941, in England. He died in Ambleside, England on January 8, 1948.

Merzbild 5 B (Bild-Rot-Herz-Kirche). April 26, 1919

Collage, tempera and conté crayon on board, 32⁷/₈ x 23⁵/₈″ (83.5 x 60 cm.)

Signed and dated l.l. "K S // 1919"

Provenance:
Mrs. Hildegarde J. Prytek, Rego Park, New York, 1952

Exhibitions:
THE SOLOMON R. GUGGENHEIM MUSEUM, New York, May 13–October 11, 1953, *Selection II* (Checklist)

ART GALLERY OF TORONTO, April 2–May 9, 1954, *A Loan Exhibition of Paintings from The Solomon R. Guggenheim Museum, New York*, no.67

THE SOLOMON R. GUGGENHEIM MUSEUM, New York, October 6, 1954–February 27, 1955, *Selection IV* (Checklist)

MONTREAL MUSEUM OF FINE ARTS, June 4–July 3, 1955, *A Selection from The Solomon R. Guggenheim Museum, New York*, no.54

THE SOLOMON R. GUGGENHEIM MUSEUM, New York, July 26–October 9, 1955, *Selection V* (Checklist)

THE SOLOMON R. GUGGENHEIM MUSEUM, New York, October 21, 1959–June 19, 1960, *Inaugural Selection* (Checklist)

PHILADELPHIA MUSEUM OF ART, November 2, 1961–January 7, 1962, *Guggenheim Museum Exhibition, A Loan Collection of Paintings, Drawings, and Prints from The Solomon R. Guggenheim Museum, New York*, no.136

WORCESTER ART MUSEUM, Massachusetts, February 6–April 7, 1963, *Aspects of Twentieth Century Painting Lent by The Solomon R. Guggenheim Museum*, no.39, ill.

GALERIE CHALETTE, New York, October 5–November 30, 1963, *Kurt Schwitters*, no.10

THE SOLOMON R. GUGGENHEIM MUSEUM, New York, June 28–October 1, 1967, *Museum Collection, Seven Decades, A Selection* (Checklist)

COLUMBUS GALLERY OF FINE ARTS, Ohio, October 5, 1968–September 7, 1969, *Paintings from The Solomon R. Guggenheim Museum*, p.25, ill.

References:
SCHMALENBACH, WERNER, *Kurt Schwitters*, Cologne, 1967, p.118, pl.17

52.1325

chwitters made his first collage of "non-artistic materials" 1919. The title of the collage was *Merzbild* (Merz-icture), "a picture in which the word 'MERZ' could be ead in between abstract forms. It was cut out and glued n from an advertisement for the KOMMERZ UND RIVATBANK. This word 'MERZ' had become a part f the picture through being attuned to the other part of he picture, and so it had to stay there. You will under-tand that I called a picture with the word MERZ the Merz-picture' in the same way that I called a picture vith 'und' the 'Und-picture' and a picture with the word Arbeiter' the 'Arbeiter-picture'. When I first exhibited these pasted and nailed pictures with the *Sturm* in Berlin, I searched for a collective noun for this new kind of picture… So I gave all my pictures the name 'MERZ-pictures' after the most characteristic of them and thus made them like a species." (Quoted in Dallas Museum of Fine Arts, *Kurt Schwitters, A Retrospective Exhibition*, November 10–December 12, 1965, p.11)

The subtitle of this relatively simple Merz-picture is inscribed on the reverse of the canvas. "Bild rot Herz-Kirche" is derived from the two forms drawn with conté crayon: a heart and a church.

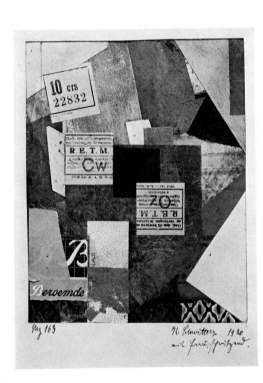

Merz 163, With Woman Sweating. 1920

Paper and cloth collage mounted on paper mat,
11⁷/₈ x 8³/₄″ (30.2 x 22.2 cm.)

Inscribed on mat l.l. "Mrz 163" and l.r. "K. Schwitters.
1920//mit Frau, schwitzend."

Provenance:

Katherine S. Dreier, West Redding, Connecticut
Gift, Katherine S. Dreier Estate, 1953

Exhibitions:

VANCOUVER ART GALLERY, November 16–December 12,
1954, *The Solomon R. Guggenheim Museum, A Selection
from the Museum Collection*, no.71, ill.

THE SOLOMON R. GUGGENHEIM MUSEUM, New York,
August 30–October 8, 1961, *Modern Masters from the
Collection of The Solomon R. Guggenheim Museum*

MARION KUGLER MCNAY ART INSTITUTE, San Antonio,
Texas, April 15–May 6, 1962, *Kurt Schwitters*, no.18;
organized by THE MUSEUM OF MODERN ART, New York,
catalogue published by PASADENA ART MUSEUM, traveled
to PASADENA ART MUSEUM, June 19–July 17; THE CURRIER
GALLERY OF ART, Manchester, New Hampshire, Septem-
ber 27–October 18; THE PHILLIPS COLLECTION, Washington,
D.C., November 4–25, 1962; UNIVERSITY OF MINNESOTA,
Minneapolis, January 7–February 4, 1963; J. B. SPEED
ART MUSEUM, Louisville, Kentucky, February 14–
March 7, 1963

GALERIE CHALETTE, New York, October 5–November 30,
1963, *Kurt Schwitters*, no.13

THE SOLOMON R. GUGGENHEIM MUSEUM, New York,
June 28–October 1, 1967, *Museum Collection, Seven
Decades, A Selection* (Checklist)

THE SOLOMON R. GUGGENHEIM MUSEUM, New York,
July 8–September 14, 1969, *Selected Sculpture and Works on
Paper*, p.76, ill.

References:

SCHMALENBACH, WERNER, *Kurt Schwitters*, Cologne, 1967,
pl.62

53.1348

"His [Schwitters] 'MERZ images' are full of secrets and
wisdom. Through them Schwitters taught us to see life
and beauty in the most insignificant things, in a tram
ticket which one discards, in a crumpled piece of paper.
He believed, as Heraclitus did, that in reality the sun is
not any larger than it appears to us…" (Jean Arp in *Onze
peintres vus par Arp*, Zürich, 1949)

Merz 199. 1921

Collage with tempera and cloth mounted on paper mat,
16⁵/₈ x 12⁷/₈" (42.2 x 32.7 cm.)

Inscribed on mat l.r. "K. Schwitters. 1921." and l.l.
"Mrz 199"

Provenance:
Katherine S. Dreier, West Redding, Connecticut
Gift, Katherine S. Dreier Estate, 1953

Exhibitions:
THE SOLOMON R. GUGGENHEIM MUSEUM, New York,
October 6, 1954–February 27, 1955, *Selection IV* (Checklist)

THE SOLOMON R. GUGGENHEIM MUSEUM, New York,
August 30–October 8, 1961, *Modern Masters from the
Collection of The Solomon R. Guggenheim Museum*

THE SOLOMON R. GUGGENHEIM MUSEUM, New York,
June 28–October 1, 1967, *Museum Collection, Seven
Decades, A Selection* (Checklist)

THE SOLOMON R. GUGGENHEIM MUSEUM, New York,
July 8–September 14, 1969, *Selected Sculpture and Works on
Paper*, p.77, ill.

References:
SCHMALENBACH, WERNER, *Kurt Schwitters*, Cologne, 1967,
cat. no.47, ill.

53.1350

"The material is as unessential as I am myself. Essential is
only creating. Because the material does not matter, I
use any material whatsoever if the picture requires it. By
tuning diversified materials to each other, I have an
advantage over 'mere-painting'; for in addition to playing
color against color, line against line, form against form,
and so on, I also play material against material, like wood
against sackcloth. I call the WELTANSCHAUUNG
from which this kind of artistic creation evolves MERZ...

"'MERZ' demands liberation from all constraint in
order to create artistically. But freedom is not lack of
restraint but the result of strict artistic discipline. 'MERZ'
also means tolerance towards any limitations imposed for
artistic reasons. Thus an artist should be permitted to
make a painting merely from two pieces of blotting
paper as long as he is really creating." (Quoted in Galerie
Chalette, New York, *Kurt Schwitters*, October–November
1963, p.5)

Georges-Pierre Seurat 1859–1891

Georges-Pierre Seurat was born December 2, 1859, in Paris. The son of a wealthy man, he received a regular allowance which enabled him to become a painter. At the age of fifteen he enrolled at a municipal art school near his home. From 1878–79 he studied at the École des Beaux-Arts under Henri Lehmann, a pupil of Ingres. The next year he spent in military service at Brest, returning to Paris in November 1880.

Seurat's early oils (1881–82) reflect the influence of Corot, Millet and the Barbizon masters. By 1883 the impact of the Impressionists is visible in his work. In 1884 when the Salon refused to exhibit his first monumental canvas *Bathing Place, Asnières*, he showed it in the first *Salon des Indépendants*, which he helped to found and supported until his death. In the spring of 1886, Seurat exhibited with Signac, Pissarro and his son Lucien Pissarro at the last Impressionist exhibition; the impact of their work, especially Seurat's *Grande Jatte*, resulted in the establishment of Neo-Impressionism as the style of the end of the century. This style was a reaction against the Impressionists who sought by choppy brushwork and intense color to record their impression of nature as it is visually perceived, instantly and without reflection. In contrast, the Neo-Impressionists used small dabs of strong and constrasting colors systematically applied to the canvas according to scientific color theories. They insisted also upon a formal ordered structure beneath the shimmering dotted surface.

Seurat, living in Paris, exhibited every year at the *Indépendants* and often with *Les XX* in Brussels. At the time of his sudden death of acute diptheria on March 29, 1891, Seurat, only thirty-one, left an œuvre that is remarkably complete; over 240 oil paintings, several hundred drawings and a large body of art theory.

GEORGES-PIERRE SEURAT

Campstool (Troupier au Pliant). c.1878–81

Conté crayon, $6^7/_8$ x $4^3/_8$″ (17.5 x 11.2 cm.)

Not inscribed

Provenance:

Félix Fénéon, Paris
Hilla Rebay, Greens Farms, Connecticut
Solomon R. Guggenheim, New York
Gift, Solomon R. Guggenheim, 1941

Exhibitions:

GALERIE BERNHEIM-JEUNE, Paris, December 14, 1908–January 9, 1909, *Rétrospective Georges Seurat*, no.105

GALERIE BERNHEIM-JEUNE, Paris, November 29–December 24, 1926, *Les dessins de Seurat*, no.21

GIBBES MEMORIAL ART GALLERY, Charleston, South Carolina, March 1–April 2, 1936, *Solomon R. Guggenheim Collection of Non-Objective Paintings*, no.124

PHILADELPHIA ART ALLIANCE, February 8–February 28, 1937, *Solomon R. Guggenheim Collection of Non-Objective Paintings*, no.199

GIBBES MEMORIAL ART GALLERY, Charleston, South Carolina, March 7–April 7, 1938, *Solomon R. Guggenheim Collection of Non-Objective Paintings*, no.273

SOLOMON R. GUGGENHEIM FOUNDATION, New York, June 1, 1939, *Art of Tomorrow* (Fifth catalogue of the Solomon R. Guggenheim Collection of Non-Objective Paintings), no.712

THE SOLOMON R. GUGGENHEIM MUSEUM, New York, February 3–May 3, 1953, *A Selection* (Checklist)

VANCOUVER ART GALLERY, November 16–December 12, 1954, *The Solomon R. Guggenheim Museum, A Selection from the Museum Collection*, no.72

ART INSTITUTE OF CHICAGO, January 16–March 7, 1958, *Seurat, Paintings and Drawings*, no.14; traveled to THE MUSEUM OF MODERN ART, New York, March 24–May 11, 1958

THE SOLOMON R. GUGGENHEIM MUSEUM, New York, August 21–October 8, 1961, *Modern Masters from the Collection of The Solomon R. Guggenheim Museum*

THE SOLOMON R. GUGGENHEIM MUSEUM, New York, April 11–May 26, 1968, *Acquisitions of the 1930's and 1940's*, p.71, ill.

THE SOLOMON R. GUGGENHEIM MUSEUM, New York, *Selected Sculpture and Works on Paper*, p.79, ill.

References:

COUSTURIER, L., *Georges Seurat*, Paris, 1926, no.36

KAHN, GUSTAV, *Les dessins de Georges Seurat*, Paris, 1928, pl.16d

DE HAUKE, C. M., *Seurat et son œuvre*, vol.II, Paris, 1961, no.420, ill.

41.712

Professor Robert L. Herbert believes this drawing may be related to the sketches of military subjects done at Brest where Seurat spent a year in military service (November 1879–November 1880). Stylistically it is characteristic of his drawings of the late 1870's.

GEORGES-PIERRE SEURAT

Farm Laborer with Hoe (Paysan à la Houe). c.1882

Oil on canvas, 18¹/₈ x 22″ (46 x 55.9 cm.)

Not inscribed

(Posthumous Inventory, canvas no.22)

Provenance:
Emile Seurat
"Mme. J. D."
Mme. Camille Platteel
Félix Fénéon, Paris, 1938
Solomon R. Guggenheim, New York
Gift, Solomon R. Guggenheim, 1941

Exhibitions:
LA REVUE BLANCHE, Paris, March 19–April 5, 1900, *Seurat,* no.8

GALERIE BERNHEIM-JEUNE, Paris, December 14, 1908–January 9, 1909, *Rétrospective Georges Seurat,* no.29

GALERIE DURAND-RUEL, Paris, May 11–June 16, 1934, *Quelques œuvres importantes de Corot à van Gogh,* no.56

GALERIE PAUL ROSENBERG, Paris, February 3–29, 1936, *Georges Seurat,* no.28

SOLOMON R. GUGGENHEIM FOUNDATION, New York, June 1, 1939, *Art of Tomorrow* (Fifth catalogue of the Solomon R. Guggenheim Collection of Non-Objective Paintings), no.716

THE SOLOMON R. GUGGENHEIM MUSEUM, New York, May 13–October 11, 1953, *Selection II* (Checklist)

THE SOLOMON R. GUGGENHEIM MUSEUM, New York, March 30–May 5, 1954, *Selection III* (Checklist)

VANCOUVER ART GALLERY, November 16–December 12, 1954, *The Solomon R. Guggenheim Museum, A Selection from the Museum Collection,* no.75, ill.

THE SOLOMON R. GUGGENHEIM MUSEUM, New York, July 26–October 9, 1955, *Selection V* (Checklist)

TATE GALLERY, London, April 16–May 26, 1957, *Paintings from The Solomon R. Guggenheim Museum,* no.70; traveled to GEMEENTEMUSEUM, The Hague, June 25–September 1; ATENEIUMIN TAIDEKOKOELMAT, Helsinki, September 27–October 20, 1957

ART INSTITUTE OF CHICAGO, January 16–March 7, 1958, *Seurat, Paintings and Drawings,* no.34, ill.; traveled to THE MUSEUM OF MODERN ART, New York, March 24–May 11, 1958

THE SOLOMON R. GUGGENHEIM MUSEUM, New York, August 30–October 8, 1961, *Modern Masters from the Collection of The Solomon R. Guggenheim Museum*

PHILADELPHIA MUSEUM OF ART, November 2, 1961–January 7, 1962, *Guggenheim Museum Exhibition, A Loan Collection of Paintings, Drawings and Prints from The Solomon R. Guggenheim Museum,* no.141

KUNSTVEREIN, Hamburg, May 4–July 14, 1963, *Seurat, Cézanne, van Gogh, Gauguin,* no.99, ill.

THE SOLOMON R. GUGGENHEIM MUSEUM, New York, April 30–September 1, 1965, *Paintings from the Collection of The Solomon R. Guggenheim Museum,* no.4, p.14, ill.

THE SOLOMON R. GUGGENHEIM MUSEUM, New York, February 9–April 7, 1968, *Neo-Impressionism,* no.69, ill.

THE SOLOMON R. GUGGENHEIM MUSEUM, New York, April 11–May 26, 1968, *Acquisitions of the 1930's and 1940's,* p.72, ill.

References:
COUSTURIER, L., "Georges Seurat," *L'Art Décoratif,* no.174, Paris, June 20, 1912, p.359, ill.

DE LAPRADE, JACQUES, *Georges Seurat,* Monaco, 1945, p.18, ill.

REWALD, JOHN, *Georges Seurat,* New York, 1946, no.51, p.85, ill.

DE LAPRADE, JACQUES, *Seurat,* Paris, 1951, p.31, ill.

DORRA, HENRI and REWALD, JOHN, *Seurat,* Paris, 1959, no.42, p.41, ill.

DE HAUKE, C. M., *Seurat et son œuvre,* Paris, 1961, vol.1, no.103, ill.

RUSSELL, JOHN, *Seurat,* New York, 1965, no.107, p.110, ill.

41.716

Seurat did many small canvases and drawings of farm scenes, workers in the fields, farm animals. Robert Herbert has pointed out that although these scenes are reminiscent of Millet and Pissarro, here "Seurat discards the complexity of Pissarro's surface movements,... and by virtue of the oblique angle of the sun, he lays out the prominent horizontal bars. These serve two functions, one is to attach themselves to the principal verticals and diagonals, the other is to subdivide the surface into geometric zones. Both force the viewer's attention on the laws of pictorial order as much as upon the subject." (Robert L. Herbert, *Neo-Impressionism,* New York, 1968, p.104)

GEORGES-PIERRE SEURAT

Farm Women at Work (Paysannes au Travail). c.1882

Oil on canvas, $15^1/8$ x $18^1/4$" (38.4 x 46.4 cm.)

Not inscribed

Provenance:
Émile Seurat
Mme. Vve. Émile Seurat
Félix Fénéon, Paris, 1938
Solomon R. Guggenheim, New York
Gift. Solomon R. Guggenheim, 1941

Exhibitions:

LA REVUE BLANCHE, Paris, March 19–April 5, 1900, *Seurat*

JOSEPH BRUMMER GALLERY, New York, December 4–27, 1924, *Georges Seurat*, no.5

GALERIE BERNHEIM-JEUNE, Paris, November 29–December 24, 1926, *Exposition Seurat*

STEDELIJK MUSEUM, Amsterdam, September-October 1930, *Tentoonstelling Vincent van Gogh en zijn Tijdgenooten*, no.273

GALERIE PAUL ROSENBERG, Paris, February 3–29, 1936, *Georges Seurat*, no.13

LEICESTER GALLERIES, London, March-April 1938, *Artists Who Died Young*, no.32

SOLOMON R. GUGGENHEIM FOUNDATION, New York, June 1, 1939, *Art of Tomorrow* (Fifth catalogue of the Solomon R. Guggenheim Collection of Non-Objective Paintings), no.713

THE SOLOMON R. GUGGENHEIM MUSEUM, New York, March 30–May 5, 1954, *Selection III* (Checklist)

VANCOUVER ART GALLERY, November 16–December 12, 1954, *The Solomon R. Guggenheim Museum, A Selection from the Museum Collection*, no.73

THE SOLOMON R. GUGGENHEIM MUSEUM, New York, July 26–October 9, 1955, *Selection V* (Checklist)

ART INSTITUTE OF CHICAGO, January 16–March 7, 1958, *Seurat, Paintings and Drawings*, no.21; traveled to THE MUSEUM OF MODERN ART, New York, March 24–May 11, 1958

THE SOLOMON R. GUGGENHEIM MUSEUM, New York, August 30–October 8, 1961, *Modern Masters from the Collection of The Solomon R. Guggenheim Museum*

PHILADELPHIA MUSEUM OF ART, November 2, 1961–January 7, 1962, *Guggenheim Museum Exhibition, A Loan Collection of Paintings, Drawings, and Prints from The Solomon R. Guggenheim Museum*, no.137

CALIFORNIA PALACE OF THE LEGION OF HONOR, San Francisco, September 29–November 4, 1962, *Barbizon Revisited*, no.110, p.205, ill.; organized by MUSEUM OF FINE ARTS, Boston, traveled to TOLEDO MUSEUM OF ART, Ohio, November 20–December 27, 1962; CLEVELAND MUSEUM OF FINE ARTS, January 15–February 24, 1963; MUSEUM OF FINE ARTS, Boston, March 14–April 28, 1963

THE SOLOMON R. GUGGENHEIM MUSEUM, New York, April 30–September 1, 1965, *Paintings from the Collection of The Solomon R. Guggenheim Museum*, no.1, p.14, ill.

THE SOLOMON R. GUGGENHEIM MUSEUM, New York, April 11–May 26, 1968, *Acquisitions of the 1930's and 1940's*, p.71, ill.

References:

DORRA, HENRI and REWALD, JOHN, *Seurat*, Paris, 1959, p.40, pl.41

HERBERT, ROBERT L., "Seurat in Chicago and New York," *The Burlington Magazine*, May 1958, p.150

DE HAUKE, C. M., *Seurat et son œuvre*, Paris, 1961, vol.1, no.60, ill.

RUSSELL, JOHN, *Seurat*, New York, 1965, no.33, p.45, ill.

HERBERT, ROBERT L., "City vs. Country: The Rural Image in French Painting From Millet to Gauguin," *Artforum*, vol.VIII, no.6, February 1970, p.52, ill.

41.713

"*Farm Women at Work*, probably painted in 1882, continues his [Seurat's] interest in Barbizon painting, for Millet's famous *Gleaners* (Louvre) is its source, but it exhibits a new use of color. The light green foliage has strokes of yellow and orange indicating reflected and partially absorbed sunlight, while the straw-colored hats have some blue to heighten its complementary orange. Rood's theory [O. N. Rood, *Modern Chromatics*, New York, 1879] is not consistently applied, however, for there are still earth colors in this canvas and not all hues are divided scientifically. The large criss-cross brush strokes make it clear that Seurat was following the advice of Blanc and Delacroix, that a vibration, not a fusion of color, is the goal." (Robert L. Herbert, "Seurat in Chicago and New York," *The Burlington Magazine*, May 1958, p.150)

Seated Woman (Paysanne assise). c.1883

Oil on canvas, 15 x 18″ (38.1 x 45.7 cm.)

Not inscribed

(Posthumous Inventory, canvas no.7)

Provenance:

Léo Gausson
Félix Fénéon, Paris
Solomon R. Guggenheim, New York
Gift, Solomon R. Guggenheim, 1937

Exhibitions:

GALERIE BERNHEIM-JEUNE, Paris, December 14, 1908–
January 9, 1909, *Rétrospective Georges Seurat*, no.8

GALERIE BERNHEIM-JEUNE, Paris, January 15–31, 1920,
Exposition Georges Seurat, no.3

CERCLE MANES, Prague, 1923, *L'Art français des XIXe et
XXe siècles*, no.159

JOSEPH BRUMMER GALLERY, New York, December 4–27,
1924, *Georges Seurat*, no.4

GALERIE BERNHEIM-JEUNE, Paris, November 29–December 24, 1926, *Les dessins de Seurat*, hors catalogue

THE MUSEUM OF MODERN ART, New York, November 20,
1934–January 20, 1935, *Fifth Anniversary Exhibition*, no.26

GIBBES MEMORIAL ART GALLERY, Charleston, South Carolina,
March 1–April 12, 1936, *Solomon R. Guggenheim Collection
of Non-Objective Paintings*, no.128

PHILADELPHIA ART ALLIANCE, February 8–28, 1937, *Solomon
R. Guggenheim Collection of Non-Objective Paintings*, no.197

GIBBES MEMORIAL ART GALLERY, Charleston, South Carolina,
March 7–April 7, 1938, *Solomon R. Guggenheim Collection of Non-Objective Paintings*, no.271

SOLOMON R. GUGGENHEIM FOUNDATION, New York, June 1,
1939, *Art of Tomorrow* (Fifth catalogue of the Solomon R.
Guggenheim Collection of Non-Objective Paintings),
no.714

M. KNOEDLER & CO., INC., New York, April 19–May 7,
1949, *Seurat, Paintings and Drawings*, no.4

THE SOLOMON R. GUGGENHEIM MUSEUM, New York,
May 13–October 11, 1953, *Selection II* (Checklist)

THE SOLOMON R. GUGGENHEIM MUSEUM, New York,
March 30–May 5, 1954, *Selection III* (Checklist)

THE SOLOMON R. GUGGENHEIM MUSEUM, New York,
July 26–October 9, 1955, *Selection V* (Checklist)

SAN FRANCISCO MUSEUM OF ART, June 17–July 10, 1955,
Art in the 20th Century, p.17

THE SOLOMON R. GUGGENHEIM MUSEUM, New York,
January 24–May 1, 1956, *Selection VI* (Checklist)

TATE GALLERY, London, April 16–May 26, 1957,
Paintings from The Solomon R. Guggenheim Museum, no.69;
traveled to GEMEENTEMUSEUM, The Hague, June 25–
September 1; ATENEIUMIN TAIDEKOKOELMAT, Helsinki,
September 27–October 20, 1957

ART INSTITUTE OF CHICAGO, January 16–March 7,
1958, *Seurat, Paintings and Drawings*, no.18, ill.; traveled
to THE MUSEUM OF MODERN ART, New York, March 24–
May 11, 1958

THE SOLOMON R. GUGGENHEIM MUSEUM, New York,
October 21, 1959–June 19, 1960, *Inaugural Selection*
(Checklist; withdrawn April 4, 1960)

THE SOLOMON R. GUGGENHEIM MUSEUM, New York,
August 30–October 8, 1961, *Modern Masters from the
Collection of The Solomon R. Guggenheim Museum*

PHILADELPHIA MUSEUM OF ART, November 2, 1961–
January 7, 1962, *Guggenheim Museum Exhibition, A Loan
Collection of Paintings, Drawings, and Prints from The
Solomon R. Guggenheim Museum*, no.139

THE SOLOMON R. GUGGENHEIM MUSEUM, New York,
April 10–June 2, 1963, *Museum Collection*

THE SOLOMON R. GUGGENHEIM MUSEUM, New York, June 5–
October 13, 1963, *Cézanne and Structure in Modern Painting*

THE SOLOMON R. GUGGENHEIM MUSEUM, New York,
April 30–September 1, 1965, *Paintings from the Collection of
The Solomon R. Guggenheim Museum*, no.2, p.15, ill.

MUSÉES DE BORDEAUX, France, May 14–September 15,
1966, *La Peinture Française dans les Collections Américaines*,
no.79, pl.48

THE SOLOMON R. GUGGENHEIM MUSEUM, New York,
February 9–April 7, 1968, *Neo-Impressionism*, no.70, ill.

THE SOLOMON R. GUGGENHEIM MUSEUM, New York,
April 11–May 26, 1968, *Acquisitions of the 1930's and 1940's*,
p.30, ill.

References:

COUSTURIER, L., *Georges Seurat*, Paris, 1921, pl.2

COQUIOT, GUSTAVE, *Georges Seurat*, Paris, 1924, p.195

COUSTURIER, L., *Seurat*, Paris, 1926, pl.7

REWALD, JOHN, *Seurat*, Paris, 1949, pl.16

HERBERT, ROBERT L., "Seurat in Chicago and New York,"
The Burlington Magazine, May 1958, pp.150–151

HOMER, WILLIAM I., "Seurat's Formative Period," *The
Connoisseur*, New York, August-September 1958, p.61,
pl.8

DORRA, HENRI and REWALD, JOHN, *Seurat*, Paris, 1959,
p.28, ill.

DE HAUKE, C. M., *Seurat et son œuvre*, Paris, 1961, vol.1,
no.59, ill.

RUSSELL, JOHN, *Seurat*, New York, 1965, p.113, ill.

COURTHION, PIERRE, *Seurat*, New York, 1968, p.77, ill.

37.714

"Seurat's early training, which concentrated so much on the human figure, begins to merge with his landscape study until, in 1883–1884, he painted his first canvas of mural scale, *Bathing Place, Asnières*. This small canvas has the palette, the technique and the feeling of the large painting. The woman has the simplified form of two artists Seurat admired, Puvis de Chavannes and Millet. The brush strokes help construct the curving planes of her body, but the meadow is painted with what Seurat called 'broomswept' strokes. They are closest, perhaps, to Camille Pissarro of the same period, say the sky of his *Cours-La-Reine* of 1883,... and Pissarro also painted in these years a number of peasant women seated or standing in fields. The distinctive note we attach to Seurat and to no other is the direct placing of the enigmatic figure against the unified background. How awkward it would be if the sky intruded itself at the top." (Robert L. Herbert, *Neo-Impressionism*, New York, 1968, p.105)

GEORGES-PIERRE SEURAT

Horse (Le Cheval Attelé). c.1883

Oil on canvas, 12³/₄ x 16¹/₈" (32.4 x 41 cm.)

Not inscribed

Provenance:
Percy Moore Turner, Paris, 1928
Félix Fénéon, Paris, 1938
Solomon R. Guggenheim, New York
Gift, Solomon R. Guggenheim, 1941

Exhibitions:
GALERIE THÉOPHILE BRIANT, Paris, March 13–April 5, 1929,
L'Adieu au Cheval, no.34

STEDELIJK MUSEUM, Amsterdam, September–October
1930, *Tentoonstelling Vincent van Gogh en zijn Tijdgenooten*,
no.271

GALERIE PAUL ROSENBERG, Paris, February 3–29, 1936,
Georges Seurat, no.11

PALAIS DE LA DÉCOUVERTE, Paris, 1937, *Exposition Internationale, la science et l'art*

LE MUSÉE D'ART VIVANT, Paris, February 3–April 10, 1938,
Oeuvres de la fin du XIXe siècle, no.1

SOLOMON R. GUGGENHEIM FOUNDATION, New York, June 1,
1939, *Art of Tomorrow* (fifth catalogue of The Solomon
R. Guggenheim Collection of Non-Objective Paintings),
no.722

ART GALLERY OF TORONTO, April 2–May 9, 1954, *A
Loan Exhibition of Paintings from The Solomon R. Guggenheim Museum*, no.68

THE SOLOMON R. GUGGENHEIM MUSEUM, New York,
October 6, 1954–February 27, 1955, *Selection IV* (Checklist)

THE SOLOMON R. GUGGENHEIM MUSEUM, New York,
August 30–October 8, 1961, *Modern Masters from
the Collection of The Solomon R. Guggenheim Museum*.

PHILADELPHIA MUSEUM OF ART, November 2, 1961–
January 7, 1962, *Guggenheim Museum Exhibition, A Loan
Collection of Paintings, Drawings, and Prints from The
Solomon R. Guggenheim Museum*, no.140

THE SOLOMON R. GUGGENHEIM MUSEUM, New York,
June 5–October 13, 1963, *Cézanne and Structure in Modern
Painting*

THE SOLOMON R. GUGGENHEIM MUSEUM, New York,
April 30–September 1, 1965, *Paintings from the Collection
of The Solomon R. Guggenheim Museum*, no.3, p.15, ill.

THE SOLOMON R. GUGGENHEIM MUSEUM, New York,
April 11–May 26, 1968, *Acquisitions of the 1930's and 1940's*,
p.75, ill.

References:
DORRA, HENRI and REWALD, JOHN, *Seurat*, Paris, 1959,
no.31, p.30, ill.

DE HAUKE, C. M., *Seurat et son œuvre*, Paris, 1961, vol.1,
no.46, ill.

FRY, ROGER, *Seurat*, London, 1965, no.5, ill.

RUSSELL, JOHN, *Seurat*, New York, 1965, p.58, no.47, ill.

COURTHION, PIERRE, *Seurat*, New York, 1968, p.75, ill.

41.722

This fourth of the small canvases of farm scenes in the
Collection depicts a harnessed horse in the fields. Seurat
has silhouetted the animal against the open sky with an
arch of trees in the distance which defines the spaces and
integrates the composition. Seurat did another version
on panel (present whereabouts unknown) centering the
horse and wagon in the middle distance and without the
semi-circular compositional device which is a barn or
shed.

GEORGES-PIERRE SEURAT

Monkey sitting up (Singe assise; The Ape; Study for "A Summer Sunday on The Grande Jatte"). 1884

Conté crayon, 6³/₄ x 8³/₈″ (17.2 x 21.3 cm.)

Not inscribed

(Posthumous Inventory, no.343)

Provenance:
Émile Seurat
Félix Fénéon
Solomon R. Guggenheim, New York
Gift, Solomon R. Guggenheim, 1937

Exhibitions:
LA REVUE BLANCHE, Paris, March 19–April 5, 1900, *Seurat*, hors catalogue

XXIe SALON DES ARTISTES INDÉPENDANTS, Paris, March 24–April 30, 1905, no.10

GALERIE BERNHEIM-JEUNE, Paris, December 14, 1908–January 9, 1909, *Rétrospective Georges Seurat*, no.190

GALERIE BERNHEIM-JEUNE, Paris, January 15–31, 1920, *Exposition Georges Seurat*, no.118

GALERIE PAUL ROSENBERG, Paris, February 3–29, 1936, *Georges Seurat*, no.118

PHILADELPHIA ART ALLIANCE, February 8–28, 1937, *Solomon R. Guggenheim Collection of Non-Objective Paintings*, no.193

GIBBES MEMORIAL ART GALLERY, Charleston, South Carolina, March 7–April 7, 1938, *Solomon R. Guggenheim Collection of Non-Objective Paintings*, no.267

SOLOMON R. GUGGENHEIM FOUNDATION, New York, June 1, 1939, *Art of Tomorrow* (Fifth catalogue of the Solomon R. Guggenheim Collection of Non-Objective Paintings), no.715

WILDENSTEIN & CO., INC., New York, April 8–May 8, 1948, *Six Masters of Post-Impressionism*, no.59

THE SOLOMON R. GUGGENHEIM MUSEUM, New York, February 3–May 3, 1953, *A Selection* (Checklist)

THE SOLOMON R. GUGGENHEIM MUSEUM, New York, October 6, 1954–February 27, 1955, *Selection IV* (Checklist)

THE SOLOMON R. GUGGENHEIM MUSEUM, New York, July 26–October 9, 1955, *Selection V* (Checklist)

ART INSTITUTE OF CHICAGO, January 16–March 7, 1958, *Seurat, Paintings and Drawings*, no.81; traveled to THE MUSEUM OF MODERN ART, New York, March 24–May 11, 1958

THE SOLOMON R. GUGGENHEIM MUSEUM, New York, August 30–October 8, 1961, *Modern Masters from the Collection of The Solomon R. Guggenheim Museum*

PHILADELPHIA MUSEUM OF ART, November 2, 1961–January 7, 1962, *Guggenheim Museum Exhibition, A Loan Collection of Paintings, Drawings, and Prints from The Solomon R. Guggenheim Museum*, no.143

THE SOLOMON R. GUGGENHEIM MUSEUM, New York, April 11–May 26, 1968, *Acquisitions of the 1930's and 1940's*, p.32, ill.

THE SOLOMON R. GUGGENHEIM MUSEUM, New York, July 8–September 14, 1969, *Selected Sculpture and Works on Paper*, p.82, ill.

References:
RICH, DANIEL CATTON, *Seurat and the Evolution of La Grande Jatte*, Chicago, 1935, pl.17

DE LAPRADE, JACQUES, *Georges Seurat*, Monaco, 1945, pl.IX

DE HAUKE, C. M., *Seurat et son œuvre*, Paris, 1961, vol.II, no.637, ill.

37.715

This is one of five conté crayon sketches made of the monkey led on a chain by the couple in the right foreground of *La Grande Jatte* (1884–86, The Art Institute of Chicago). This pose of the monkey sitting up was replaced in the final version by a monkey running on all fours.

Child in White (Study for "A Summer Sunday on The Grande Jatte"; l'Enfant Blanc). 1884

Conté crayon and chalk, 12 x 9¹/₄″ (30.5 x 23.5 cm.)

Not inscribed

Provenance:

Félix Fénéon, Paris
Solomon R. Guggenheim, New York
Gift, Solomon R. Guggenheim, 1937

Exhibitions:

XXIe SALON DES ARTISTES INDÉPENDANTS, Paris, March 24–April 30, 1905, no.7

GALERIE BERNHEIM-JEUNE, Paris, December 14, 1908–January 9, 1909, *Rétrospective Georges Seurat*, no.189

GALERIE BERNHEIM-JEUNE, Paris, January 15–31, 1920, *Exposition Georges Seurat*, no.43

GALERIE BERNHEIM-JEUNE, Paris, November 29–December 24, 1926, *Les dessins de Seurat*, no.109

GIBBES MEMORIAL ART GALLERY, Charleston, South Carolina, March 1–April 12, 1936, *Solomon R. Guggenheim Collection of Non-Objective Paintings*, no.125

PHILADELPHIA ART ALLIANCE, February 8–28, 1937, *Solomon R. Guggenheim Collection of Non-Objective Paintings*, no.194

GIBBES MEMORIAL ART GALLERY, Charleston, South Carolina, March 7–April 7, 1938, *Solomon R. Guggenheim Collection of Non-Objective Paintings*, no.268

SOLOMON R. GUGGENHEIM FOUNDATION, New York, June 1, 1939, *Art of Tomorrow* (fifth catalogue of the Solomon R. Guggenheim Collection of Non-Objective Paintings), no.717

THE SOLOMON R. GUGGENHEIM MUSEUM, New York, February 3–May 3, 1953, *A Selection* (Checklist)

THE SOLOMON R. GUGGENHEIM MUSEUM, New York, October 6, 1954–February 27, 1955, *Selection IV* (Checklist)

THE SOLOMON R. GUGGENHEIM MUSEUM, New York, July 26–October 9, 1955, *Selection V* (Checklist)

ART INSTITUTE OF CHICAGO, January 16–March 7, 1958, *Seurat, Paintings and Drawings*, no.72; traveled to THE MUSEUM OF MODERN ART, New York, March 24–May 11, 1958

THE SOLOMON R. GUGGENHEIM MUSEUM, New York, August 30–October 8, 1961, *Modern Masters from the Collection of The Solomon R. Guggenheim Museum*

PHILADELPHIA MUSEUM OF ART, November 2, 1961–January 7, 1962, *Guggenheim Museum Exhibition, A Loan Collection of Paintings, Drawings, and Prints from The Solomon R. Guggenheim Museum*, no.142

UNIVERSITY GALLERY, UNIVERSITY OF MINNESOTA, Minneapolis, March 26–April 23, 1962, *The Nineteenth Century: 125 Master Drawings*, no.109; THE SOLOMON R. GUGGENHEIM MUSEUM, New York, May 15–July 1, 1962

MUSEUM FRIDERICIANUM, Kassel, Germany, June 27–October 5, 1964, *Documenta III*, p.209, no.11

WASHINGTON UNIVERSITY GALLERY, St. Louis, Missouri, March 13–April 9, 1966, *Master Drawings*

THE SOLOMON R. GUGGENHEIM MUSEUM, New York, April 11–May 26, 1968, *Acquisitions of the 1930's and 1940's*, p.33, ill.

THE SOLOMON R. GUGGENHEIM MUSEUM, New York, July 8–September 14, 1969, *Selected Sculpture and Works on Paper*, p.83, ill.

References:

ZERVOS, CHRISTIAN, "Un Dimanche à La Grande Jatte et la technique de Seurat," *Cahiers d'art*, no.9, 1928, p.370, ill.

KAHN, GUSTAVE, *Les dessins de Georges Seurat*, Paris, 1928, pl.93

RICH, DANIEL CATTON, *Seurat and the Evolution of La Grande Jatte*, Chicago, 1935, pl.8

DORRA, HENRI and REWALD, JOHN, *Seurat*, Paris, 1959, p.152, no.138b, ill.

DE HAUKE, C. M., *Seurat et son œuvre*, vol.II, Paris, 1961, no.631, ill.

RUSSELL, JOHN, *Seurat*, New York, 1965, no.153, p.167, ill.

37.717

This is a preliminary sketch of the child, dressed in white and wearing a straw hat, that appears in the center of *La Grande Jatte* (1884–86, The Art Institute of Chicago).

GEORGES-PIERRE SEURAT

The Clipper (Le Clipper, Étude pour "Gravelines, Petit Fort-Philippe"). 1890

Conté crayon on off-white laid paper, 9¼ x 12½"
(23.1 x 31 cm.)

Not inscribed

Provenance:
Family of Seurat
Félix Fénéon, Paris
Solomon R. Guggenheim, New York
Gift, Solomon R. Guggenheim, 1937

Exhibitions:
LA REVUE BLANCHE, Paris, March 19–April 5, 1900, *Seurat*,
hors catalogue

GALERIE BERNHEIM-JEUNE, Paris, December 14, 1908–
January 9, 1909, *Rétrospective Georges Seurat*, no.203

GALERIE BERNHEIM-JEUNE, Paris, January 15–31, 1920,
Exposition Georges Seurat, no.47

GALERIE DEVAMBEZ, Paris, October 1922, *Georges Seurat*,
no.18

GALERIE BERNHEIM-JEUNE, Paris, November 29–December 24, 1926, *Les dessins de Seurat*, no.89

GALERIE BERNIER, Paris, May 25–June 13, 1929, *Mers et plages de Delacroix à nos jours*, no.20

GIBBES MEMORIAL ART GALLERY, Charleston, South Carolina, March 1–April 12, 1936, *Solomon R. Guggenheim Collection of Non-Objective Paintings*, no.126

PHILADELPHIA ART ALLIANCE, February 8–28, 1937, *Solomon R. Guggenheim Collection of Non-Objective Paintings*, no.195

GIBBES MEMORIAL ART GALLERY, Charleston, South Carolina, March 7–April 7, 1938, *Solomon R. Guggenheim Collection of Non-Objective Paintings*, no.269

VANCOUVER ART GALLERY, November 16–December 12, 1954, *The Solomon R. Guggenheim Museum, A Selection from the Museum Collection*, no.76

ART INSTITUTE OF CHICAGO, January 16–March 7, 1958, *Seurat, Paintings and Drawings*, no.145; traveled to THE MUSEUM OF MODERN ART, New York, March 24–May 11, 1958

THE SOLOMON R. GUGGENHEIM MUSEUM, New York, August 30–October 8, 1961, *Modern Masters from the Collection of The Solomon R. Guggenheim Museum.*

PHILADELPHIA MUSEUM OF ART, November 2, 1961–January 7, 1962, *Guggenheim Museum Exhibition, A Loan Collection of Paintings, Drawings, and Prints from The Solomon R. Guggenheim Museum, New York*, no.144

References:
KAHN, GUSTAVE, *Les dessins de Georges Seurat*, Paris, 1928, pl.73

DORRA, HENRI and JOHN REWALD, *Seurat*, Paris, 1959, p.266, cat. no.204a, ill.

DE HAUKE, C. M., *Seurat et son œuvre*, Paris, 1961, vol.II, p.292, cat. no.703, ill.

37.718

Seurat spent the summer of 1890 at the seaport of Gravelines on the Channel coast. This is a study of the ship in the center of the oil painting, *Channel at Gravelines, Small Fort Philippe*, now in the collection of the John Herron Art Institute, Indianapolis (de Hauke, no.208).

Gino Severini 1883–1966

Gino Severini was born in Cortona, Italy in 1883. Settling in Rome in 1899, he studied drawing and attended life classes. In 1901 he met Boccioni, the future theoretician of Futurism, and in the following year, another fellow student, Balla. He moved to Paris in 1906, where he associated with Picasso, Braque and other artists who were to become involved with Cubism. Severini's work in these early years was profoundly influenced by Seurat. Drawn to the Futurist aesthetic, in 1910 he signed the *Technical Manifesto of Futurist Painting* with Carrà, Boccioni, Russolo, Marinetti and Balla.

In the 1920's Severini turned away from Futurism to a calmer, more objective figurative style based often on classical motifs, close in spirit to Metzinger and Gris. He became interested in mural painting, and executed frescoes and mosaics in a number of churches in Switzerland, Italy and France. He published many books, among them *Du Cubisme au Classicisme*.

Severini lived in Paris from 1950 until his death in 1966.

Red Cross Train. 1915

Oil on canvas, $35^{1}/_{4}$ x $45^{3}/_{4}$" (89.6 x 116.2 cm.)

Signed l.r. "G. Severini"

Provenance:
the artist, c.1917
John Quinn, New York
Estate of John Quinn, by auction, 1927
J. B. Neumann, New York, 1944

Exhibitions:
GALLERY OF THE PHOTO-SECESSION, New York, March 1917, *Severini*

TOLEDO MUSEUM OF ART, Ohio, November 6–December 11, 1938, *Contemporary Movements in European Painting*, no.99

WILMINGTON MUSEUM OF ART, Delaware, November 1–22, 1939, *Classic and Romantic Tradition in Abstract Art*; organized by THE MUSEUM OF MODERN ART, New York, traveled to UNIVERSITY OF PITTSBURGH, December 2–23, 1939; SPRINGFIELD ART ASSOCIATION, Illinois, January 1–22, 1940 and March 1–31; DES MOINES ART ASSOCIATION, Iowa, April 12–May 3; DUKE UNIVERSITY, Durham, North Carolina, May 14–June 4, 1940

THE SOLOMON R. GUGGENHEIM MUSEUM, New York, May 13–October 11, 1953, *Selection II* (Checklist)

ART GALLERY OF TORONTO, April 2–May 9, 1954, *A Loan Exhibition of Paintings from The Solomon R. Guggenheim Museum*, no.70

VANCOUVER ART GALLERY, November 16–December 12, 1954, *The Solomon R. Guggenheim Museum, A Selection from the Museum Collection*, no.78, ill.

MONTREAL MUSEUM OF FINE ARTS, June 4–July 3, 1955, *A Selection from The Solomon R. Guggenheim Museum, New York*, no.56, ill.

TATE GALLERY, London, April 16–May 26, 1957, *Paintings from The Solomon R. Guggenheim Museum*, no.71; organized by THE SOLOMON R. GUGGENHEIM MUSEUM, traveled to GEMEENTEMUSEUM, The Hague, June 25–September 1, no.71; ATENEIUMIN TAIDEKOKOELMAT, Helsinki, September 27–October 20, no.71; GALLERIA NAZIONALE D'ARTE MODERNA, Rome, December 5, 1957–January 8, 1958, no.27, pl.27; WALLRAF–RICHARTZ–MUSEUM, Cologne, January 26–March 30; no.70; MUSÉE DES ARTS DÉCORATIFS, Paris, April 23–June 1, 1958, no.36, pl.36

PASADENA ART MUSEUM, October 7–November 16, 1958, *The New Renaissance in Italy*, no.95, ill.

PALAZZO REALE, Milan, April 12–June 26, 1960, *Arte Italiana del XX Secolo da Collezioni Americane*, no.175, ill.; organized by The International Program of THE MUSEUM OF MODERN ART, New York, traveled to GALLERIA NAZIONALE D'ARTE MODERNA, Rome, July 10–September 10, 1960

MUSÉE NATIONAL D'ART MODERNE, Paris, October 20, 1960–January 20, 1961, *Les Sources du XXe Siècle*, no.668

PHILADELPHIA MUSEUM OF ART, November 2, 1961–
January 7, 1962, *Guggenheim Museum Exhibition, A Loan
Collection of Paintings, Drawings, and Prints from The
Solomon R. Guggenheim Museum, New York*, no.146

THE SOLOMON R. GUGGENHEIM MUSEUM, New York,
June 5–October 13, 1963, *Cézanne and Structure in Modern
Painting*

THE SOLOMON R. GUGGENHEIM MUSEUM, New York,
April 30–September 1, 1965, *Paintings from the Collection of
The Solomon R. Guggenheim Museum*, no.39, ill.

BALTIMORE MUSEUM OF ART, October 25–November 27,
1966, *Twentieth Century Italian Art*

THE SOLOMON R. GUGGENHEIM MUSEUM, New York,
June 28–October 1, 1967, *Museum Collection, Seven
Decades, A Selection* (Checklist)

THE SOLOMON R. GUGGENHEIM MUSEUM, New York,
April 11–May 26, 1968, *Acquisitions of the 1930's and
1940's*, p.85, ill.

References:

*The John Quinn Collection of Paintings, Watercolours,
Drawings and Sculptures,* Huntington, New York, 1926,
p.15

ARNASON, H. H., *History of Modern Art*, New York, 1968,
pl.371

REID, B. L., *The Man from New York, John Quinn and His
Friends*, New York, 1968, pp.263, 656

44.944

Severini and the other Futurists celebrate the beauty and
dynamism of the machine and modern life in their paintings. The Futurists believed that their work should be
deeply involved with contemporary life, and sought to
express their feelings about World War I in a series of
war paintings or "guerrapittura". *Red Cross Train* is one of
these war paintings. Severini painted it (as well as another
version now in the Stedelijk Museum, Amsterdam) when
he lived near a railroad line at Vigny in the summer of
1915 and could watch the trains moving to and from the
battlefield.

Red Cross Train is typical of the Futurist concern with
movement. The small brushstrokes, though derived from
Neo-Impressionism, seem to have been applied rapidly
and are slanted in varying directions, thus conveying a
vivid sense of motion. The strong horizontal of the train
cuts through the center of the composition. The feeling of
its power and speed is echoed and heightened by the
billowing white smoke and the shifting sharp-edged
triangular planes that fragment the landscape.

David Smith 1906–1965

David Roland Smith was born March 9, 1906, in Decatur, Indiana. In 1921 he moved with his family to Paulding, Ohio, where he began studying art by correspondence from the Cleveland Art School. In 1924–1925 he studied briefly at Ohio University in Athens and at Notre Dame University in South Bend, Indiana, spending the summer of 1925 as a welder and riveter at the Studebaker plant in South Bend. In 1926, Smith lived briefly in Washington, D.C. after which he moved to New York where he studied art at the Art Students League.

Having started his career as a painter, it was not until 1931 that the artist executed his first sculptures. In 1934 he rented studio space for working and welding in the Terminal Iron Works, Brooklyn (until 1940). Aside from two trips to Europe and the Soviet Union, he divided his time between New York City and his house at Bolton Landing, New York where he settled permanently in 1940.

"The three phases in Smith's career that may be specifically isolated are, first, a period of intensive assimilation of advanced European 20th century artistic styles, i.e. cubism, constructivism, and surrealism, during the ten year period of 1930–40... Secondly, beginning in 1939–40 with his MEDALS FOR DISHONOR... and lasting until *circa* 1951–1952... Smith developed a unique symbolic and expressive style, based in part on the lessons he had learned from European art, but also deriving both from his own great gift for the creation of verbal and visual metaphor and from his ability to transform and objectify his inner psychic pressures. Thirdly, from *circa* 1951–52 until his death... he drew upon the combined resources of both his own previous work and whatever other ideas, materials, and examples he found useful to his purpose, to create a public, increasingly monumental sculptural style, discarding and sublimating in the process his previous symbolic interests in favor of formal plastic innovation." (Edward F. Fry, *David Smith,* New York, 1969, p.10).

Between 1948 and 1965 Smith taught in several colleges and universities and his work was shown regularly in both group and one-man exhibitions. In 1962 he executed twenty-six sculptures in Voltri near Genoa, Italy for the Festival of Two Worlds at Spoleto. The artist died in an automobile accident near Bennington, Vermont on May 23, 1965.

DAVID SMITH

Cubi XXVII. 1965

Welded stainless steel, 111³/₈ x 87³/₄ x 34″ (282.9 x 222.9 x 86.4 cm.)

Inscribed at top of lower horizontal "DAVID SMITH MAR 3 1965"

Provenance:
the artist
Estate of the artist, through Marlborough-Gerson Gallery, New York, 1967

Exhibitions:
LOS ANGELES COUNTY MUSEUM OF ART, November 3, 1965–January 30, 1966, *David Smith, A Memorial Exhibition*, no.11, ill.

THE SOLOMON R. GUGGENHEIM MUSEUM, New York, October 20, 1967–February 4, 1968, *Guggenheim International Exhibition 1967: Sculpture from Twenty Nations*, p.40, ill.; traveled to ART GALLERY OF ONTARIO, Toronto, February 23–March 24; THE NATIONAL GALLERY OF CANADA, Ottowa, April 26–June 9; MONTREAL MUSEUM OF FINE ARTS, June 27–August 18, 1968

THE SOLOMON R. GUGGENHEIM MUSEUM, New York, March 29–May 11, 1969, *David Smith*, no.97, ill.; traveled to DALLAS MUSEUM OF FINE ARTS, June 25–September 1; CORCORAN GALLERY OF ART, Washington, D.C., October 18–December 7, 1969

References:
CONE, JANE HARRISON and PAUL, MARGARET, "The Sculpture of David Smith: A Handlist", in *David Smith 1906–1965, A Retrospective Exhibition*, Fogg Art Museum, Harvard University, Cambridge, Massachusetts, 1966, no.543, p.82

BANNARD, DARBY, "Cubism, Abstract Expressionism, David Smith", *Artforum*, vol.VI, no.8, April 1968, p.31, ill.

KRAMER, HILTON, "Greatest of All American Artists", *The New York Times Magazine*, February 16, 1969, p.41, ill.

MILLARD, CHARLES W., "David Smith", *The Hudson Review*, vol.XXII, no.2, Summer 1969, pp.271–77, ill.

67.1862

Smith's Cubi series of twenty-eight works, the culminating point in his career as the outstanding figure in modern American sculpture, was begun in 1961 and ended with the artist's death in May, 1965. *Cubi XXVII* is one of the last and greatest works in the series and marks the final step in Smith's life-long struggle to reconcile the aesthetics of painting and sculpture. Smith made three monumental "gates" cubis, but it was in *Cubi XXVII* that he was most successful in transforming a pictorial frame into a subtle yet firmly articulated three-dimensional sculpture. Similarly, Smith's choice and treatment of his material contributes to this same unity of sculpture with painting, for the reflective surfaces of polished stainless steel fuse the conflicting principles of the pictorial and the plastic into a single gleaming opticality.

Leon Polk Smith 1906–

Leon Polk Smith was born May 20, 1906, in Chickasha, Indian Territory, Oklahoma. He received a Bachelor of Arts degree from East Central Oklahoma State College in 1934 and a Master of Arts degree in art and educational psychology from Columbia University Teachers' College, New York, in 1938. Between 1939 and 1957 he was active in art education. His first one-man exhibition was held at the Uptown Gallery, New York, in 1941.

Throughout his career, Smith has been considered a geo-metric artist, receiving his initial stimulus from Mondrian, whom he discovered, together with Arp, in the Gallatin Collection in 1946. What he learned from Mondrian was "the interchangeability of form and space" and what he sought was to "release Mondrian from the rectangle". Smith's work of the forties was usually based on a grid struc-ture, but in the early 1950's he discovered a means to free form. The curved outlines of zones of pure color which re-sulted were his solution to the problem of creating conti-nuous space. There is never a figure-ground relationship in Smith's work; instead there is a juxtaposition of positive and negative space. Although Smith's point of departure was European geometric art, the large scale, shaped can-vases, and distinct areas of pure color relate his painting to recent American abstraction. He has exhibited widely, mostly in America but also in Europe. Leon Polk Smith resides at present in Shoreham, Long Island, New York.

LEON POLK SMITH

Constellation. 1968–9

Acrylic on cotton canvas, $86^{1}/_{2}$ x $54^{1}/_{2}''$ (219.8 x 138.4 cm.)

Inscribed on reverse of top oval "LEON POLK SMITH// CON-//STELLATION I 1968" and on reverse of bottom oval "I 1968"

Provenance:
the artist
Gift, Dr. and Mrs. Arthur Lejwa, 1969

69.1919

Constellation I shows several characteristic aspects of Leon Polk Smith's recent style. The curved forms, initiated in 1954, and inspired by the continuous surfaces and flowing seams of baseballs, tennis balls and basket balls, here become the structure of the canvas. The two shaped canvases, connected by a rod, in turn generate the internal image. The economy of color emphasizes its intensity, further accentuated by the absence of texture, modeling and surface detail. Color, space and support coincide in an image of forceful impact.

Kurt R. H. Sonderborg 1923–

Sonderborg was born K. R. H. Hofmann on April 5, 1923, in Sonderborg, Denmark of German parents. He decided to become a painter in 1946 and attended the School of Fine Arts in Hamburg from 1947 to 1949. He began painting consistently after 1951 and in 1953 worked at printmaking at Hayter's *Atelier 17* in Paris. It was at this time that his mature style began to emerge.

Sonderborg's earliest paintings rely greatly on automatic gesture and imagery. After 1953 one can speak of a constructive/destructive technique in which the painter organized the surface through broad swatches of black paint and then attacked them with equally broad sweeps of a spatula, razor blade or other sharp instrument. Working on a gelatin coated photographic paper (which is only later mounted on canvas), he thus creates subtle contrasts of full and scraped surfaces.

Sonderborg habitually works with great speed and spontaneity of gesture. His palette is usually restricted to black, white and red. Color is secondary to his preoccupation with rhythm, the visual and vital rhythms of the urban landscape and technology. As much a draftsman as a painter, in his paintings rhythm is transposed in a loose often lyrical idiom whereas his drawings consist of more rapid and staccato notations.

Sonderborg had his first one-man exhibition at the Kestner Gesellschaft, Hanover, in 1956. Since then his work has been shown frequently both alone and in group exhibitions including the Venice Biennale (1958) and Documenta II and III (1959, 1964). The artist resides in Paris and Stuttgart.

Untitled. 1961

Tempera on paper mounted on canvas, 43 x 27⅝″ (109.3 x 70.2 cm.)

Signed and dated l.l. "Sonderborg//61"

Provenance:
Galerie Karl Flinker, Paris, 1963

Exhibitions:
VII BIENAL DE SÃO PAULO, September –December 1963, *K. R. H. Sonderborg*, no.31, ill.

XXXII BIENNALE INTERNAZIONALE D'ARTE VENEZIA, Venice, June 20–October 18, 1964, *Today's Art in Museums: The Solomon R. Guggenheim Museum*, no.17, p.34

References:
BAYL, FRIEDRICH, "K. R. H. Sonderborg", *Art International*, October 25, 1963, p.53, ill.

HAHN, OTTO, *Sonderborg*, New York, 1964, p.61, ill.

63.1646

This painting is also identified as *Villa Santos Dumont, 20.11.61, 23.22–24.05 h.,* indicating the place, date and time of execution (a villa in Paris, November 20, 1961, 11:22 p.m.–12:05 a.m.). "That since 1953 I ceased to name my paintings and limited myself to the noting of time and place of my executions, has led to many misunderstandings. My products are quickly born – it bores me. Already Monet painted fast, up to three paintings a day. A title is an intolerably banal concession to everything which does not concern what I am doing... My time is not the clock's time. 10.x.58, 8.21 h – 8.27 h, rue Boromée, Paris, this is the only way to indicate what so fleetingly vanishes.

"Work-notes, facts for catalogues, that is enough for me; maybe this explains why I cannot and will not say more than 'when' and 'where'. I know nothing. My works tell me ever and again that everything is other, telling me something I do not know and forget." (Quoted in Galerie Karl Flinker, *Sonderborg*, Paris, 1960).

The swiftness of execution (forty-three minutes) is characteristic of Sonderborg's creative technique. When he has prepared his materials and is ready to paint, he proceeds swiftly and without hesitation. The controlled and balanced masses of this painting are found in other works of 1961, one of the relatively more ordered and structured periods of the artist's work.

Jesús Rafael Soto 1923–

Jesús Rafael Soto was born in Cuidad Bolivar, Venezuela in 1923. He studied at the School of Plastic Arts in Caracas from 1942 to 1947 and was Director of the Maracaibo School of Fine Arts, Venezuela, from 1947 to 1950. In 1950 he moved to Paris where he now lives. He had his first one-man exhibition in Caracas in 1948. Subsequently his work has been in such important exhibitions as the Bienal de São Paulo, the Venice Biennale, the World's Fair, Brussels and Expo '67 in Montreal. The Kunsthalle in Bern held a Soto exhibition in the summer of 1968.

Since his arrival in Paris, Soto has been experimenting with optical problems; he was very much influenced by Mondrian's late works which he believes were moving toward optical illusion. By 1954 he was dealing with the problem of optical movement on the surface by working out different spatial relationships between small dots of the same size but of varying colors. In 1954, Soto discovered superimposition. Still working with dots painted on the picture surface, he spaced a perspex sheet, also painted with dots, several inches in front of the picture plane. His most recent work is characterized by surfaces painted with thin white lines upon a black ground over which a structure of welded wire is imposed. As the viewer moves in front of the work, the solidity of the wire disappears at different points and the optical experience becomes one of lyrical waves of motion. The visual disintegration of mass in favor of an experience which occurs in two dimensions prohibits consideration of the object as sculpture.

Vibration. 1965

Metal and wood with oil, $62^3/_8$ x $42^1/_4$ x $5^3/_4''$ (158.4 x 107.4 x 14.6 cm.)

Signed and dated on reverse "Soto//1965"

Provenance:
from the artist through Galerie Edouard Loeb, Paris; Gift, Miss Eve Clendenin, New York, 1967

Exhibitions:
GALERIE EDOUARD LOEB, Paris, June 1–July 31, 1965, *Soto*
ATENEO DE CARACAS, January 10–February 10, 1965, and MUSEO DE BELLAS ARTES, Caracas, January 10–24, 1965, *Evaluación de la Pintura Latinoamericana Años '60,* no.69
ANDREW D. WHITE MUSEUM, Cornell University, Ithaca, New York, October 8–November 8, 1965, *The Emergent Decade;* organized by THE SOLOMON R. GUGGENHEIM MUSEUM, New York, traveled to DALLAS MUSEUM OF FINE ARTS, December 18, 1965–January 18, 1966; THE NATIONAL GALLERY OF CANADA, Ottawa, April 1–May 1; THE SOLOMON R. GUGGENHEIM MUSEUM, New York, May 20–June 19; KRANNERT ART MUSEUM, University of Illinois, Champaign, September 16–October 9; DECORDOVA MUSEUM, Lincoln, Massachusetts, November 6–December 4, 1966; JOHN AND MABLE RINGLING MUSEUM OF ART, Sarasota, April 9–May 7, 1967
DELAWARE ART CENTER, Wilmington, March 9–April 7, 1968, *Contemporary Latin American Artists*
ART GALLERY/CENTER FOR INTER-AMERICAN RELATIONS, New York, July 2–September 14, 1969, *Latin American Paintings From the Collection of The Solomon R. Guggenheim Museum,* p.30, ill.

References:
MACLEISH, WILLIAM H., "Cornell's Latin American Year", *Art in America,* vol 54, no.3, May–June 1966, p.105, ill.
MESSER, THOMAS M., *The Emergent Decade,* New York, 1966, p.143, ill.

67.1855

"I always work with the fewest and most anonymous elements, to get as far away as possible from description. French painters have tended always to use 'beautiful' forms, forms still close to figuration, forms with a decorative function. The elements I use are absolutely without value in themselves, they are used simply to demonstrate relations. By means, for example, of the endless repetition of the square, the square itself disappears and produces pure movement." (Jesús Rafael Soto, April, 1965, quoted in Guy Brett, "Pure Relations – The Art of Jesús Rafael Soto", *Art International,* October, 1965, p.18)

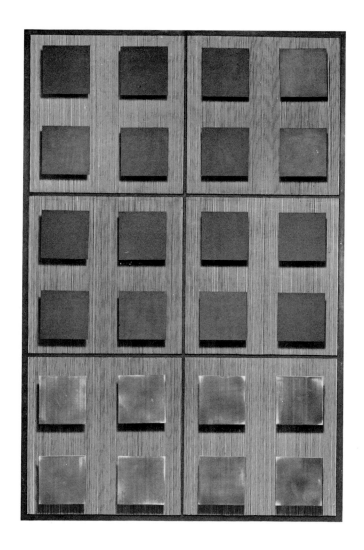

Pierre Soulages 1919–

Pierre Soulages was born December 24, 1919, at Rodez in southern France. After finishing high school he decided to be a painter and went to Paris to study (1939). The war and the German Occupation interrupted his activity. He did not return to Paris nor to painting until 1946.

Soulages's early paintings of 1946, already characterized by dark tones on a white ground, were comparable to "action painting" in that they were legible as dynamic gesture. By 1947, he had exchanged the brush for the palette knife, thus translating gesture into planar configurations. His subsequent work consists of dark massive equivocal calligraphic forms on a light background, sometimes accentuated in certain areas by a glow of color. More architectonic than gestural, they evoke a sense of anonymous primeval forces rather than the transience of individual gesture.

Soulages began exhibiting his work at the *Salon des Sur-indépendants* and the *Salon de Mai* in 1947. His first one-man show was held in 1949 (Galerie Lydia Conti, Paris). Throughout the fifties and sixties his work has been widely exhibited both separately and in groups, the latter including the São Paulo Bienal (1953) and Documenta I, II, and III (1955, 1959, 1964). The artist resides in Paris.

PIERRE SOULAGES

Painting. November 20, 1956

Oil on canvas, 76³/₄ x 51¹/₈″ (194 x 129.9 cm.)

Inscribed l.r. "Soulages 56" and on reverse "Soulages//20 Nov. 1956//Peinture"

Provenance:
from the artist, Paris, 1957

Exhibitions:
THE SOLOMON R. GUGGENHEIM MUSEUM, New York, October 21, 1959–June 19, 1960, *Inaugural Selection* (Checklist)
THE NEW GALLERY, Hayden Library, Massachusetts Institute of Technology, Cambridge, January 10–30, 1962, *Pierre Soulages*, no.10
MUSEUM OF FINE ARTS OF HOUSTON, April 20–May 22, 1966, *Pierre Soulages Retrospective Exhibition*
MUSÉE NATIONAL D'ART MODERNE, Paris, March 22–May 21, 1967, *Soulages*, no.29
COLUMBUS GALLERY OF FINE ARTS, Ohio, October 5, 1968–September 7, 1969, *Paintings from The Solomon R. Guggenheim Museum*, p.38, ill.

57.1469

As a boy growing up in the south of France, Soulages was deeply impressed by the Romanesque architecture of that region. In fact, it was in the church of Ste. Foy de Conques (as reported by James Johnson Sweeney, *Soulages: Paintings since 1963*, M. Knoedler & Co., Inc., New York, 1968) that Soulages decided to become a painter. The impressions of monumentality, primitive force, stability and clearly organized volumes characteristic of the Romanesque style, as well as the mystery and sobriety of the dark church interiors, are metaphorically transmitted by Soulages's mature style.

Yves Tanguy 1900–1955

Raymond Georges Yves Tanguy was born January 5, 1900, in Paris, the son of a retired sea captain. The stark, haunting landscapes that characterize his art were no doubt in part inspired by the Breton landscape, with its menhirs and dolmens, which he saw during vacations at Locrona as a child. Studying at the Lycées Montaigne and St. Louis in Paris, Tanguy met Pierre Matisse, who became his life-long friend and dealer. In 1918, he joined the Merchant Marine and traveled to South America and Africa. Two years later he formed a lasting friendship with the film-maker and poet, Jacques Prévert, with whom he shared a literary interest, notably in the Comte de Lautréamont, a hero of the yet-to-be-formed Surrealist movement.

When, in 1923, Tanguy saw a picture by de Chirico in Paul Guillaume's gallery, he decided to become a painter (until then he had only sketched in his spare time). By 1927 he had met André Breton and joined the Surrealist group. In the early thirties, after a trip to Africa, Tanguy's forms shifted in kind from vegetal to mineral. His images began to resemble boneyards, with forms metamorphosing into one another to become chains of indeterminate beings in an infinite landscape; "land" blends with "sky" to create a great sea of space where objects rest, hover, and float.

In 1939, Tanguy met the American Surrealist, Kay Sage, whom he married the following year, after immigrating to America at the outbreak of the war. In 1941, they moved to Woodbury, Connecticut, where they bought a farmhouse with a studio-barn five years later. Tanguy died on January 15, 1955, in Woodbury.

YVES TANGUY

Untitled. 1949

Ink and paper collage on paper, $19^7/_8$ x $14^3/_4''$ (50.5 x 37.5 cm.)

Signed and dated l.r. "YVES TANGUY 49"

Provenance:

Kay Sage Tanguy, Woodbury, Connecticut
Gift, Kay Sage Tanguy Estate, 1963

Exhibitions:

PIERRE MATISSE GALLERY, New York, March 26–April 13, 1963, *Exhibition of Gouaches and Drawings by Yves Tanguy*, no.64, ill.

THE SOLOMON R. GUGGENHEIM MUSEUM, New York, May 30–September 2, 1968, *Rousseau, Redon, and Fantasy*

THE SOLOMON R. GUGGENHEIM MUSEUM, New York, July 8–September 14, 1969, *Selected Sculpture and Works on Paper*, p.86, ill.

References:

GRUEN, JOHN, "Much in Little", *New York*, July 7, 1969, p.56, ill.

63.1663

The series of pen drawings that Tanguy produced after coming to America "are the monologues of a solitary man. We follow the traced line as it rises from the bottom of the sheet or moves from one side to the other, firm, sharp, as if traced by a knife. Occasionally in its advance the artist's hand turns full circle to embrace a form or note an image that has flashed through the mind – only to proceed thereupon to another point where a new land-mark is to be erected. Here and there small sign-posts gradually give rise to areas in which particles of shells or man-made tools oppose their cluttered existence to the emptiness of the plains. So much labor is involved in forming these precious little objects that the pen's advance is, seemingly, endlessly retarded...

"Having traced the artist's voyage over the sheet we come to the realization that the work should now be viewed in terms of the final product, unmistakably a surrealist image. Tanguy possessed the secret of putting automatism at the service of recognizable forms." (Quoted in Nicolas Calas, *Exhibition of Gouaches and Drawings by Yves Tanguy*, Pierre Matisse Gallery, New York, 1963).

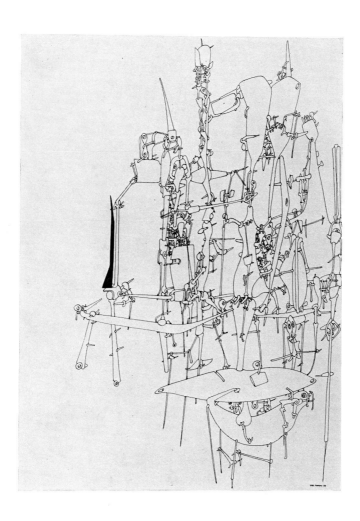

Antoni Tàpies 1923–

Antoni Tàpies was born in Barcelona in 1923. Self-taught as an artist, in 1946 he abandoned his law studies to devote himself to painting. He was a founding member of the group and review *Dau al Set* in Barcelona in 1948. At this time Tàpies was influenced by Miró and Klee in his emphasis on a calligraphic sign language, and by Torres-Garcia in his use of an all-over compositional grid. A strong Surrealist flavor is also apparent in the dream-like atmosphere of his early canvases.

Tàpies received a French government scholarship which enabled him to work in Paris from 1950–51. He has subsequently re-visited Paris regularly. From about 1953, Tàpies's work began to reveal the influence of "matter painting" and its central figure Dubuffet. The materiality of his painting increased as he started to use pigment weighted with sand or marble dust, massive planes and pitted textures.

Since his participation in the Carnegie International in 1950, he has exhibited regularly in group and one-man shows. He has had numerous museum retrospectives, one at The Solomon R. Guggenheim Museum in 1962. Tàpies lives in Barcelona.

Great Painting. 1958

Mixed media on canvas, 79 x 102⁵/₈″ (200.7 x 260.7 cm.)

Not inscribed

Provenance:
from the artist through Martha Jackson Gallery, New York, 1959

Exhibitions:
MARTHA JACKSON GALLERY, New York, February 24– March 21, 1959, *Antonio Tàpies*, no.1

THE SOLOMON R. GUGGENHEIM MUSEUM, New York, October 21, 1959–June 19, 1960, *Inaugural Selection* (Checklist)

THE SOLOMON R. GUGGENHEIM MUSEUM, New York, March 21–April 9, 1962, *Antoni Tàpies*, ill.

References:
CIRLOT, JUAN-EDUARDO, "La Pintura de Antonio Tàpies", *Goya*, no.34, 1960, p.234, ill.

59.1551

Tàpies's use of color in *Great Painting* is characteristically Spanish: austere, somber, earthy. The dense surface – achieved through the mixture of sand with thick oil paint – the massive, frontal, wall-like plane, and the rough surface characterize this painting almost as relief sculpture. The composition is a stable, almost static mass, symmetrically divided into large rectangular areas, enlivened by the scarred and gouged texture rather than by brushwork.

Typical of much of Tàpies's painting, the canvas brings to mind an ancient object or archaeological site. The heavy pigment is like dried earth, the regularly rectangular areas evoke either a map or a crumbling wall and the incised lines and scars suggest hieroglyphics or eroded graffiti.

Ernest Trova 1927–

Ernest T. Trova was born February 19, 1927, in St. Louis, Missouri. Self-taught as an artist, his paintings of the early fifties were essentially in an expressionist vein, strongly influenced by de Kooning, Matta, Bacon and Dubuffet. In the late fifties and early sixties Trova worked at assemblages and objects, first composed of junk, and subsequently incorporating mechanical objects and forms. Thus progressed his transition from expression to clearly defined signifying objects.

In 1961 appeared the stereotyped image of his armless, faceless, sexless *Falling Man*. Perfected and repeated on canvas through 1963, in 1964 it was projected into three dimensions. Since that time the artist has experimented with this modular figure in diverse materials (chrome-plated bronze, silicone bronze, nickel-plated bronze, aluminum, enamel) and contexts (light boxes, plexiglas mazes, "car kits", isolated or in groups), as well as in combinations with machinery (wheels, aqualungs, pistons), creating diverse formal, functional and signifying attitudes. However the image itself is immutable. To some observers it connotes despair with the modern human condition, embodied by this impotent standardized mannequin. To Trova it is a sign, signifying man as an imperfect but dignified entity.

Trova had his first one-man show in 1959 at the Image Gallery, St. Louis. He had his first New York one-man exhibition at the Pace Gallery in 1963 where his work has been shown regularly ever since. The artist resides in St. Louis.

Wheel Man. 1965

Silicone bronze, 60^1/$_8$ x 47^3/$_4$ x 21″ (152.7 x 121.3 x 53.3 cm.)

Signed with monogram and dated on back of base "[monogram] 3. 6 65"

Provenance:
Pace Gallery, New York
Gift, John G. Powers Fund, 1965

Exhibitions:
CITY ART MUSEUM, St. Louis, Missouri, September 29–November 12, 1967, *Seven for '67*

NATIONAL GALLERY OF CANADA, Ottawa, April 26–June 9, 1968, *Guggenheim International Exhibition, 1967: Sculpture from Twenty Nations* (hors catalogue); traveled to MONTREAL MUSEUM OF FINE ARTS, June 20–August 18, 1968

66.1777

As with the other members of his *Falling Man* series of the mid-1960's, Trova uses the human image in *Wheel Man* not for expressionistic or literary effects but as a generalized sign. This figure, anonymous, smoothly unheroic, and psychologically detached, functions both as a dehumanized component of a machine and as an arbitrary element within a neo-Dada juxtaposition.

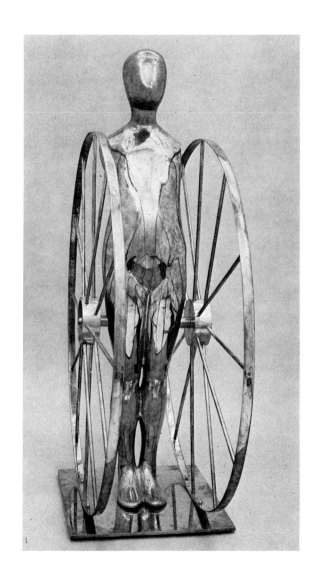

Kandahar. 1950–52

Oil on pressed board, 39³/₈ x 42⁵/₈″ (100 x 108.3 cm.)

Not inscribed

Provenance:
from the artist through Galerie Denise René, Paris, 1954

Exhibitions:
GALERIE DENISE RENÉ, Paris, May 1952, *Vasarely*
GALERIE SAMLAREN, Stockholm, September 1952, *Vasarely*
THE SOLOMON R. GUGGENHEIM MUSEUM, New York,
December 2, 1953–May 2, 1954, *Younger European
Painters*, no.31, ill.; traveled to WALKER ART CENTER,
Minneapolis, August 8–September 24; PORTLAND ART
MUSEUM, Portland, Oregon, October 8–November 14;
SAN FRANCISCO MUSEUM OF ART, November 26, 1954–
January 25, 1955; THE DALLAS MUSEUM OF FINE ARTS,

Victor Vasarely 1908–

Victor Vasarely was born April 9, 1908, in Pecs, Hungary.
He studied medicine at the University of Budapest but he
gave it up in 1929 to join the Budapest Bauhaus. Here, for
the first time, he was exposed to abstraction (Cubism, Suprematism, Constructivism) as well as to the principles and
techniques of applied art.

In 1930, Vasarely settled in Paris. From 1931 to 1935 he
worked in advertising and commercial art. Always a prolific draftsman, between 1936 and 1944 he did no painting
but executed a series of drawings in which he meticulously
studied the properties of materials, problems of dimensions
and perspective in their relationships to surface plane, color
modulation, illusions of movement. According to the
artist, his goal was to elaborate a highly perfected commercial art.

These graphic works were shown at the Galerie Denise
René in Paris in 1944. The artist did not begin to paint until
a few years later. In 1947 he began to use a reductive language translating the shapes of nature into the most simply
structured forms. In the ensuing years, Vasarely's works
became progressively complex. His interest in pictorial
space, not as a structure of figure/ground relationships but
as a continuous surface of contrasting yet level planes, and
his experiments with *trompe-l'oeil* and optical illusion, led
him to the eventual incorporation of movement (and time)
into his paintings. In 1955 he published the *Manifeste jaune*,
a manifesto for kinetic art.

Vasarely's artistic theories and applications – his stress on
perception as the medium not only for apprehending spatial
relationships but temporal sequences – have had an enor-
mous influence on younger kinetic artists such as Soto,
Agam, Yvaral. His work has been exhibited widely and
infinitely reproduced, not only through the media of silk-
screens and multiples but in all areas of the graphic and
decorative arts. The artist resides in France.

February 1–March 1; UNIVERSITY OF ARKANSAS, Fayette-ville, March 7–April 9; THE DAYTON ART INSTITUTE, Dayton, Ohio, April 15–May 13; ADDISON GALLERY OF AMERICAN ART, Phillips Academy, Andover, Massachusetts, October 1–31; CARPENTER ART GALLERIES, Dartmouth College, Hanover, New Hampshire, November 5–December 31, 1955; DWIGHT ART MEMORIAL, Mount Holyoke College, South Hadley, Massachusetts, January 3–31, 1956; DAVISON ART CENTER, Wesleyan University, Middletown, Connecticut, February 6–March 18, 1956

THE SOLOMON R. GUGGENHEIM MUSEUM, New York, October 21, 1959–June 19, 1960, *Inaugural Selection* (Checklist)

PHILADELPHIA MUSEUM OF ART, November 2, 1961–January 7, 1962, *Guggenheim Museum Exhibition, A Loan Collection of Paintings, Drawings, and Prints from The Solomon R. Guggenheim Museum, New York*, no.155

THE SOLOMON R. GUGGENHEIM MUSEUM, New York, June 28–October 1, 1967, *Museum Collection, Seven Decades, A Selection* (Checklist)

COLUMBUS GALLERY OF FINE ARTS, Ohio, October 5, 1968–September 7, 1969, *Paintings from The Solomon R. Guggenheim Museum*, p.37, ill.

References:

VASARELY, VICTOR, *Vasarely*, Neuchâtel, 1965, pl.15

54.1396

Vasarely believes that art is not to be restricted to an elite cultivated class but should be addressed to all society. "…every man, no matter who he is, Papou or French-man, laborer or doctor, ignorant or knowledgeable, responds to rhythms, forms, and colors. [This is] because the shock of beauty is an emotional experience, not an intellectual one." (Quoted in *Vasarely*, Galleri K.B., Oslo, February 16–27, 1962, p.18). To this end, the artist developed a pictorial language based on the fundamental experience of perception: rhythms and contrasts of shapes and hues.

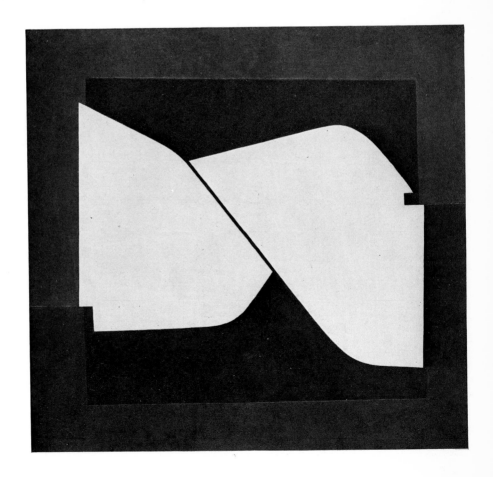

Wols 1913–1951

Wols was born Alfred Otto Wolfgang Schulze on May 27, 1913, in Berlin. His youth was spent in Dresden until in 1932 he returned to Berlin, intending to join the Bauhaus. He was discouraged from doing so by Moholy-Nagy who persuaded him to continue studying independently.

In 1932 Wols arrived in Paris where he earned a meager living as a photographer and teacher of German. Drafted in 1933, he took refuge in Spain but was finally arrested in 1935. Wols spent 1937–1940 in concentration camps in France. Upon his liberation, he settled in Cassis on the Mediterranean coast. In 1942 he moved inland to Dieulefit and in 1945 he returned to live in Paris.

Wols was essentially a graphic artist, his preferred mediums being watercolor, gouache and ink. His earliest watercolors date from 1932–1933. Inspired by the artist's fascination with nature, they depict fantastic landscapes, based on organic yet subjectively interpreted forms. The work done in Spain having been lost, the next series is from 1936 to 1939 or the period of the artist's imprisonment. By this time he had started drinking heavily as a means of escape from the outside world. Although the imagery of these drawings and watercolors is of similar origins, it has become more fantastic, more explicitly erotic and more ominous in its connotations: obsessive outgrowths of the artist's hallucinations. This predicts the direction his work will subsequently take. Dreamscapes depicting a paradoxically vital disintegration of form, his late works evoke simultaneously creation and destruction through their organic yet shattered configurations.

Wols had his first one-man exhibition in 1945 (Galerie René Drouin, Paris). In 1949, in view of his alarming health (through alcoholism), he entered a sanatorium from which he emerged apparently completely cured. He spent his last two years painting in Champigny near Paris. There he died accidentally on September 1, 1951 at the age of thirty-eight.

WOLS

Houses. Undated

Watercolor and ink on paper, 6¹/₄ x 4³/₈″ (15.9 x 11.2 cm.)

Signed l.r. "WOLS"

Provenance:
Karl Nierendorf, New York
Estate of Karl Nierendorf, 1948

Exhibitions:
THE SOLOMON R. GUGGENHEIM MUSEUM, New York, February 24–April 17, 1966, *European Drawings*, no.141; traveled to UNIVERSITY GALLERY, University of Minnesota, Minneapolis, May 10–31; DECORDOVA MUSEUM, Lincoln, Massachusetts, June 26–September 4; MUSEUM OF ART, Rhode Island School of Design, Providence, September 14–October 8; THE NATIONAL GALLERY OF CANADA, Ottawa, November 28–December 25, 1966; MILWAUKEE ART CENTER, January 5–Februay 5, 1967; HIGH MUSEUM OF ART, Atlanta, March 1–31; DALLAS MUSEUM OF FINE ARTS, April 15–May 15; KRANNERT ART MUSEUM, University of Illinois, Champaign, May 28–June 25;

NORTH CAROLINA MUSEUM OF ART, Raleigh, July 15–August 15, 1967
THE SOLOMON R. GUGGENHEIM MUSEUM, New York, July 8–September 14, 1969, *Selected Sculpture and Works on Paper*, p.87, ill.

48.1172x423

Houses and cities were a theme which preoccupied Wols throughout his lifetime. He once wrote in his notebook: "All my dreams take place in a large and very beautiful unknown city."

Perhaps Wols's predilection for drawing houses can be traced to the influence exerted on him by Paul Klee during the years he was exposed to the Bauhaus. However Wols's houses do not show the same whimsical interpretation as Klee's.

In contrast to Wols's "hallucinatory" images, views of houses provided a more rigid structural context. In view of the artist's quest for spiritual detachment, one could suggest that this theme offered an escape from depicting the pressures of his earthly condition.

Adja Yunkers 1900–

Adja Yunkers was born July 15, 1900, in Riga, Latvia. He left his home at fourteen to study art in Leningrad. By the early twenties he had left Russia and traveled to Hamburg and Berlin where he was impressed by the German Expressionists and the School of Paris he saw at *Der Sturm*. In 1924, he moved to Paris, but soon traveled to Germany, Cuba, Mexico, back to Paris, Sweden and in 1947, to New York. He was awarded a Guggenheim Fellowship, 1949–50 (renewed 1954–55) and a Ford Foundation Grant in 1959. He has taught at the New School for Social Research, New York, the University of New Mexico, Cooper Union, Columbia University and teaches at present at Barnard College.

Yunkers's early abstract style is characterized by a will to suggest rather than to define form. He has worked extensively with pastel, developing the quality inherent in this medium to produce an ambiguity of form which infuses his works with a certain mystery. The latter pertains primarily to the psychological experience of the artist and only secondarily to the subject portrayed. The impact of his recent work – large collages with a reduced number of clearly defined abstract shapes – depends on the sensuous color and forms rather than on associations of subject matter.

Yunkers has been given numerous one-man shows including an exhibition at the Baltimore Museum of Art in 1960. He now lives in New York City.

ADJA YUNKERS

Aegean IV. 1967

Acrylic and collage on canvas, $72^1/_2$ x $62^1/_2''$ (184.2 x 158.7 cm.)

Signed on reverse "AEGEAN IV//ADJA YUNKERS// 1967//$72^1/_4$ x $62^1/_2''$//COLLAGE-Acrylic

Provenance:
the artist
Rose Fried Gallery, New York
Gift, May Walker, 1968

Exhibitions:
ROSE FRIED GALLERY, New York, February 14–March 9, 1968, *Recent Paintings by Adja Yunkers*

68.1870

Unlike the abrupt changes that occur in most collages, here there is an equivocal relationship between the expanse of the total field and the superimposed piece of canvas. While the eye attempts to define the nuances of surface transitions, it is almost playfully diverted by the painted forms – the strip of black and curve of yellow which push toward the edges of the picture. The artist's use of a minimal amount of clearly defined forms is personal and expressive; paradoxically, his economy of means allows a wealth of interpretations.

EXHIBITION 70/3

10,000 copies of this catalogue designed by Malcolm Grear
have been printed by Johan Enschedé en Zonen, Haarlem,
The Netherlands in April 1970 for the Trustees of
The Solomon R. Guggenheim Foundation on the occasion
of the exhibition
"Selections from The Guggenheim Museum Collection
1900–1970"

Photography Credits:
ROBERT E. MATES AND PAUL KATZ, New York